GCSE/KEY STAGE 4
SCIENCE

LONGMAN
REVISE
GUIDES

Di Barton

Longman

LONGMAN REVISE GUIDES

SERIES EDITORS:
Geoff Black and Stuart Wall

TITLES AVAILABLE:
Biology*
Business Studies*
Chemistry*
Economics*
English*
English Literature*
French
Geography
German
Information Systems*
Mathematics*
Mathematics: Higher Level*
Music
Physics*
Psychology
Religious Studies*
Science*
Sociology
Spanish
Technology*
World History

* new editions for Key Stage 4

Addison Wesley Longman Limited
Edinburgh Gate, Harlow,
Essex CM20 2JE, England
and Associated Companies throughout the world.

First published 1988
Second Edition 1993
Seventh Impression 1996

British Library Cataloguing in Publication Data

Barton, D.
   GCSE science. – (Longman GCSE revise guide)
   1 England. Secondary Schools. Curriculum subjects: Science.
   GCSE Examinations.
   Techniques
   I. Title
   570'.6

ISBN 0-582-228298

Set by 17QQ in 10/12pt Century Old Style

Produced by Longman Singapore Publishers Pte Ltd
Printed in Singapore

CONTENTS

EDITORS' PREFACE

Longman Revise Guides for GCSE/Key Stage 4 are written by experienced examiners and teachers, and aim to give you the best possible foundation for success in examinations and other modes of assessment. Much has been said in recent years about declining standards and disappointing examination results. While this may be somewhat exaggerated, examiners are well aware that the performance of many candidates falls well short of their potential. The books encourage thorough study and a full understanding of the concepts involved and should be seen as course companions and study guides to be used throughout the year. Examiners are in no doubt that a structured approach in preparing for examinations and in presenting coursework can, together with hard work and diligent application, substantially improve performance.

The largely self-contained nature of each chapter gives the book a useful degree of flexibility. After starting with Chapters 1 and 2, all other chapters can be read selectively, in any order appropriate to the stage you have reached in your course. As well as the examination-type questions and answers at the end of each chapter, you will also find a 'Review Sheet' to test yourself on the content of that chapter.

We believe that this book, and the series as a whole, will help you establish a solid platform of basic knowledge and examination technique on which to build.

Geoff Black and Stuart Wall

ACKNOWLEDGEMENTS

I am grateful to the following Examination Groups for permission to reproduce questions which have appeared in their examination papers. The questions from the Sample Assessment material for Key Stage 4 are included to give a reasonable idea of the type of questions which will appear in the Key Stage 4 examinations. However, the answers, or hints on any answers, are solely the responsibility of the author.

Midland Examining Group (MEG)
Northern Examinations and Assessment Board (NEAB)
Southern Examining Group (SEG)
University of London Examinations and Assessment Council (ULEAC)
University of Cambridge Local Examinations Syndicate (UCLES)
Welsh Joint Education Committee (WJEC)
Northern Ireland Council for Curriculum, Examinations and Assessment (NICCEA)

I would like to acknowledge the major contribution made by Mike Evans to the following chapters: Matter and Particles, The Periodic Table, Chemical Reactions, Acidity, Metals and Polymers, and also the major contribution made by Stuart Farmer to the chapters on Variation, Evolution and Inheritance, and Feedback and Control.

I would also like to thank Geoff Black and Stuart Wall for their help and guidance during the preparation of this book.

Di Barton

GETTING STARTED

Science has become an essential subject for all learners to study either as a single or a double award for Key Stage 4. The double award Science courses usually involve you in twice the amount of time for a single subject and lead to two qualifications. The double award is a good foundation for studying separate Sciences and some of the newer modular Science courses at A level or AS level.

The syllabuses from the examination groups are all based on the requirements of the National Curriculum for Science. However the syllabuses do vary in their interpretation of what you should study. It is well worth checking with your teacher exactly which syllabus you are studying and at what level so that you do not attempt to revise topics which may be at a higher level than you need.

At the end of each chapter there are some questions from the different examination groups, and outline answers. There are also some typical student answers with comments from an examiner. Some of the examination questions are based on the GCSE examination, others are based on sample assessment questions for Key Stage 4. However all the questions are of a similar style and assess similar abilities and will give you good experience in answering examination questions.

Remember you need to be actively involved in your revision, and to take responsibility for planning and organising your revision time. Meeting deadlines for submitting Coursework has become part of your school life. Try to plan your revision so that you meet the examination deadline as well.

ASSESSMENT IN SCIENCE

ATTAINMENT TARGETS

THE SYLLABUSES

TARGET RANGES OF LEVELS

ACHIEVING THE TARGETS

THE TERMINAL EXAMINATION PAPERS

YOUR FINAL CERTIFICATE

NEAB, ULEAC and WJEC

MEG

NICCEA

GCSE AND KEY STAGE 4 SCIENCE

The GCSE Science syllabuses offered by the various Examining Groups have been approved by the Schools Curriculum Assessment Authority (SCAA) and are designed to fulfil the requirements of the statutory National Curriculum Orders for Science. The syllabuses match both the Double Science and Single Science models of the National Curriculum at Key Stage 4.

1 ▷ ATTAINMENT TARGETS

All the syllabuses are based on the four **Attainment Targets** for Science and all syllabuses have to include the knowledge, skills and understanding specified in Attainment Targets 2, 3 and 4. These Targets are further divided into a number of *strands* as described below:

- **Attainment Target 1: Scientific Investigation** (see below)

- **Attainment Target 2: Life and Living Processes**
  Pupils should develop knowledge and understanding of:
    i)* life processes and the organisation of living things;
    ii)* variation and the mechanisms of inheritance and evolution;
    iii) populations and human influences within ecosystems;
    iv) energy flows and cycles of matter within ecosystems.

- **Attainment Target 3: Materials and Their Properties**
  Pupils should develop knowledge and understanding of:
    i)* the properties, classification and structure of materials;
    ii)* explanations of the properties of materials;
    iii) chemical changes;
    iv) the Earth and its atmosphere.

 *Topics are for Single Science award only*

- **Attainment Target 4: Physical Processes**
  Pupils should develop knowledge and understanding of:
    i)* electricity and magnetism;
    ii)* energy resources and energy transfer;
    iii) forces and their effects;
    iv) light and sound
    v) the Earth's place in the Universe.

Each Attainment Target is weighted at 25% in the Scheme of Assessment. The assessment of Attainment Target 1 will be by Coursework and assessed by your teachers during your course. Attainment Targets 2, 3 and 4 will be assessed by written examination papers, set and marked by the examination group.

Statements of Attainment

Each Attainment Target is sub-divided into **Statements of Attainment**, which are grouped at different levels. For the purposes of assessment at Key Stage 4 only levels 4 to 10 are stated. The Statements simply describe what a learner should be able to do at a particular level. For example in Attainment Target 2, Life and Living Processes, one of the five Statements of Attainment for *level 6* reads 'know that variation in living organisms has both genetic and environmental causes.' In the notes for guidance, one example of this would be 'to explain some possible causes of variation in human birth weight.'

Programmes of Study

Each Attainment Target is accompanied by a **Programme of Study** which sets out the essential ground to be covered to enable pupils to meet the attainment targets. The Programmes of Study are basically descriptive accounts of *how* learners should approach the Statements of Attainment. For example, the Programme of Study linked with the Statement of Attainment described above, states that 'Pupils should consider the interaction of genetic and environmental factors (including radiation) in variation.'

THE SYLLABUSES

Each **syllabus** divides up these 4 Attainment Targets in different ways. For example one Examining Group has divided the Attainment Targets into 18 *units* of study, such as Feedback and Control, Electricity and Magnetism, Fuels and Energy Sources, etc. Another has developed 55 *themes* based on the same four attainment targets.

The themes or units in each syllabus define fully the knowledge, skills and understanding that an examiner is entitled to expect of candidates. This is one reason why you, as a candidate, should attempt to obtain a copy of the correct syllabus for the Science course you are studying.

AIMS

The **aims** are a description of the purpose of the Syllabus and are often long-term goals which cannot necessarily be assessed in a written examination. It is hoped that you, as a learner, will meet these aims during your studies in Science. An example of a long term aim is:

'to stimulate an interest in, and care for, the environment.'

Aims and objectives

ASSESSMENT OBJECTIVES

The **assessment objectives** are a list of the abilities which you should develop as a result of studying Science and on which you will be assessed. There are two main groups of objectives: those associated with Attainment Target 1, Scientific Investigation, and those associated with Attainment Targets 2, 3 and 4, Knowledge and Understanding of Science.

Attainment Target 1: Scientific Investigation

Candidates should develop the intellectual and practical skills which will allow them to explore and investigate the world of Science and develop a fuller understanding of scientific phenomena, the nature of the theories explaining these, and the procedures for scientific investigation. This should take place through activities that require a progressively more systematic and quantified approach which develops and draws on an increasing knowledge and understanding of science. The activities should encourage the ability to plan and carry out investigations in which pupils:

One quarter of the marks involve investigation

- ask questions, predict and hypothesise;
- observe, measure and manipulate variables;
- interpret their results and evaluate scientific evidence.

Attainment Targets 2, 3 and 4: Knowledge and Understanding of Science

Candidates should be able to

Three quarters of the marks involve knowledge and understanding

- demonstrate the knowledge, skills and understanding specified by the Statements of Attainment in Attainment Targets 2, 3 and 4 (50%).
- Through the knowledge, skills and understanding specified, candidates should demonstrate the ability to:
  - communicate scientific observations, ideas and arguments effectively (5%);
  - select and use reference materials and translate data from one form to another (15%);
  - interpret, evaluate and make informed judgements from relevant facts, observations and phenomena (15%);
  - solve qualitative and quantitative problems (15%).

The figures in brackets represent one Examination Group's target weightings of these Assessment Objectives in the written examination.

The *scheme of assessment* in each Syllabus should describe how each of the Assessment Objectives will be assessed by the different components of the examination.

It is important that you, as a candidate, realise that the examination papers are not just going to test the recall of facts. The target weighting for the assessment of 'recall of facts' should not be more than 33% of the written examination papers, and should only form 25% of the total assessment.

TARGET RANGES OF LEVELS

Most of the Examining Groups offer terminal examination papers at three 'tiers' of entry. You will only be entered for one 'tier', i.e. for one examination which covers a specified range of target levels. Discussion between you, your teacher and your parents should help to decide on the most realistic entry option for you. If, however, you enter for a paper which proves to have been targeted at too high a level there is provision made for the award of *one grade lower* than the target grades. If, for example, you entered for the highest level paper, target levels 8-10, and failed to achieve level 8, you could still be awarded a level 7 if your work merited such an award.

The Examining Groups offer three options or tiers targeted at *overlapping* ranges of levels:

66 Options and Tiers of entry 99

Tier/ Option	Levels targeted	Levels available	Grades available
Basic Option P	4, 5, 6	3, 4, 5, 6 (7)	G to D(C)
Central Option Q	6, 7, 8	5, 6, 7, 8 (9)	(F)E to B(A)
Further Option R	8, 9, 10	7, 8, 9, 10	(D, C)B to A*

The award of grade C for the Basic tier (Option P) and the award of grade A for the Central tier (Option Q) will be considered in exceptional circumstances only.

We now look at how you can achieve each target level for each of the four attainment targets. You can use this as a checklist at various times in your course. The targets outlined here are for the double science award, although they are very similar for the single science award.

---

4 ▷ ACHIEVING THE TARGETS

ATTAINMENT TARGET 1: SCIENTIFIC INVESTIGATION

We have already outlined the broad objectives of this Attainment Target. Here are the specific requirements for reaching each level.

Statements of Attainment

Pupils should carry out investigations in which they:

Level 4
a) ask questions, suggest ideas and make predictions, based on some relevant prior knowledge, in a form which can be investigated.
b) carry out a fair test in which they select and use appropriate instruments to measure quantities such as volume and temperature.

66 Achieving the levels for each Target 99

c) draw conclusions which link patterns in observations or results to the original question, prediction or idea.

Level 5
a) formulate hypotheses where the causal link is based on scientific knowledge, understanding or theory.
b) choose the range of each of the variables involved to produce meaningful results.
c) evaluate the validity of their conclusions by considering different interpretations of their experimental evidence.

Level 6
a) use scientific knowledge, understanding of theory to predict relationships between continuous variables.
b) consider the range of factors involved, identify the key variables and those to be

controlled and/or taken account of, and make qualitative or quantitative observations involving fine discrimination.
c) use their results to draw conclusions, explain the relationship between variables and refer to a model to explain the results.

Level 7
a) use scientific knowledge, understanding or theory to predict the relative effect of a number of variables.
b) manipulate or take account of the relative effect of two or more independent variables.
c) use observations or results to draw conclusions which state the relative effects of the independent variables and explain the limitations of the evidence obtained.

Level 8
a) use scientific knowledge, understanding or theory to generate quantitative predictions and a strategy for the investigation.
b) select and use measuring instruments which provide the degree of accuracy commensurate with the outcome they have predicted.
c) justify each aspect of the investigation in terms of the contribution to the overall conclusion.

Level 9
a) use a scientific theory to make quantitative predictions and organise the collection of valid and reliable data.
b) systematically use a range of investigatory techniques to judge the relative effect of the factors involved.
c) analyse and interpret the data obtained, in terms of complex functions where

appropriate, in a way which demonstrates an appreciation of the uncertainty of evidence and the tentative nature of conclusions.

Level 10
a) use scientific knowledge and an understanding of laws, theories and models to develop hypotheses which seek to explain the behaviour of objects and events they have studied.
b) collect data which is sufficiently valid and reliable to enable them to make a critical evaluation of the law, theory or model.
c) use and analyse the data obtained to evaluate the law, theory or model in terms of the extent to which it can explain the observed behaviour.

ATTAINMENT TARGET 2: LIFE AND LIVING PROCESSES

Pupils should develop knowledge and understanding of:
i) life processes and the organisation of living things;
ii) variation and the mechanisms of inheritance and evolution;
iii) populations and human influences within ecosystems;
iv) energy flows and cycles of matter within ecosystems.

Statements Of Attainment

Pupils should:

Level 4
a) be able to name and locate the major organs of the human body and of the flowering plant.
b) be able to assign plants and animals to their major groups using keys and observable features.
c) understand that the survival of plants and animals in an environment depends on successful competition for scarce resources.
d) understand food chains as a way of representing feeding relationships in an ecosystem.

Level 5
a) be able to name and outline the functions of the major organ systems in mammals and in flowering plants.
b) know that information in the form of genes is passed on from one generation to the next.
c) know how pollution can affect the survival of organisms.
d) know about the key factors in the process of decay.

Level 6
a) be able to relate structure to function in plant and animal cells.
b) know the ways in which living organisms are adapted to survive in their natural environment.
c) know that variation in living organisms has both genetic and environmental causes.
d) understand population changes in predator-prey relationships.
e) know that the balance of materials in a biological community can be maintained by the cycling of these materials.

Level 7
a) understand the life process of movement, respiration, growth, reproduction, excretion, nutrition and sensitivity in animals.
b) understand the life processes of photosynthesis, respiration and reproduction in green plants.
c) understand how selective breeding can produce economic benefits and contribute to improved yields.
d) know how population growth and decline is related to environmental resources.
e) understand pyramids of numbers and biomass.

Level 8
a) be able to describe how the internal environment in plants, animals and the human embryo is maintained.
b) know how genetic information is passed from cell to cell and from generation to generation by cell division.
c) understand the principles of a monohybrid cross involving dominant and recessive alleles.
d) understand that the impact of human activity on the Earth is related to the size of the population, economic factors and industrial requirements.
e) understand the role of microbes and other living organisms in the process of decay and in the cycling of nutrients.

Level 9
a) be able to explain the coordination in mammals of the body's activities through nervous and hormonal control.
b) understand the different sources of genetic variation.
c) understand the relationships between variation, natural selection and reproductive success in organisms and the significance of these relationships for evolution.
d) understand the basic scientific principles associated with a major change in the biosphere.
e) understand how materials for growth and energy are transferred through an ecosystem.

Level 10
a) understand how homeostatic and metabolic processes contribute to maintaining the internal environment of organisms.
b) understand how DNA replicates and controls protein synthesis by means of a base code.
c) understand the basic principles of genetic engineering, selective breeding and cloning, and how these give rise to social and ethical issues.
d) understand how food production involves the management of ecosystems to improve the efficiency of energy transfer, and that such management imposes a duty of care.

ATTAINMENT TARGET 3: MATERIALS AND THEIR PROPERTIES

Pupils should develop knowledge and understanding of:
i) the properties, classification and structure

of materials;
ii) explanations of the properties of materials;
iii) chemical changes;
iv) the Earth and its atmosphere.

Statements Of Attainment

Pupils should:

Level 4
a) be able to classify materials as solids, liquids and gases on the basis of simple properties which relate to their everyday uses.
b) know that materials from a variety of sources can be converted into new and useful products by chemical reactions.
c) know that the combustion of fuel releases energy and produces waste gases.
d) know how measurements of temperature, rainfall, windspeed and direction describe the weather.
e) know that weathering, erosion and transport lead to the formation of sediments and different types of soil.

“ Attainment Target 3: Materials and their Properties ”

Level 5
a) know how to separate and purify the components of mixtures using physical processes.
b) be able to classify aqueous solutions as acidic, alkaline or neutral, using indicators.
c) understand that rusting and burning involve a reaction with oxygen.
d) understand the water cycle in terms of the physical processes involved.

Level 6
a) be able to distinguish between metallic and non-metallic elements, mixtures and compounds using simple chemical and physical properties.
b) understand the physical differences between solids, liquids and gases in simple particle terms.
c) understand oxidation processes, including combustion, as reactions with oxygen to form oxides.
d) be able to recognise variations in the properties of metals and make predictions based on the reactivity series.
e) know that some chemical reactions are exothermic, while others are endothermic.
f) know about the readily observable effects of electrolysis.
g) understand how different airstreams give different weather related to their recent path over land and sea.
h) understand the scientific processes involved in the formation of igneous, sedimentary and metamorphic rocks including the timescales over which these processes operated.

Level 7
a) be able to relate the properties of a variety of classes of materials to their everyday uses.
b) know that the periodic table groups contain families of elements with similar properties, which depend on their electronic structure.
c) understand changes of state, including the associated energy changes, mixing and diffusion in terms of the proximity and motion of particles.
d) understand the relationships between the volume, pressure and temperature of a gas.
e) understand the difference between

elements, compounds and mixtures in terms of atoms, ions and molecules.
f) understand the factors which influence the rate of a chemical reaction.
g) be able to relate knowledge and understanding of chemical principles to manufacturing processes and everyday effects.
h) understand how some weather phenomena are driven by energy transfer processes.

Level 8
a) know the major characteristics of metals and non-metals as reflected in the properties of a range of their compounds.
b) understand the structure of the atom in terms of protons, neutrons and electrons and how this can explain the existence of isotopes.
c) understand radioactivity and nuclear fission and the harmful and beneficial effects of ionising radiations.
d) be able to relate the properties of molecular and giant structures to the arrangement of atoms and ions.
e) be able to explain the physical and chemical processes by which different chemicals are made from oil.
f) be able to use symbolic equations to describe and explain a range of reactions including ionic interactions and those occurring in electrolytic cells.
g) understand how the atmosphere has evolved and how its composition remains broadly constant.
h) be able to interpret evidence of modes of formation and deformation of rocks.

Level 9
a) understand how the properties of elements depend on their electronic structure and their position in the periodic table.
b) understand the nature of radioactive decay, relating half-life to the use of radioactive materials.
c) be able to interpret chemical equations quantitatively.
d) be able to use scientific information from a range of sources to evaluate the social, economic, health and safety and environmental factors associated with a major manufacturing process.
e) be able to use appropriate scientific ideas to explain changes in the atmosphere that cause various weather phenomena.
f) be able to describe and explain the supporting evidence, in simple terms, for the layered structure of the inner Earth.

Level 10
a) be able to use data on the properties of different materials in order to make evaluative judgements about their uses.
b) understand chemical reactions in terms of the energy transfers associated with making and breaking chemical bonds.
c) be able to relate the bulk properties of metals, ceramics, glass, plastics and fibres to simple models of their structure.
d) be able to interpret electrolytic processes quantitatively.

ATTAINMENT TARGET 4: PHYSICAL PROCESSES

Pupils should develop knowledge and understanding of:
 i)   electricity and magnetism;
 ii) energy resources and energy transfer;
 iii) forces and their effects;
 iv) light and sound;
 v)   the Earth's place in the Universe.

Statements Of Attainment

Pupils should:

Level 4
a) be able to construct circuits containing a number of components in which switches are used to control electrical effects.
b) understand that an energy transfer is needed to make things work.
c) know that more than one force can act on an object and that forces can act in different directions.
d) know that light travels faster than sound.
e) be able to explain day and night, day length and year length in terms of the movements of the Earth around the Sun.

Level 5
a) know how switches, relays, variable resistors, sensors and logic gates can be used to solve simple problems.
b) understand that energy is transferred in any process and recognise transfers in a range of devices.
c) understand the difference between renewable and non-renewable energy resources and the need for fuel economy.
d) know that the size and direction of the resultant force on an object affects its movement.
e) understand how the reflection of light enables objects to be seen.
f) know that sound is produced by a vibrating object and travels as a wave.
g) be able to describe the motion of planets in the solar system.

Level 6
a) understand the qualitative relationships between current, voltage and resistance.
b) understand that energy is conserved.
c) understand that the Sun is ultimately the major energy source for the Earth.
d) understand the relationship between an applied force, the area over which it acts and the resulting pressure.
e) understand the relationship between speed, distance and time.
f) be able to relate loudness and amplitude, pitch and frequency, of a sound wave.
g) know that the solar system forms part of a galaxy which is part of a larger system called the Universe.

Level 7
a) understand the magnetic effect of an electric current and its application in a range of common devices.
b) understand how energy is transferred through conduction, convection and radiation.
c) be able to evaluate methods of reducing wasteful transfers of energy by using a definition of energy efficiency.
d) understand the quantitative relationships between force, distance, work, power and time.
e) understand the law of moments.
f) be able to use the wave model of light to explain refraction at a plane surface.
g) know that gravity acts between all masses and the magnitude of the force diminishes with distance.

Level 8
a) be able to explain charge flow and energy transfer in a circuit.
b) be able to use the quantitative relationship between change in internal energy and temperature change.
c) understand the quantitative relationship between force, mass and acceleration.
d) understand the quantitative relationship between speed, frequency and wavelength.
e) be able to explain resonance in oscillating systems and how this can be advantageous and disadvantageous.
f) be able to use data on the solar system or other stellar systems to speculate about the conditions elsewhere in the Universe.

Level 9
a) be able to use the quantitative relationships between charge, current, potential difference, resistance and electrical power.
b) be able to evaluate the economic, environmental and social benefits of different energy sources, using quantitative secondary sources of information.
c) be able to use the quantitative relationships between mass, weight, potential energy, kinetic energy and work.
d) be able to relate the physical properties of the main areas of the electromagnetic spectrum to their uses and effects.
e) be able to relate the theory of gravitational force to the motion of the satellites.

Level 10
a) understand the principles of electro-magnetic induction.
b) understand that in many processes energy is spread out into the surroundings and shared amongst many particles, so reducing the possibility of further useful energy transfers.
c) understand the concept of momentum and its conservation.
d) be able to relate an understanding of the nature of electromagnetic radiation to its behaviour in the processes of interference, diffraction, and polarisation.
e) be able to relate current theories about the origin and future of the Universe to the astronomical evidence.

All the written terminal examination papers set by the Examining Groups are similar in format and style. They all contain compulsory, structured questions which are answered on the question paper. Spaces and lines are left for your answer so that you can see how much you need to write. The number of marks allocated for each answer are given in brackets on the question paper. The papers for the basic (lower) tier, aimed at levels 4 to 6, contain more short-answer questions. The papers aimed at levels 6 to 10 provide more opportunity for extended writing. For example, you may be given 8 or 10 marks and a page of lines on which to compose your answer. The papers will also contain calculations of appropriate complexity for that level of paper.

Where the assessment is only by Terminal Examination and Coursework, the examination papers are worth 75% of the total assessment and the Coursework is 25%. In the *modular* schemes, the various Module Tests are worth 25%, the Coursework is worth a further 25%, and the value of the Terminal Examination is reduced to 50%.

SPELLING, PUNCTUATION AND GRAMMAR

In each written terminal examination paper, 5% of the marks have been allocated for the use of accurate spelling, punctuation and grammar according to the following criteria. Each 'level' corresponds to a particular level of competence in spelling, punctuation and grammar.

Pay attention to spelling, punctuation and grammar

- *Threshold performance*. Candidates spell, punctuate and use the rules of grammar with reasonable accuracy; they use a limited range of specialist terms appropriately.
- *Intermediate performance*. Candidates spell, punctuate and use the rules of grammar with considerable accuracy; they use a good range of specialist terms with facility.
- *High performance*. Candidates spell, punctuate and use the rules of grammar with almost faultless accuracy, deploying a range of grammatical constructions; they use a wide range of specialist terms adeptly and with precision.

In a written paper of 100 marks, the number of marks allocated for reaching each level of competence is as follows:

- *level 1*: 1 mark allocated
- *level 2*: 2-3 marks allocated
- *level 3*: 4-5 marks allocated

6 ▷ YOUR FINAL CERTIFICATE

Your examination result for Key Stage 4 will be reported using letter grades A–G which correspond to the levels of the National Curriculum 10-point scale. Certificates will be issued to candidates gaining level 4 and above. The chart shows the link between the new Levels and the GCSE grades. Note that level 9 is represented by A and Level 10 by starred A (A*)

GCSE Grades	Key Stage 4 Levels
A*	10
A	9
B	8
C	7
D	6
E	
F	5
G	4
U	3

In the Science: Double Award scheme, candidates will receive double certificates as *pairs of identical levels* for the whole subject; for example 5, 5 (never different levels such as 6, 4). In the Science: Single Award scheme, candidates will receive a single certificate.

There is no stated 'pass mark' for a particular level. The number of marks required for a particular level will be agreed by the Examination Group depending on the difficulty of the exam paper. The same *standard* will however be maintained from one year to the next.

THE SCHEMES OF ASSESSMENT OF EACH EXAMINING GROUP

Three of the Examining Groups offer almost identical schemes of Assessment:

- Northern Examinations and Assessment Board (NEAB)
- University of London Examinations and Assessment Council (ULEAC)
- Welsh Joint Examinations Council (WJEC)

Schemes of Assessment

These Groups offer three different schemes for assessment:

- **Co-ordinated/Combined Scheme:** the separate areas of Science may be taught by different teachers. This is assessed by Terminal Examination and Coursework (Single and Double Award).
- **Integrated Scheme:** the syllabus is arranged to stress the inter-relationships between the different themes. This is assessed by Terminal Examination and Coursework (Double Award only).
- **Modular Scheme:** the themes are arranged into a range of modules or units of study. This is assessed by Terminal Examination, Module Tests and Coursework (Single or Double Award).

In the Co-ordinated and Integrated schemes, the Terminal Examination is 75% and the Coursework is 25%. In the Modular Scheme, the Module Tests together carry 25%, Coursework a further 25%, and the Terminal Examination 50%.

CO-ORDINATED SCIENCE: DOUBLE AWARD

Terminal Examination AT 2, 3 and 4 (75%)

	Levels		Grades
Option P (Tier F)	4-6(7)	Paper 1 ($1\frac{1}{2}$ hrs) and Paper 2 ($1\frac{1}{2}$ hrs) Short answer and structured questions	G to D (C)
Option Q (Tier I)	(5)6-8(9)	Paper 3 (2 hrs) and Paper 4 (2 hrs) Structured questions	(F)E to B(A)
Option R (Tier H)	(7)8-10	Paper 5 ($2\frac{1}{2}$ hrs) and Paper 6 ($2\frac{1}{2}$ hrs) Structured questions	(D, C)B to A*

This pattern applies to NEAB and ULEAC. For WJEC there are three papers for each option. For option P, papers 1, 2 and 3 are each 1 hour, for option Q, papers 4, 5 and 6 are each $1\frac{1}{2}$ hours and for option R, papers 7, 8 and 9 are each 2 hours.

All papers will have opportunity for extended writing and may contain calculations of appropriate complexity.

Coursework AT 1 (25%)

Coursework will assess the three skills stated under AT 1. A single overall assessment for each of the three skills must be submitted based on assessments made during normal Coursework.

CO-ORDINATED SCIENCE: SINGLE AWARD

Terminal Examination AT 2, 3 and 4 (75%)

	Levels		Grades
Option P (Tier F)	4-6(7)	Paper 1 ($1\frac{1}{2}$ hrs) Short answer and structured questions	G to D(C)
Option Q (Tier I)	(5)6-8(9)	Paper 2 (2 hrs) Structured questions	(F)E to B(A)

Option R (Tier H)	(7)8-10	Paper 3 ($2\frac{1}{2}$ hrs) Structured questions	(D, C)B to A*

All papers will have opportunity for extended writing and may contain calculations of appropriate complexity.

Common questions will be used in these papers and the Co-ordinated Science Double Award Scheme.

Coursework AT 1 (25%)

Coursework will assess the three skills stated under AT 1. A single overall assessment for each of the three skills must be submitted based on assessments made during normal Coursework.

INTEGRATED SCIENCE: DOUBLE AWARD

Terminal Examination AT 2, 3 and 4 (75%)

	Levels		Grades
Option P (Tier F)	4-6(7)	Paper 1 ($1\frac{1}{2}$ hrs) and Paper 2 ($1\frac{1}{2}$ hrs) Short answer and structured questions	G to D(C)
Option Q (Tier I)	(5)6-8(9)	Paper 3 (2 hrs) and Paper 4 (2 hrs) Structured questions	(F)E to B(A)
Option R (Tier H)	(7)8-10	Paper 5 ($2\frac{1}{2}$ hrs) and Paper 6 ($2\frac{1}{2}$ hrs) Structured questions	(D, C)B to A*

All papers will have opportunity for extended writing and may contain calculations of appropriate complexity.

Coursework AT 1 (25%)

Coursework will assess the three skills stated under AT 1. A single overall assessment for each of the three skills must be submitted based on assessments made during normal Coursework.

THE MODULAR SCHEMES - SCIENCE: DOUBLE AWARD AND SINGLE AWARD

Terminal Examination AT 2, 3 and 4 (50%)

Science: Double Award

	Levels		Grades
Option P (Tier F)	4-6(7)	Paper 1 (1 hr) and Paper 2 (1 hr) Short answer and structured questions	G to D(C)
Option Q (Tier I)	(5)6-8(9)	Paper 3 ($1\frac{1}{2}$ hrs) and Paper 4 ($1\frac{1}{2}$ hrs) Structured questions	(F)E to B(A)
Option R (Tier H)	(7)8-10	Paper 5 (2 hrs) and Paper 6 (2 hrs) Structured questions	(D, C)B to A*

Science: Single Award

	Levels		Grades
Option P (Tier F)	4-6(7)	Paper 1 (1 hr) Short answer and structured questions	G to D(C)
Option Q (Tier I)	(5)6-8(9)	Paper 2 ($1\frac{1}{2}$ hrs) Structured questions	(F)E to B(A)
Option R (Tier H)	(7)8-10	Paper 3 (2 hrs) Structure questions	(D, C)B to A*

Different papers are used for the Single and Double Award examination but many of the questions are common.

All papers will have opportunity for extended writing and may contain calculations of appropriate complexity.

Module Tests (25%)

Candidates take different sections of the module test appropriate to their expected attainment in that module.

	Levels		Grades
General (G) Section A	4-7(8)	(20/30 minutes)	G to C(B)
Higher (H) Section B	(6)7-10	(20/30 minutes)	(E)D to A*

The number of Module Tests varies between Groups depending on how the course is arranged. For example, in the ULEAC Modular Science, the module tests are set and marked by the Examining Group for each of the nine modules studied. Each test consists of 18 multiple choice questions and lasts for 20 minutes. Double award candidates take all nine modules, single award candidates take five module tests.

Coursework AT 1 (25%)

Coursework will assess the three skills stated under AT 1. A single overall assessment for each of the three skills must be submitted based on assessments made during normal Coursework.

Summary of Modules   (S indicates Single Award modules)

S	1	Processes of Life
S	2	Reproduction and Inheritance
	3	Ecosystems
	4	Earth and Space
S	5	Materials
	6	Chemical Changes
S	7	Electricity and Magnetism
	8	Light and Sound
S	9	Forces and Energy

COMBINED SCIENCE: ULEAC

ULEAC also offer Combined Science Double Award (1524) and Combined Science Single Award (1527)

Combined Science: Double Award (1524)

Terminal Examination AT 2, 3 and 4 (75%)

	Levels		Grades
Foundation tier	4-6(7)	Paper 2F ($1\frac{1}{2}$ hrs) (AT 2) Paper 3F ($1\frac{1}{2}$ hrs) (AT 3) Paper 4F ($1\frac{1}{2}$ hrs) (AT 4)	G to D(C)
Intermediate tier	(5)6-8(9)	Paper 2I ($1\frac{1}{2}$ hrs) (AT 2) Paper 3I ($1\frac{1}{2}$ hrs) (AT 3) Paper 4I ($1\frac{1}{2}$ hrs) (AT 4)	(F)E to B(A)
Higher tier	(7)8-10	Paper 2H ($1\frac{1}{2}$ hrs) (AT 2) Paper 3H ($1\frac{1}{2}$ hrs) (AT 3) Paper 4H ($1\frac{1}{2}$ hrs) (AT 4)	(D, C)B to A*

Combined Science: Single Award (1527)

Terminal Examination AT 2, 3 and 4 (75%)

	Levels		Grades
Foundation tier	4-6(7)	Paper 2F (1 hr) (AT 2) Paper 3F (1 hr) (AT 3) Paper 4F (1 hr) (AT 4)	G to D(C)
Intermediate tier	(5)6-8(9)	Paper 2I (1 hr) (AT 2) Paper 3I (1 hr) (AT 3) Paper 4I (1 hr) (AT 4)	(F)E to B(A)
Higher tier	(7)8-10	Paper 2H (1 hr) (AT 2) Paper 3H (1 hr) (AT 3) Paper 4H (1 hr) (AT 4)	(D, C)B to A*

Coursework AT 1 (25%)

Coursework for both Double and Single Award will assess the three skills stated under AT 1.

SUMMARY OF THEMES COMMON TO NEAB, ULEAC, WJEC SYLLABUSES

2.1.1 Organs, organ systems and life processes
2.1.2 Lifestyle and health
2.1.3 Technology and Life Processes
2.1.4 Homeostasis

2.2.1 Diversity and variation
2.2.2 The mechanisms of inheritance
2.2.3 Selection, evolution and genetic engineering

2.3.1 Habitats
2.3.2 Populations
2.3.3 Human influences on the environment

2.4.1 Energy flows in ecosystems
2.4.2 Microbes, decay and cycles of matter within ecosystems

3.1.1 Metals, non-metals and the periodic table
3.1.2 Reactivity series of metals
3.1.3 Acids
3.1.4 Properties and uses of materials
3.1.5 Mixtures

3.2.1 Gas laws
3.2.2 Particles model of matter
3.2.3 Different sorts of particles
3.2.4 Radioactivity

3.3.1 Types of chemical reactions
3.3.2 Rates of reactions
3.3.3 Chemical equations
3.3.4 Energy transfer in chemical reactions
3.3.5 The chemical industry

3.4.1 Atmosphere and weather

3.4.2 Origins and maintenance of the atmosphere and oceans
3.4.3 Rocks - weathering, formation and age
3.4.4 Earth structure and tectonics

4.1.1 Using mains electricity
4.1.2 Electrostatics
4.1.3 Magnets and electromagnets
4.1.4 Electromagnetic induction
4.1.5 Electrical measurements
4.1.6 Circuits
4.1.7 Charge flow

4.2.1 Energy transfers
4.2.2 Energy measurements
4.2.3 Energy conservation and efficiency
4.2.4 Energy resources

4.3.1 Forces and motion
4.3.2 Momentum
4.3.3 Pressure
4.3.4 Forces on materials and structures
4.3.5 Machines, turning effects and stability
4.3.6 Floating and sinking

4.4.1 Properties of sound
4.4.2 Using sound
4.4.3 Properties of light
4.4.4 The electromagnetic spectrum
4.4.5 Optical devices

4.5.1 Observing and explaining the solar system
4.5.2 The nature of the Sun and the planets
4.5.3 Solar System and Universe - origins and evolution

8 SOUTHERN EXAMINING GROUP (SEG)

There are four different Schemes of Assessment on offer:
Science: Single Award (2420); Science: Double Award (2421);
Science (Modular) Single Award (2422); Science: Double Award (2423).

SCIENCE: DOUBLE AWARD (2421)

Terminal Examination AT 2, 3 and 4 (75%)

	Levels		Grades
Foundation tier	4-6(7)	Paper 2 ($1\frac{1}{2}$ hrs) (AT 2)	G to D(C)
		Paper 3 ($1\frac{1}{2}$ hrs) (AT 3)	
		Paper 4 ($1\frac{1}{2}$ hrs) (AT 4)	
Intermediate tier	(5)6-8(9)	Paper 5 ($1\frac{1}{2}$ hrs) (AT 2)	(F)E to B(A)
		Paper 6 ($1\frac{1}{2}$ hrs) (AT 3)	
		Paper 7 ($1\frac{1}{2}$ hrs) (AT 4)	
Higher tier	(7)8-10	Paper 8 ($1\frac{1}{2}$ hrs) (AT 2)	(C)B to A*
		Paper 9 ($1\frac{1}{2}$ hrs) (AT 3)	
		Paper 10 ($1\frac{1}{2}$ hrs) (AT 4)	

All papers consist of compulsory structured questions with answers written on the question paper. There will be opportunity for some extended writing.

SCIENCE: SINGLE AWARD (2420)

The pattern is similar for Science: Single Award except that each paper lasts one hour.

Coursework AT 1 (25%)

Coursework will assess each of the three skills stated under AT 1. The investigations used must be set in the context of the subject content for Attainment Targets 2, 3 and 4.

Summary of themes. (D) indicates double award only

Sc 2 Life and living process
A   Life processes and the organisation of living things
B   Variation and the mechanism of evolution
C   Populations and human influences within ecosystems (D)
D   Energy flows and cycles of matter within ecosystems (D)

Sc 3 Materials and their properties
A   The properties, classification and structure of materials
B   Explanations of the properties of materials
C   Chemical changes (D)
D   The Earth and its atmosphere (D)

Sc 4 Physical processes
A   Electricity and magnetism
B   Energy resources and energy transfer
C   Forces and their effects
D   Light and Sound (D)
E   The Earth's place in the Universe (D)

SCIENCE: SINGLE AWARD (MODULAR) (2422)

Terminal Examination AT 2, 3 and 4 (50%)

	Levels		Grades
Foundation tier	4-6(7)	Paper 1 (90 marks) ($1\frac{1}{2}$ hrs)	G to D(C)
Intermediate tier	(5)6-8(9)	Paper 2 (120 marks) (2 hrs)	(F)E to B(A)
Higher tier	(7)8-10	Paper 3 (120 marks) (2 hrs)	(C)B to A*

The papers will consist of 3 sections:
Section A will contain questions on modules 1 and 2 (AT 2)
Section B will contain questions on module 5 (AT 3)
Section C will contain questions on modules 7 and 9 (AT 4).

The papers will consist of short answer and structured questions all compulsory, with some opportunity for extended writing.

Module Tests (25%)

Candidates will take five module tests which are set and marked by the Examining Group. Each test will consist of 18 multiple choice questions and last for 20 minutes. There are two tiers of test available and candidates can take different tiers for different modules if appropriate.

	Levels	Grades
General Tier	4-8	G to C(B)
Higher Tier	(6, 7)8-10	(E)D to A*

Coursework AT 1 (25%)

Coursework will assess each of the three skills stated under AT 1. The investigations used must be set in the context of the subject content for Attainment Targets 2, 3 and 4.

SCIENCE: DOUBLE AWARD (MODULAR) 2423

First Terminal Examination 2, 3 and 4 (25%)

	Levels		Grades
Foundation tier	4-6(7)	Paper 1 (90 marks) (1$\frac{1}{2}$ hrs)	G to D(C)
Intermediate tier	(5)6-8(9)	Paper 2 (120 marks) (2 hrs)	(F)E to B(A)
Higher tier	(7)8-10	Paper 3 (120 marks) (2 hrs)	(C)B to A*

The paper will consist of 3 sections:

Section A will contain questions on modules 1 and 2 (AT 2)
Section B will contain questions on module 5 (AT 3)
Section C will contain questions on modules 7 and 9 (AT 4)

These papers are common to the single and double award syllabuses.

Second Terminal Examination 2, 3 and 4 (25%)

	Levels		Grades
Foundation tier	4-6(7)	Paper 4 (90 marks) (1$\frac{1}{2}$ hrs)	G to D(C)
Intermediate tier	(5)6-8(9)	Paper 5 (120 marks) (2 hrs)	(F)E to B(A)
Higher tier	(7)8-10	Paper 6 (120 marks) (2 hrs)	(C)B to A*

The papers will consist of 3 sections:

Section A will contain questions on module 3 (AT 3)
Section B will contain questions on part of module 4 and all of 6 (AT 3)
Section C will contain questions on part of module 4 and all of 8 (AT 4).

The papers will consist of short answer and structured questions, all compulsory, with some opportunity for extended writing.

Module Tests (25%)

Candidates will take nine module tests which are set and marked by the Examining Group. Each test will consist of 18 multiple choice questions and last for 20 minutes. There are two tiers of test available and candidates can take different tiers for different modules if appropriate.

	Levels	Grades
General Tier	4-8	G to C(B)
Higher Tier	(6, 7)8-10	(E)D to A*

Coursework AT 1 (25%)

Coursework will assess each of the three skills stated under AT 1. The investigations used must be set in the context of the subject content for Attainment Targets 2, 3 and 4.

The 9 Modules to be studied for Double Science are as listed below:
(the S prefix indicates the five modules studied for Single Science)

Modules for SEG Double Science

S1	Processes of Life	AT 2
S2	Reproduction and Inheritance	AT 2
3	Ecosystems	AT 2
4	Earth and Space	AT 3 and 4
S5	Materials	AT 3
6	Chemical Changes	AT 3
S7	Electricity and Magnetism	AT 4
8	Light and Sound	AT 4
S9	Forces and Energy	AT 4

9 ▶ MIDLAND EXAMINING GROUP (MEG)

MEG offers several different schemes of assessment:

- Science: Double Award (1770)
- Science: Single Award (1771)
- Nuffield Co-ordinated Sciences: Double Award (1772)
- Nuffield Co-ordinated Sciences: Single Award (1773)
- Co-ordinated Science (The Suffolk Development) (1777)
- Science: (Salters) Double Award(1774)
- Science: (Salters) Single Award (1775)

SCIENCE DOUBLE AWARD (1770) AND SINGLE AWARD (1771)

Syllabus Content

For Science: Double Award (1770), 18 units of work are required and 10 units (marked *) are required for Science: Single Award (1771):

Units for MEG Double Award and Single Award*

1	Sound and Hearing	10*	Fuels and Energy Sources
2	Light and Sight	11	Energy Flow and Ecosystems
3	Space and Communication	12	Weather and Atmosphere
4*	Feedback and Control	13	Rocks
5	Raw Materials	14*	Plants
6	Reactions	15*	Animals
7*	Structures and Properties	16*	The Body at Work
8*	Patterns and Trends	17*	Plants at Work
9*	Electricity and Magnetism	18*	Forces and Machines

NUFFIELD CO-ORDINATED SCIENCES: DOUBLE AWARD (1772) AND SINGLE AWARD (1773)

Syllabus Content

For Nuffield Co-ordinated Sciences: Double Award (1772) there are 65 'chapters of work' under four broad headings, Biology (B1-23), Chemistry (C1-18), Physics (P1-21), Earth and Environment (E1-3). For the Single Award (1773) the content is a sub-set of these 65 'chapters', i.e. only those statements printed in bold type in the syllabus need be studied.

B1, B2	The Principles of Biological Classification and the Diversity of Organisms	B 4	How do Animals Feed?
		B 5	Digestion
		B 6	Diet and Good Health
B 3	Photosynthesis	B 7	Gaseous Exchange in Animals

Chapters of work for Nuffield Double Award

B 8	Transport Systems	C 12	Chemicals in the Medicine Cupboard
B 9	Aerobic and Anaerobic Respiration	C 13	Fuels and Fires
B 10	Support in Terrestrial Organisms	C 14	Batteries
		C 15	Soil
B 11	Responding to Changes in the Environment	C 16	Fertilisers
		C 17	The Periodic Table
B 12	Homeostasis	C 18	Atoms and Bonding
B 13	The Nature of the Environment		
B 14	Food Relationships between Organisms	P 1	The Strength of Solids
		P 2	Particles in Motion
B 15	Cycles of Minerals in the Ecosystem	P 3	Radioactivity
		P 4	Motion
B 16	Colonising the Habitat	P 5	Force and Motion
B 17	Affecting the Environment	P 6	Kinetic Energy and Momentum
B 18	Conservation of Habitats	P 7	Gravity
B 19	Reproduction	P 8	Machines and Engines
B 20	Human Sexuality	P 9 and	
B 21	Growth and Development	P 10	Transferring Energy
B 22	Inheritance	P 11	Energy Transmission
B 23	Evolution	P 12	Energy Resources
		P 13	Light and Sound
C 1	The Elements of Chemistry	P 14	Making Waves
C 2	Petrochemicals	P 15	Making Use of Waves
C 3	Chemical from Plants	P 16	Electricity
C 4	Chemical and Rocks	P 17	Energy and Electricity
C 5	Materials and Structures	P 18	Making more use of Electricity
C 6	Glasses and Ceramics	P 19	Electronics
C 7	Metals and Alloys	P 20	Control - An Introduction to Electronics
C 8	Polymers		
C 9	Foams, Emulsions, Sols and Gels	P 21	Communication
C 10	Keeping Clean	E 1	Weather
C 11	Dyes and Dyeing	E 2	Geology
C 12	Chemicals in the Medicine	E 3	Space

SCHEMES OF ASSESSMENT

Science: Double Award (1770), Single Award (1771)

Terminal Examination AT 2, 3 and 4 (75%)

	Levels		Double	Single		Grades
Basic Tier	4-6(7)	Paper 1	$(1\frac{1}{4}$ hrs)	$[1\frac{1}{2}$ hrs] Paper 2	$(1\frac{1}{4}$ hrs)	G to D(C)
Central Tier	(5)6-8(9)	Paper 3	(1 hr)	[2 hrs] Paper 4	$(1\frac{3}{4}$ hrs)	(F)E to B(A)
Further Tier	(7)8-10	Paper 5	(2 hrs)	$[2\frac{1}{4}$ hrs] Paper 6	(2 hrs)	(D, C)B to A*

The terminal examination papers consist of compulsory short answer structured questions with opportunity for some extended writing, especially on the higher level papers. There will be some common question material on the papers of different levels.

Nuffield Co-ordinated Sciences: Double Award (1772), Single Award (1773) *Terminal Examination AT 2, 3 and 4* (75%)

Tier	Levels		Double	Single	Grades
Basic	4-6(7)	Paper 1, 2, 3	(1 hr)	$[\frac{3}{4}$ hr]	G to D(C)
Central	5-8(9)	Paper 4, 5, 6	$(1\frac{1}{2}$ hrs)	[1 hr]	F to B(A)
Further	7-10	Paper 7, 8, 9	$(1\frac{3}{4}$ hrs)	$[1\frac{1}{4}$ hrs]	D to A*

Each of the three papers covers a separate attainment target, for example papers 1, 4 and 7 cover AT 2, papers 2, 5 and 8 cover AT 3 and papers 3, 6, and 9 cover AT 4. There is common question material between some of the papers and all questions are compulsory, short answer structured questions with some opportunity for extended writing in the Central and Further Tier papers.

Coursework (25%)

On each paper questions will be set from AT 2, 3 and 4 and the marks will be divided equally between the three Attainment Targets. The weighting of each AT is 25% overall.

There is an alternative assessment scheme for the Basic Tier of the Double Award in which one of the Terminal examination papers is replaced by 9 module tests each of 30 minutes duration, over the two year course. Each module test will cover two of the units of work. The terminal examination paper (Paper 9) will be 1 hour 30 minutes. Both the module tests and Paper 9 will contain a mixture of question types including sentence completion, matching pairs, short answer and structured questions. In the Single Award the alternative modular assessment scheme for the Basic Tier requires candidates to take five end of module tests each for 30 minutes. The written terminal paper will be of 1 hour duration.

Coursework AT 1 (25%)

Coursework will assess each of the three skills stated under AT 1 as three different strands. The assessment must be set in the context of complete investigations.

CO-ORDINATED SCIENCE THE SUFFOLK DEVELOPMENT (1777)

Syllabus Content

There are 21 units of study, 7 in each of the Attainment Targets 2, 3 and 4. The first four units should be covered in the first year of the course and are assessed by End-of-Unit Tests

B 1 Importance of Plants	C 5 Controlling Chemical Reactions
B 2 Ecology	C 6 Chemical Economics
B 3 Staying Alive	C 7 Chemistry in the Home
B 4 Growth and Development	
B 5 How Living Things Work	P 1 Movement and Forces
B 6 Managing the Earth	P 2 Energy in the Home
B 7 The Living Inheritance	P 3 Sound and Light
	P 4 Structures
C 1 Periodic Table	P 5 Space
C 2 Structure and Properties	P 6 Communications
C 3 Energy and Earth	P 7 Using Electricity
C 4 Energy and the Environment	

The terminal examination will assess units covered in Year 11 (B 5-7, C 5-7, P 5-7) and the main themes which are developed throughout the course.

T 1 Energy and the Balance of Life
T 2 Energy and Balance in Chemical Changes
T 3 Controlling and Transferring Energy

SCHEMES OF ASSESSMENT

Co-ordinated Science: The Suffolk Development (1777) (Double Certificate only)

There are three methods of assessment in this scheme:

Terminal Examination AT 2, 3 and 4 (50%)

Foundation tier	Levels 4, 5	Paper I (45 mins) (AT 2)
		Paper II (45 mins) (AT 3)
		Paper III (45 mins) (AT 4)

Merit tier	Levels 6, 7	Paper I (45 mins) (AT 2)
		Paper II (45 mins) (AT 3)
		Paper III (45 mins) (AT 4)
Special tier	Levels 8, 9, 10	Paper I (45 mins) (AT 2)
		Paper II (45 mins) (AT 3)
		Paper III (45 mins) (AT 4)

The written papers will consist of compulsory, short answer and structured questions with some opportunity for extended writing. They will assess the work covered in year 11 (the second year of the 2 year course) as well as some of the work covered in Year 10 which will have been assessed by End-of-Unit tests. (see above for list of units of study.)

End-of-Unit Tests AT 2, 3 and 4 (25%)

These tests are set on the first four units in each Attainment Target (B 1-4, C 1-4, P 1-4) which are covered during Year 10 (the first year of the two year course). There are three tiers of tests, Foundation, Merit and Special. A candidate may take tests at different levels during the course. The tests consist of short answer and structured questions with some opportunity for extended writing. There are 25 marks available and the tests take approximately 20 minutes.

Coursework AT 1 (25%)

Coursework will assess four skills by criterion matching:

- predicting and planning
- performing
- interpreting and evaluating
- communicating

The investigations will form part of the normal activities of the course. Each skill must be assessed at least once within the context of the Attainment Targets using whole investigations.

THE SCIENCES: DOUBLE AWARD

10 NORTHERN IRELAND COUNCIL FOR CURRICULUM, EXAMINATIONS AND ASSESSMENT (NICCEA)

There are four schemes on offer:

Science: Double Award (Non-modular) (Modular)

Science: Single Award (Non-modular) (Modular limited grade C to G)

The syllabus content covers the following: (S denotes Single Award)

1	S	Living Things and the Processes of Life
2		The Living World-Survival and Development
3		Use of Chemical Names, Symbols, Formulae, Equations, etc.
4	S	Using Materials and Understanding Reactions
5		Patterns, Problems, Processes
6	S	Forces and Energy
7		Electricity and Magnetism: Sound, Light and Waves
8		Environment

The scheme of assessment follows the pattern of most of the Examining groups with three tiers of entry, P, Q and R. The Double Award Non-Modular is assessed by four terminal papers and the Single Non-Modular is assessed by three terminal papers. The Double Award Modular scheme also includes four module tests on topics 1, 4, 6 and 8 from the above list, each of 1 hr consisting of 15 short questions. The module tests are weighted 25%, and the terminal examination reduced to 50% weighting. The Single Award Modular scheme includes three module tests each of 1 hr and consisting of 6 short questions per test, as well as a terminal examination of two papers, one of $1\frac{1}{2}$ hrs and one of 1 hr.

EXAMINATION TECHNIQUE AND COURSEWORK

GETTING STARTED

Just as a tennis player learns new techniques and trains for a tournament, so there are a number of techniques which you can develop which will help you to improve your performance in the examination, and gain more marks. For example, you can practise answering questions to a set time limit, and without using books to help you, before the exam. You will then be better prepared to cope with the actual conditions you will meet in the exam.

Examination questions are written by examiners to find out how much you know and understand. They also test your ability to handle information and to apply what you know to new situations. You are often given information in a question to help you answer the question, so a lot depends on reading the question fully, and making use of all the available facts. You will only gain marks for answering the questions which are set by the examiner, not for answering your own version of the question!

Coursework is the work that you will have completed at school or college prior to the written examination. This work will have been marked by your teacher and you may have had some feedback about how well you are doing. Remember that Coursework counts for 25% of your total assessment in Science, and that the written Terminal Examination (together with Module Tests where applicable) counts for 75%.

E S S E N T I A L   P R I N C I P L E S

The Terminal Written Examination is the examination you take at the end of your course of study, usually in May or June of Year 11 and is worth 75% of your marks, unless you are taking a modular course where the terminal exam is worth only 50%. As described in Chapter 1, all the Examining Groups set examination papers which are similar in style and format, consisting of compulsory, *structured questions* which are answered on the question paper in the spaces provided. The papers aimed at the higher levels provide more opportunity for *extended writing* and *calculations*.

> **1 > STRUCTURED QUESTIONS**

The structured questions are divided into sub-questions (a) (b) (c), etc. If you are unable to answer part (a) for example, you should still be able to go on to attempt (b) or (c) without doing (a). Sometimes the sub questions are further divided into say, (b) (i), (b) (ii), etc.; you will usually need to have answered (i) before doing (ii). The marks allocated for each part of the question are indicated in brackets. If a question asks you for 'TWO changes' there are usually two lines for your answer with the numbers 1 and 2 on the lines. There may sometimes be a table for you to complete with your answers. The examiners are really trying to help you to write down what you know and understand!

Structured questions are usually based on a particular topic or theme from the syllabus, such as 'acidity', 'electricity', or 'reproduction'. The questions are usually based on some 'stimulus material' such as one of the following.

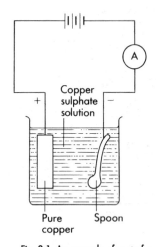

- A diagram of some apparatus which you may be familiar with; for example, an electrical circuit or a chemistry experiment.

- A diagram of something you have seen in a book; for example, the human body.

- A table (chart) showing information; for example about the heights of pupils in a class.

- A graph; for example, showing the motion of a car over a period of time.

- A photograph or sketch with some explanatory information.

- Some written information; for example, a newspaper article.

Fig. 2.1 An example of part of a typical structured question.

The question usually starts with an introductory sentence telling you what the question is about, followed by the 'stimulus material' as described above. This is in turn followed by a series of short questions requiring a few words for an answer or a few sentences.

i) Which part of the apparatus is the anode?

_____

> **66 Example of a structured question 99**

ii) Name the electrolyte _____
iii) Explain how the process of plating takes place.

_____

_____
(4)
(ULEAC)

At the end of the space for your answer you may see how many marks are being awarded for that part of the question. Your answer should aim to fill the space which is provided, but you can write more if you wish. Try and use as many scientific words as possible so that the examiner can see evidence of your knowledge and understanding in Science and can award you marks. Remember the general rule that one correct fact usually gains one mark.

If you are asked for the answer to a calculation, always include the units for any number which you write: for example, the rate of doing work is 10 W or 10 watts, not just 10.

These questions appear more frequently on the intermediate and higher level papers. They are often aimed at assessing level 9 and 10 candidates. They usually require a longer answer in the form of a few sentences and may allocate up to 10 marks for your answer. These questions may ask you to 'explain how something happens' or to 'suggest reasons' for a particular observation. You may find it helpful to write the main points of your answer in pencil on the question paper before answering the question. Check that you have matched the number of points you have made to the marks allocated and remember to cross out any rough notes you have made.

3 ⟩ MODULE TESTS

The number and frequency of Module Tests vary from syllabus to syllabus. They seem to have a variety of question styles, involving the use of short answer and structured questions of the type already considered. However the module tests also make use of a variety of types of *multiple choice* (or *objective*) questions.

MULTIPLE CHOICE OR OBJECTIVE QUESTIONS

These questions test your knowledge and understanding of a wide range of topics from the syllabus. Each question has a 'stem', which is the main part of the question. The stem may include diagrams or tables of figures, and you need to read the stem carefully to obtain as much information as possible before you read the list of suggested answers, called 'options'. These options are usually labelled A to E, and only one of them is the correct answer, which is the 'key'. The incorrect answers are the 'distractors'.

One way of approaching this type of question is to look for the correct answer and to ignore the distractors. Alternatively, you can work through the list of options and *reject each distractor* until you are only left with the 'key'. Look at the following example.

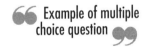 **Example of multiple choice question**

Many types of different waves and rays bombard the Earth. Which one of the following makes us feel hot?
A gamma rays **B** infra-red rays **C** radio waves **D** visible rays **E** X-rays

You may know the correct answer to this (key = **B**), or you may be able to reject each of the distractors. For example, you may know that radio waves are involved in communication and so **C** can therefore be *rejected* as an answer to this question, and so on.

In the exam, you may be able to use rough paper or the question paper to work out your answer. You mark the answer which you have chosen on a special answer grid using a soft HB pencil. You can then rub out an answer if it is wrong and make a new mark. Remember, there is only *one* correct answer to each question, and every question carries

 Check your answers

one mark. If you get stuck on a question, leave it and go on to the next. You may have time to come back to that question later and at least have a guess at the answer before the exam ends. When you have completed as many questions as possible, you should *check* each of your answers carefully, making sure that you have put your answer against the number on the grid which corresponds to the question you have answered. Try to use all the time you have in the exam in this positive way instead of just doing nothing!

Sometimes the type of objective question may involve *sentence completion* or selecting *matching pairs* out of a range of possible answers.

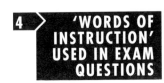

An examiner asks you to answer the question in a certain way by giving you help in the form of a 'word of instruction' in each sub-question. For example, if you are asked to 'Explain . . .' then writing a list will not qualify you for the marks. Some examples of the *words of instruction* which are often used are given:

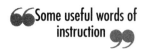
Some useful words of instruction

'**Describe**' means what actually happens, your observations, or what you would do.

'**Explain**' means that you must give reasons, and make some reference to a scientific principle or fact.

'**Suggest**' means apply your knowledge to a new situation or write about some reasonable scientific ideas.

'**Calculate**' is used when a numerical answer is required, with your working shown, together with the units used.

'**Define**' means that a fairly exact statement is required.

'**State**' means that a short, factual answer is required.

Some of the questions aimed at the basic and intermediate levels use simpler terms such as:

- Label on the diagram
- Complete the table/equation
- Name two . . .
- Make a graph
- What is . . .
- Put these into a list
- Which . . .

5 LANGUAGE AND LITERACY SKILLS AND MATHEMATICAL REQUIREMENTS

LANGUAGE AND LITERACY SKILLS

As well as the ability to use correct spelling, grammar and punctuation described in Chapter 1 the following skills are required:

- recording and storage of information in appropriate forms
- using and understanding information gained from various sources
- communicating ideas to others
- summarising and organising information in order to communicate adequately
- using appropriate language to explain the results of observations in a variety of contexts
- using and interpreting scientific nomenclature, symbols and conventions

MATHEMATICAL REQUIREMENTS

You are expected to have some skills in mathematics to answer some of the questions in a Science examination. They vary from one Exam Group to another but are basically as follows.

Some useful mathematical skills

Levels 4–6	National Curriculum Mathematical reference
add, subtract, multiply and divide whole numbers	2.2b, 2.3c
recognise and use expressions in decimal form	2.4c
make approximations and estimates to obtain reasonable answers	2.4e
use simple formulae expressed in words	3.4b
undertake mensuration of triangles, rectangles and cuboids	4.4d
understand and use averages	5.4e
read, interpret and draw simple inferences from tables and statistical diagrams	1.5b, 5.5c
find fractions or percentages of quantities	2.5b
construct and interpret pie-charts	5.5c
construct bar charts	5.5c
calculate with fractions, decimals, percentage or ratio	2.6a
solve simple equations	3.6b
substitute numbers for letters in simple equations	3.6b
interpret and use graphs	5.6
plot graphs from data provided, given the axes and scales	5.6

Levels 7–10	National Curriculum Mathematical reference
use appropriate limits of accuracy	2.7c
make approximation to a given number of significant figures or decimal places	2.7c
undertake mensuration of a cylinder	4.7d
choose by simple inspection and then draw the best smooth curve through a set of points on a graph	5.7a
recognise and use expressions in standard form	2.8a
manipulate simple equations	3.8a
select appropriate axes and scales for graph plotting	3.8c
determine the intercept of a linear graph	3.8c
understand and use inverse proportion	

A NOTE ABOUT GRAPHS

If you are asked to draw a graph in the exam there are some important points to remember:

a) use the axes and scale if they are given in the question;
b) if the axes and scale are not given in the question then decide on a scale which will fit the figures given in the data;
c) the *x* axis goes along the bottom or on the horizontal, the *y* axis goes upwards or on the vertical;
d) the factor which changes regularly, such as time, goes on the *x* axis;
e) label your axes, and indicate the scale used;
f) write a heading on your graph;
g) draw either a smooth curve through the points on the graph or the best-fitting straight line.

Marks are usually given for:

■ use of appropriate scale and correct axes;

■ correctly labelled axes and title;

■ accurate plot of points;

■ best straight line or best smooth curve.

6 DIAGRAMS

You may be asked to draw diagrams to show apparatus, or possibly diagrams to show something like a magnetic field pattern or the arrangement of the planetary bodies in a solar eclipse.

■ Use a *sharp* HB pencil.
■ Try to make the diagram fit the space allowed on the exam paper, or use about a third to a half page of A4 if answering on lined paper.
■ State the *magnification/scale* (if relevant).
■ Write a *heading* above the diagram to state what it is showing.
■ Use *labelling lines* to label the different parts of the diagram clearly. For example, Figure 2.2 opposite shows how you can use radial *labelling lines* around a diagram. Alternatively, as in Figure 14.1 (page 277), you can use a *list of labels* at the side of a diagram.
■ Include as much *accurate detail* on the diagram as possible.
■ When you draw apparatus, only draw the *relevant parts* of the apparatus and omit standard equipment such as retort stands, Bunsen burners, etc. The diagrams in this book may be useful to study for guidance.

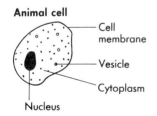

Fig 2.2 How to use radial labelling lines around a diagram.

Look at the *number of marks* allocated for the diagram. Five marks may mean that it's better to only spend about five minutes on a diagram. You can always come back to it if you have extra time at the end.

7 ❯ COURSEWORK

The Coursework component of all Science courses, both Double and Single Award, is worth 25% of your overall assessment for Key Stage 4. It should form part of your normal Science course and assess those skills which you have had a chance to develop during the course. The assessments will be based on whole investigations during the units of work you are studying for Attainment Targets 2, 3 and 4.

The emphasis in Coursework is that you, as a learner, take responsibility for making decisions in planning, carrying out and reporting investigations, instead of your teacher, who is there to assist you in developing these skills and to assess you.

Coursework is designed to assess the three *strands* in Attainment Target 1, as follows.

Candidates should use the knowledge, skills and understanding specified in the syllabus to plan and carry out investigations in which they do the following:

- ask questions, predict and hypothesise; (**strand 1**)
  for example this could mean:
  - suggesting your own questions
  - predicting the outcome of an experiment you have planned
  - planning a solution to a problem, deciding how to make a fair test

Three Key elements or 'strands' used in describing AT 1

- observe, measure and manipulate variables; (**strand 2**)
  for example this could mean:
  - deciding what to measure
  - choosing the most appropriate apparatus
  - deciding how to organise your apparatus to achieve results
  - deciding how to record and display your results

- interpret their results and evaluate scientific evidence; (**strand 3**)
  for example this could mean:
  - deciding what your results mean
  - arriving at your own conclusions
  - evaluating what you have done

In similar terms these three 'strands' are described by other Exam Groups as:
- Designing investigations / Predicting
- Carrying out investigations / Implementing
- Interpreting investigations / Concluding

Some examples of the statements used to describe what you should be able to do to reach specified target levels for AT 1

For each level (1–10) there are *statements* describing what you should be able to do within each strand.

In *strand 1* for example, a level 8 candidate would be expected to:

'use scientific knowledge, understanding or theory to generate quantitative predictions and a strategy for the investigations'.

In *strand 2* within the context of an investigation where one independent variable is given, a level 8 candidate would be expected to:

'take readings using the measuring instruments chosen to provide quantitative results to a high degree of accuracy'

In *strand 3* a level 10 candidate would be expected to:

'use and analyse the data obtained to evaluate the law, theory or model in terms of the extent to which it can explain the observed behaviour'

These statements are included here to give you an idea of how your teacher will be assessing your work in general terms. Your teacher will probably use more specific descriptive statements for a particular investigation. You should have an opportunity to discuss the quality of your coursework with your teacher and to improve on your level of achievement where appropriate.

LEVELS FOR AT1

There are 10 levels described in *each* of the three 'strands'. These marks are described by one Exam Group as relating to the levels of achievement as follows:

Mark	Level	Mark	Level
11–13	4	20–22	7
14–16	5	23–25	8
17–19	6	26–28	9
		27–30	10

However, at this stage, this information can only be taken as an approximate guide to the relationship between marks and levels.

There are normally two different methods by which you can be assessed on practical skills. One way is by your teacher watching you carry out a particular practical, perhaps involving you in the handling of apparatus or in following instructions. The second method is by your teacher assessing what you have written during a practical investigation.

The work you hand in for assessment may include your observations and a presentation of your results, perhaps as a chart or graph. Your teacher can then use your written work to assess your ability to make and record observations. You are usually assessed on more than one occasion for a particular skill, so don't worry if you haven't done too well on any one particular piece of work. You may be assessed on the same skill at a later date, or you may be able to arrange this with your teacher. The best person with whom to discuss the standards you have reached on your practical assessments is your teacher at school. He or she may not be able to tell you the actual mark for any particular skill, but may be able to give you some guidance about how you can improve your level of performance in a particular skill area.

Points to remember when submitting coursework:

a) There should be a clear heading or title, and an introduction which describes the investigation, and shows that you understand what the investigation is about.

b) You should have your name, the date and your form or set, clearly written on the work.

c) Underline the headings and subheadings.

d) All diagrams, charts, graphs, photos, etc. should have a heading and labels.

e) List all relevant equipment and apparatus.

 **Presentation is very important**

f) Describe any safety precautions which you have taken, for example wearing safety goggles, using small amounts of chemical substances, using a fume cupboard.

g) Present your results as a chart or graph. Refer to, and make use of, your results when writing up your coursework.

h) Describe any problems you had during the investigation and suggest possible solutions.

i) Identify possible sources of error and suggest further investigations.

j) List any references which you may have used.

You will find it useful to keep all your coursework in a folder, as the exam boards usually look at the coursework from a random selection of about 10% of candidates from a centre. Your work may therefore go to an examiner, called a coursework moderator, who is responsible for ensuring that standards are similar between different schools.

8 SOME GENERAL HINTS

During your revision

Use 'active' revision techniques

■ Plan your revision time so that you have time to study your notes on *all* the topics in the weeks leading up to the exam.

■ Make your revision as active as possible, perhaps by looking at your notes and then writing a *summary* of key facts about a topic, or explaining a difficult idea to a friend, or even to your teddy bear! Practice drawing key charts and diagrams *before* the exam.

■ Some students find it useful to *tape record information* using a cassette recorder. You can then listen to the tape as a change from reading notes, or swop tapes on key topics with a friend.

■ Practice answering questions without using any books, and working to the actual time allowed in the exam. Then check your answers and see where you are right and wrong.

THE HUMAN BODY

GETTING STARTED

Chapters 3 to 7 of this book will take you through the main topics and points needed to cover Attainment Target 2: Life and Living Processes.

Taking responsibility for your own body, for what you eat, and for how fit you are, is an important part of your everyday living. If you have a basic understanding about how your body works, you will be more able to understand the importance of a balanced diet, regular exercise and relaxation, and the need to avoid cigarette smoking, excessive alcohol and dangerous drugs. In this chapter we look at the basic structure of your body, and then consider nutrition, circulation and respiration in more detail. The chapter concludes by reviewing the main functions of the skeleton in supporting the body and giving the muscles a firm attachment when they contract to move bones.

ESSENTIAL PRINCIPLES

1 > CELLS, TISSUES AND ORGANS

Your body is made of about 50 million million tiny *cells*, which can be thought of as the building blocks of your body. The cells carry out a variety of different functions: for example, red blood cells carry oxygen around your body to the muscle cells; nerve cells transmit impulses from sense organs to the brain.

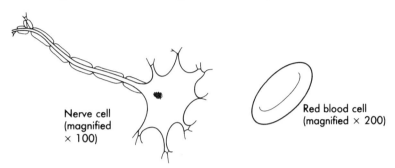

Fig 3.1 Two different cells in your body.

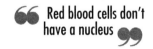
Red blood cells don't have a nucleus

Every cell, except the red blood cells, has a *nucleus* which controls the cell's activities and contains the *chromosomes,* the site of the genetic information of the cell. The nucleus is surrounded by *cytoplasm* which is surrounded by a *cell membrane.*

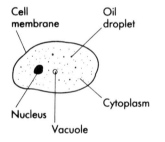

Fig 3.2 A typical cell showing cell structure.

Most of the cells in your body are grouped together to form *tissues,* so that they work more effectively. For example, the large muscle in your upper arm, the biceps muscle, is a group of millions of tiny muscle cells which contract and relax so that you can raise and lower your arm.

When different tissues join together, they form *organs,* which make up the seven main systems in your body. The hierarchy of structures in your body is as follows:

cells → tissues → organs → organ systems

The seven main *systems* in your body are:

1 The *circulatory system,* which carries oxygen, glucose and amino acids to every cell, and carries waste products such as urea and carbon dioxide away from the cells.
2 The *respiratory system,* which takes in oxygen and removes carbon dioxide.
3 The *digestive system,* which breaks down and absorbs the food taken into your body.
4 The *excretory system,* which removes unwanted, harmful waste produced by your body, such as urea produced by the liver and removed by your kidneys.
5 The *skeletal system,* which protects and supports your organs and muscles, and enables your muscles to move your body.
6 The *nervous system,* which controls all the organs in your body and enables you to respond to the information received by sensory cells in your body.
7 The *reproductive system,* which enables you to make eggs or sperm so that you can pass on genetic information to create the next generation.

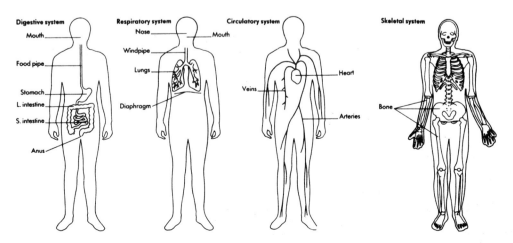

Fig 3.3 Organ systems

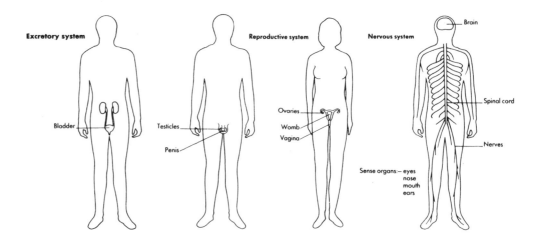

The cells in your body are made from many different elements, such as carbon, hydrogen, oxygen, nitrogen, sulphur and phosphorous. Plants and animals obtain these elements from their environment in different ways: by photosynthesis and by absorbing minerals from the soil in the case of plants; by eating plants or other animals in the case of animals.

A BALANCED DIET

Human beings require a *balanced diet*, which should include some of each of the seven main types of food shown in the chart below:

Items in a balanced diet

Type of food	Reason	Source
Carbohydrate	glucose, sucrose, starch } for energy	jams, sweets, bread, potato
Protein	amino acids – for growth and repair of cells	meat, cheese
Fats	fatty acids – storage and energy	butter, oils
Vitamins	A, B, C, D – good health	fresh vegetables and fruit
Minerals	eg iron, calcium – good health	fruit, green vegetables
Roughage	to help bowel movement	vegetables
Water	for all the reactions in the body	fruit and vegetables

If you eat too much energy containing food, the surplus is stored as fat which can make you overweight and can increase the stress on your heart. Too much saturated (animal) fat in your diet can also increase the risk of heart disease as the fat can be deposited inside the blood vessels and block them. An average 15-year-old girl needs about 10,400 kilojoules of energy each day whereas an average 15-year-old boy needs about 12,100 kilojoules of energy each day.

Your daily dietary requirements will vary according to age, pregnancy, illness, and how active a person you are. For example, if you do a lot of exercise you will use up a lot of energy and will need more carbohydrate and fats which can be broken down to supply energy to your muscle cells. A young person who is still growing will need more protein than an adult who has stopped growing, to supply amino acids for the growth of extra body cells to make more tissues and muscles.

Deficiencies

Many people in under-developed countries suffer from a lack of one or more of the different types of food from their daily diet. For example, a lack of *protein* causes a disease called *kwashiorkor* and children are unable to grow and develop properly. A lack of *vitamin A* causes 250 000 children to go blind every year, and many more children suffer severe eye problems. A lack of *vitamin D* causes soft bones which can lead to a condition known as *rickets*. A lack of *iodine* in the diet causes many children in less developed countries to suffer *mental retardation*. A lack of *iron* in the diet can cause *anaemia*.

Food additives

Food additives include chemical preservatives, artificial colourings and flavourings. They are added to improve the colour and taste of food as well as the 'shelf life', i.e. how long it will last.

Some additives however may have long term effects on people and may cause allergic reactions in children. For example, *tartrazine*, an orange colouring found in fruit drinks, is thought to cause *hyperactivity* in some children.

All food must state the substances they contain. Chemical preservatives are described in terms of an international code of E numbers. For example many jams contain E220, sulphur dioxide.

Fig 3.4 Food label

INGREDIENTS:
CHERRIES, SUGAR, WATER,
COLOUR E124, FLAVOURING,
PRESERVATIVES E211, E220.

Food tests

These tests help to identity the different type of foodstuff which may be present in a sample of food. You have probably carried out simple food tests in the laboratory to see if carbohydrate, protein or fat is present in a food. The summary chart will help you to remember these food tests.

 **Some useful food tests**

Type of Food	Substance used	Positive result
starch	iodine solution	blue-black colour
reducing sugar	add Benedict's solution and warm tube gently	green / red colour
protein	Biuret test : add sodium hydroxide solution then a few drops of copper sulphate solution	violet / purple colour
fat	rub food onto filter paper	a translucent grease stain forms

DIGESTION

The food which you eat contains large molecules which have to be *broken down* into smaller molecules so that they can pass through the wall of your gut into your

Some students find digestion confusing, but it's going on inside you most of the time! Remember, digestion is just breaking down food molecules

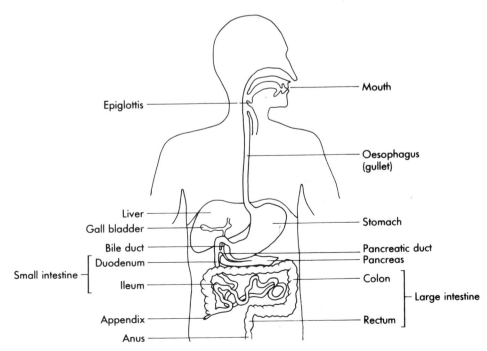

Fig 3.5 The human digestive system.

Mouth
Epiglottis
Oesophagus (gullet)
Liver
Gall bladder
Bile duct
Duodenum
Small intestine
Ileum
Appendix
Anus
Stomach
Pancreatic duct
Pancreas
Colon
Large intestine
Rectum

bloodstream. The process of breaking down the large molecules is described as 'digestion'. In your body you make chemical catalysts, called *enzymes*, which speed up the rate of breakdown of your food.

1 The process of digestion starts in your mouth when your teeth crush and chew the food, which is mixed with *saliva*. The saliva contains an enzyme called *amylase* which starts to break down or digest the large molecules of starch.

2 The food is then swallowed and goes to your *stomach* for about 3 or 4 hours. The stomach lining secretes a dilute acid to create an acidic environment so that the enzyme *pepsin* can break down the large protein molecules into smaller molecules.

3 The partly digested food is then passed into the next part of the gut, the *small intestine*, where enzymes from the *pancreas* continue the process of digestion. The starch is eventually converted into the small molecules of glucose, the protein is broken down into amino acids, and the fats are broken down into fatty acids.

4 The small molecules are then absorbed through the *lining of the gut* into the bloodstream.

5 The undigested food and other waste products then pass into the *large intestine*, where water is absorbed and faeces are formed.

6 The faeces then pass out of the body through the *rectum* and *anus*.

Eating a good amount of fibre or roughage in your diet each day helps you to pass faeces out of your body at regular intervals. If you do not eat sufficient fibre in your diet, then you become constipated and it is difficult to pass the faeces out of your body.

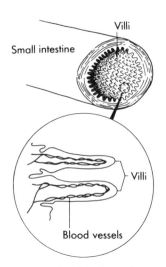

Fig 3.6 The villi in the small intestine increase the area for absorption.

3 ENERGY FROM FOOD

The blood system carries the small molecules of glucose and amino acids, together with oxygen, to every cell in your body. A chemical process called *respiration* takes place in the cells to release the energy from the food.

food + oxygen → carbon dioxide + water + energy

The carbon dioxide and water are carried by the blood to your lungs and breathed out. The energy is used by your cells for the various functions of the cells. Muscle cells need energy for contraction, gut cells need energy for secretion and absorption.

You may have investigated the energy released from different foods by letting them burn under a measured volume of water, and measuring the change in temperature, as shown in Figure 3.7.

The energy values of 100 g of different foods are shown in the table.

Food	Energy in kJ
butter	3041
sugar	1680
milk	272
cheese	1682
chicken	599
fish	322
eggs	612
peas	212
potatoes	339
chips	1065
bread	918
apple	196

As you can see, foods such as butter, sugar, cheese and chips have high energy values and would need to be eaten in moderation!

Fig 3.7 Finding out how much energy is released when a peanut is burned.

4 THE BLOOD SYSTEM, ARTERIES AND VEINS

The blood is like a transport system which carries many substances such as glucose, oxygen, carbon dioxide, hormones, and urea to and from every cell of your body. The blood flows in a series of tubes or blood vessels called *arteries* and *veins*, which divide into very small blood vessels called *capillaries*.

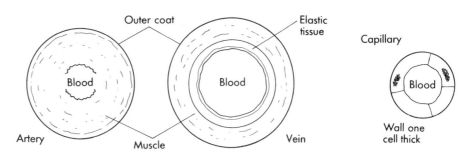

Fig 3.8a) The arteries have much thicker walls than the veins.

Fig 3.8b) This chart compares arteries, veins and capillaries.

Comparison	Artery	Vein	Capillary
Internal (lumen) diameter	Fairly narrow; can expand (= pulse)	Fairly wide	Very narrow; red blood cells squeeze through
Wall structure	The wall is relatively thick and also elastic, to withstand pressure	The wall is relatively thin; there are valves to keep blood moving in one direction	Wall is composed of a single cell layer; gaps between cells allow exchange of materials with surrounding tissues
Blood direction	Blood flows away from the heart	Blood flows towards the heart	Blood flows from arteries to veins
Blood pressure	High	Low	Very low
Blood flow rate	Rapid, irregular	Slow, regular	Very slow

Check you know the differences between arteries and veins

Arteries have thick muscular walls, as they carry blood *away* from the heart under pressure. *Veins* have much thinner walls, and possess valves to help the blood to flow one way *towards* the heart. The blood in the veins is at a lower pressure than blood in the arteries, and the muscles of your arms and legs help to squeeze the blood back to the heart.

HOW OXYGEN AND FOOD REACH THE CELLS

1 Oxygen and food molecules diffuse out of the blood into the tissue fluid which surrounds every cell.
2 These substances then diffuse into the cell.
3 Waste products diffuse out of the cell into the tissue fluid and into the blood through the walls of the capillaries, to be carried away from the cells to the excretory organs.

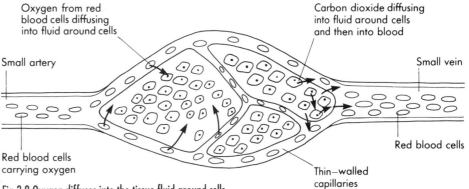

Fig 3.9 Oxygen diffuses into the tissue fluid around cells

5 ▶ RED AND WHITE BLOOD CELLS

Red and white blood cells do different jobs

There are about 25 million million *red* blood cells in your body; their job is to carry oxygen from the blood capillaries around the lungs, to the body cells.

There are about 20 million *white* blood cells, whose function it is to protect the body against disease. Some of the white blood cells produce *antibodies* which kill bacteria, while others destroy bacteria by engulfing them.

Some white blood cells produce *antibodies* or *antitoxins* which counteract the *toxins* (poisons) which are released by infective bacteria. Antibodies stay in the blood for a long time and give you a built-in resistance (immunity) to a particular disease. The Human Immune Deficiency Virus (HIV) infects and destroys the white blood cells which produce antibodies so the body is unable to protect itself against disease. This condition is known as AIDS (Acquired Immune Deficiency Syndrome).

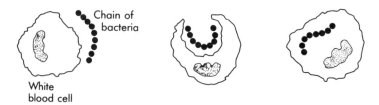

Fig 3.10 White blood cells engulf and destroy bacteria in your body.

6 ⟩ THE HEART

The heart is basically two muscular pumps which work side by side. Each side is divided into two chambers, an *upper atrium* and a *lower ventricle*. The *right atrium* takes in deoxygenated blood which has been round the body, and the *right ventricle* pumps the blood to the lungs, via the pulmonary artery. The *left atrium* takes in oxygenated blood from the lungs, via the pulmonary vein, and the more muscular *left ventricle* pumps the blood under great pressure around the body, via the *aorta*, the thick-walled main artery. *Valves* in the heart force the blood to flow in the right direction.

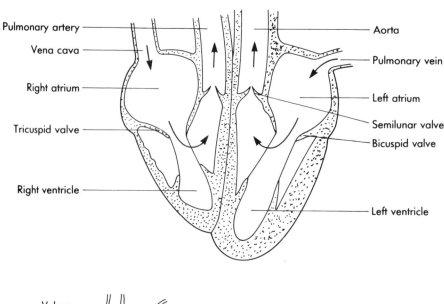

Fig 3.11a) The heart is a powerful pump which pumps blood round the body and to the lungs

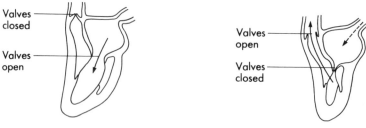

a) **Ventricle relaxed**: blood is forced from the atrium into the ventricle. Valves prevent blood flowing 'backwards'

b) **Ventricle contracted**: blood is forced from the ventricle and out of the heart. The atrium meanwhile re-fills with more blood

Fig 3.11b) The heart in action.

The beating of the heart is controlled automatically so that it beats in a continuous series of rhythmic muscular contractions. Each cycle of contractions is called the *cardiac cycle* and the average adult rate of this cycle is about 72 beats per minute. To control the heart beat artificially a small electrical device known as a *pacemaker* can be implanted into the chest of a person whose own natural pacemaker fails to work properly.

7 ⟩ BREATHING

At rest you are breathing about 15 times a minute. If you put your hands over your ribs and take a deep breath you can feel your chest cavity getting larger as you breathe in. The *intercostal* muscles, between your ribs, contract to pull your ribs up and out and the *diaphragm* muscle at the base of your chest flattens so that your chest cavity is made larger. Air outside your chest cavity is at greater pressure than air inside your chest, this difference in pressure causes air to rush into your lungs.

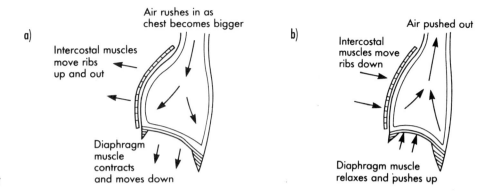

Fig 3.12 a) Breathing in
b) Breathing out

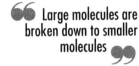

Large molecules are broken down to smaller molecules

Your lungs are basically two sponge-like structures in your chest which fill up with air. Oxygen diffuses over the moist surface of the air sacs or *alveoli,* from the air into the blood in the capillaries, where it combines with haemoglobin in the red blood cells, to make a new substance called *oxyhaemoglobin.* The blood is pumped by the heart muscle to the rest of the body through arteries and eventually capillaries. The oxygen diffuses into your cells, and carbon dioxide from the cells diffuses into your blood and is carried back to the lungs. The intercostal muscles and diaphragm make your chest cavity smaller, therefore increasing the pressure in the lungs, so the air is pushed out.

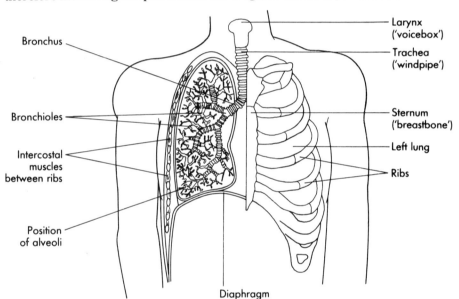

Fig 3.13 The human chest cavity.

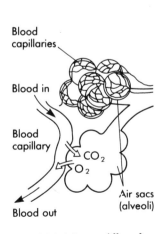

Fig. 3.14 a) Oxygen diffuses from the air sacs into your blood stream.

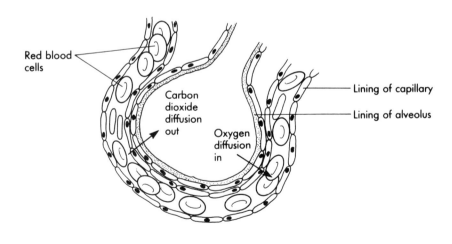

Fig 3.14 b) Inside one alveolus.

Inhaled and Exhaled air

The summary chart shows the difference in composition between inhaled (atmospheric) and exhaled air.

Component	Inhaled air	Exhaled air
oxygen	21%	16%
carbon	0.04%	4%
water vapour	variable:	saturated
	average = 1.3%	= 6.2%
temperature	ambient	38°C

8 THE EFFECT OF EXERCISE

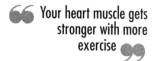

Your heart muscle gets stronger with more exercise

When your muscles are working harder during vigorous exercise they need more energy. Your heart rate increases to pump blood carrying glucose more quickly to your cells, and your rate of breathing increases so that more oxygen is taken in to release the energy from glucose. More carbon dioxide is produced which is removed by the increased rate of breathing.

People who are fit generally have a lower heart rate and therefore a lower pulse rate than people who are unfit, because exercise develops the heart muscle, just like any other muscle. Fit people and non-smokers get back to their resting pulse rate more quickly than unfit people and smokers. Regular exercise, eating a good, well-balanced diet without too much fat, and not smoking, can reduce the risk of heart disease.

9 TOBACCO AND ALCOHOL

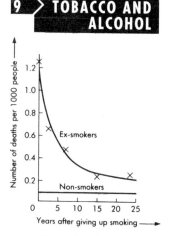

Fig 3.15 You reduce the risk of dying from lung cancer if you are a non-smoker.

Cigarette Smoking

Cigarette smoking can affect the body in many ways:

1 Chemicals in the tobacco smoke can cause cancer in the lungs, and as a result the lungs are destroyed.
2 Carbon monoxide, a gas in cigarette smoke, mixes with haemoglobin in the red blood cells and makes the blood less efficient at carrying oxygen. As a result the blood vessels around the heart become weak and this may result in a heart attack.
3 The tiny hairs in the lungs which remove dust and mucus from the lungs become paralysed, so sticky *phlegm* collects in the lungs, causing infection. Smokers try to move the phlegm by heavy coughing which damages the lining of the lungs and reduces the number of air sacs in the lungs. There is less surface area for oxygen to diffuse into the blood stream so the smokers become out of breath and may suffer from bronchitis.
4 Pregnant women who smoke can give birth to babies which are undersized and sometimes born prematurely.

The effect of alcohol on the body

Alcohol is a chemical found in beers, wines and spirits. It affects the nervous system and slows down a person's reaction time, causing a lack of co-ordination of the muscles. It can also lead to a lack of self control, unconsciousness or even a coma. Drinking excessive amounts of alcohol over a number of years can result in a diseased liver, an ulcerated stomach, weak heart muscles, high blood pressure and depression.

Alcohol and its effects on the body can be a serious problem for motorists and is a major cause of many road accidents. One in three drivers who are killed in road accidents have drunk alcohol just prior to the accident. In Britain there are strict controls about the amount of alcohol a person can drink when they are driving. Anyone found driving a car or motorcycle with over 80 milligrams of alcohol in their blood would be prosecuted. The legal limit for drinking and driving is three units of alcohol which is about three standard drinks as shown in the diagram (Fig. 3.16).

Fig 3.16 The legal limit for driving is three units of alcohol

½ pint of beer = 1 glass of table wine = 1 glass of sherry = 1 single whisky = 1 unit of alcohol

Solvent abuse

Many glues and other household products contain a chemical *solvent* to stop them solidifying. Solvent abuse is sometimes referred to as *glue sniffing* because people breathe in the fumes given off by the solvent. The fumes affect the brain and produce a temporary pleasant sensation which may lead to delirium and unconsciousness. As a result of glue sniffing many people have died, often from choking on their own vomit. Glue sniffers are often irritable and moody and usually develop a cough, sore eyes, sores around the mouth. It is a very dangerous habit and can become addictive.

Addictive drugs

There are many dangers associated with using illegal drugs, such as cannabis and heroin, especially those which are injected into the blood. There is no control over the quality of the drug which may be mixed with impurities which can cause serious side effects. The strength of the drug is unknown so it can be difficult to control the amount of drug being injected. Injecting with unsterilised needles can cause other diseases such as blood poisoning, hepatitis and HIV. People who are addicted to illegal drugs are often unable to have a regular job and do not earn the money to pay for the drugs they need and often steal money from others. Over a period of time the drugs can affect behaviour and may cause damage to the brain, liver and kidneys.

Aerobic respiration means *using oxygen* to breakdown carbohydrates and fats to release energy. The word equation for this process is as follows:

food and oxygen → carbon dioxide and water and energy

The chemical equation for this process using glucose as food is:

$$C_6H_{12}O_6 + 6O_2 \rightarrow 6CO_2 + 6H_2O + 2830kJ$$

Aerobic respiration takes place in the cells of your body, for example, muscle cells. Your blood carries food and oxygen to the cells and transports waste products, carbon dioxide and water from the cells. These waste products are removed by the lungs when you breathe out.

One way of investigating aerobic respiration in living organisms is to identify the carbon dioxide produced. For example, the gas produced by a mouse can be bubbled through limewater. If the limewater turns cloudy, then the gas is carbon dioxide.

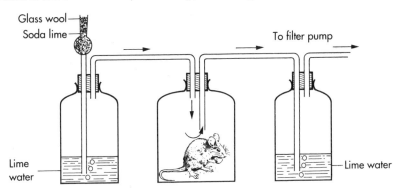

Fig 3.17 Testing for aerobic respiration

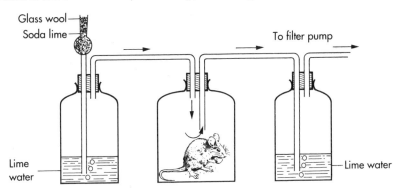

Anaerobic respiration is the breakdown of carbohydrates and fats to release energy, *without using oxygen*. The food is broken down to substances such as lactic acid and alcohol. Less energy is released compared to aerobic respiration, which uses oxygen.

An example of anaerobic respiration occurs in your muscles when you are doing vigorous exercise. There is not enough oxygen supplied to your muscles to break down the food quickly enough and release the energy needed by the body. Some energy is released from the food anaerobically and lactic acid is produced as a waste product. When you stop the exercise, your rapid breathing provides extra oxygen to remove the lactic acid, repaying the 'oxygen debt'.

Athletes in sprint races usually use only anaerobic respiration to release energy quickly when they run a 100 metres race.

Micro-organisms can also use anaerobic respiration in the process which is known as *fermentation*. For example, yeast (a micro-organism) digests sugars in the absence of air and produces alcohol and carbon dioxide. Wine, beer and bread are all produced as a result of fermentation by yeast.

The diagram (Figure 3.18) shows an investigation to show that carbon dioxide is produced by yeast during anaerobic respiration.

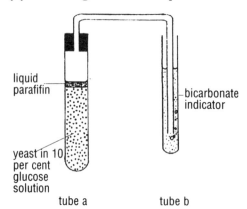

liquid parafifin

bicarbonate indicator

yeast in 10 per cent glucose solution

tube a   tube b

Fig 3.18 Anaerobic respiration in yeast

13 > THE SKELETON

The function of the skeleton is to support the body and give the muscles a firm attachment when they contract to move bones.

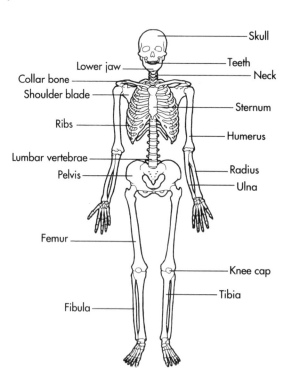

Skull

Lower jaw

Teeth

Neck

Collar bone

Shoulder blade

Sternum

Ribs

Humerus

Lumbar vertebrae

Pelvis

Radius

Ulna

Femur

Knee cap

Tibia

Fibula

Fig 3.19 Skeleton

The backbone or vertebral column is made up of many vertebrae which allow attachment for other bones and muscles. The main function of the backbone is to protect the spinal cord. Other parts of the skeleton also have a protective function, for example, the cranium protects the brain; the rib cage and sternum protect the heart and lungs.

Movement and Joints

Movement is possible due to *joints* between the bones. For example, at the *shoulder*, is a ball and socket joint which allows the arm to swivel around in any direction. At the *elbow* is a hinge joint which allows the lower arm to move backwards and forwards.

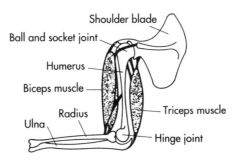

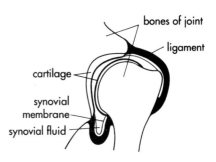

Fig 3.20 Various joints

a) The bones and muscles of the upper arm showing the elbow and shoulder joints

b) Typical synovial joint (shoulder)

In order to move the lower arm up, the biceps muscle contracts to pull up the radius. The triceps muscle then contracts to pull the lower arm down. These muscles work as a pair of *antagonistic muscles* working against each other. The muscles are attached to bones by *tendons* which transmit the pulling force from the muscle to the bone. The bones are held together by *ligaments*. Inside the joint the *synovial fluid* acts as a cushion and shock absorber to prevent the bones rubbing on each other.

E X A M I N A T I O N   Q U E S T I O N S

MULTIPLE CHOICE

QUESTION 1

The diagram opposite shows a section through the heart.

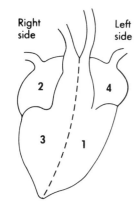

What is the correct order of blood flow from the vena cava to the aorta?

A 1,4,2,3   D 3,2,4,1
B 2,3,1,4   E 4,1,3,2
C 2,3,4,1

QUESTION 2

What is the function of white blood cells?
A to carry nerve impulses to the brain
B to produce hormones to clot the blood
C to help clot the blood
D to transport oxygen to the cells
E to destroy bacteria in the body

QUESTION 3

The diagram opposite shows the human gut.

What is the part labelled X?

A the duodenum
B the ileum
C the large intestine
D the stomach
E the pancreas

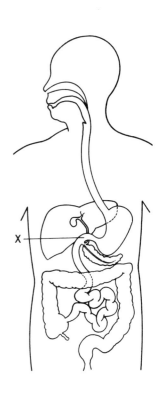

QUESTION 4

In which part of the gut does the digestion of protein start?
A the mouth   D the small intestine
B the food tube   E the large intestine
C the stomach

QUESTION 5

What is the function of the excretory system?
A to break down food which you eat
B to get rid of undigested food from your body
C to remove harmful waste produced by your body
D to control all the organs in your body
E to take in oxygen and transport it to the cells

QUESTION 6

Which of the following is used for growth and repair of cells?
A starch   D proteins
B fats   E roughage
C minerals

QUESTION 7

The diagram below shows the chest cavity.

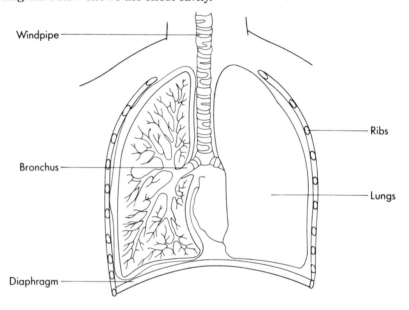

Which one of the following contracts when you breathe in?
A bronchus   D ribs
B diaphragm   E windpipe
C lungs

QUESTION 8

The table below shows the composition of a well-known breakfast cereal. Study the label and answer the questions which follow.   *(2)*

	Per 100g		Per 100g
Energy	1400kJ	Dietary Fibre	12.9g
		Vitamins:	
Protein	10.5g	Niacin	10.0mg
Fat	2.0g	Riboflavin (B_2)	1.0mg
Available		Thiamin (B_1)	0.7mg
Carbohydrate	66.8g	Iron	6.0mg

a) Which two food groups are carbohydrates?

i) _____

ii) _____

b) What use does the body make of *(4)*

   i) carbohydrates_____

   ii) proteins? _____

c) The cereal supplies 1400 kJ of energy per 100 g; what does kJ stand for? *(1)*

   _____

d) What is the total mass of vitamins the cereal contains per 100 g? *(2)*

   _____ mg

e) To which food group does iron belong? *(1)*

   _____

f) Which food group supplies dietary fibre? *(1)*

   _____

(NICCEA)

QUESTION 9

The illustration opposite shows a child suffering from malnutrition.

a) What do you understand by malnutrition? (2 lines available) *(2)*

b) Which food group would be of most benefit to the child shown in the picture? *(1)*

   _____

The histogram shows the consumption of different types of food in three areas of the world.

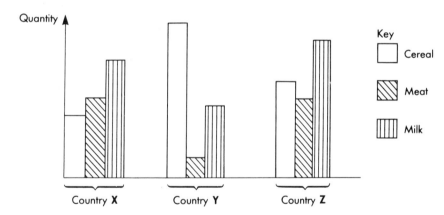

c) From the data given, from which country do you think it is likely that the child comes? *(2)*

   _____

(NICCEA)

QUESTION 10

a) *Scurvy, rickets* and *anaemia* are illnesses which can affect different parts of the body. Match these illnesses to the part of the body they most affect:

	Part of body	*Illness it can be affected by*
i)	Skin	_____
ii)	Bones	_____
iii)	Blood	_____

(3)

b) Each illness listed in (a) is caused by a particular substance missing from the diet. Name the substance and state **one** food which contains the substance.

Illness	Substance missing from diet	One *food which contains missing substance*
i) scurvy		
ii) rickets		
iii) anaemia		

(3)
(WJEC)

QUESTION 11

A pupil was provided with samples of the following foods: starch, fat, sugar and protein.

The pupil selected one of these foods and placed equal amounts of it in each of three test tubes containing an enzyme in solution.

One test tube was kept at 10°C, one at 37°C, and the third was heated until the contents boiled.

A sample was removed from each test tube at intervals and tested for the presence of sugar.

The results are shown in the table below.

Test tube	Amount of sugar present			
	at 0 min	*after 5 min*	*after 10 min*	*after 20 min*
1	none	a little	a lot	a lot
2	none	none	a little	a lot
3	none	none	none	none

a) Which one of the following foods was placed in each of the three test tubes: starch, fat, sugar, protein?

_____

b) Name the enzyme which was present. _____

c) Which test tube was kept at 10°C? _____

d) In which test tube had the enzyme been boiled?

_____

e) Which test tube was kept at 37°C? Give a reason for your answer.

_____

_____

(6)
(ULEAC)

QUESTION 12

The table below gives information about the food values of 100 grams (g) of a number of foods.

Food	Energy measured in kilojoules (kJ)	Fat measured in grams (g)	Protein measured in grams (g)	Carbohydrate measured in grams (g)	Calcium measured in milligrams (mg)	Iron measured in milligrams (mg)
potato	370	0.0	2.0	21.0	7.0	0.7
fish	300	0.7	16.0	0.0	32.0	1.1
butter	3340	85.0	0.4	0.0	14.0	0.0
rice	1500	1.0	6.0	86.0	4.0	0.4

sugar	1620	0.0	0.0	100.0	0.0	0.0
soya	1810	24.0	40.0	13.0	210.0	7.0
orange	150	0.0	0.7	8.0	42.0	4.0
meat	1600	20.0	15.0	6.0	40.0	0.6

a) i) Which food listed in the table has the most fat?

_____

(1)

ii) Which food listed in the table only gives energy?

_____

(1)

iii) Suggest **one** food in the table which nearly gives a balanced diet. Explain your answer.?

Food _____

(1)

Explanation (3 lines available) _____

(2)

iv) Name one other important group of substances needed for a healthy diet which has been left out of the table.

_____

(1)

b) i) What pattern can you see between the fat content and the energy given by butter, rice, soya and meat? (3 lines available)

ii) Suggest **one** other food listed in the table which does not fit your pattern.

_____

(1)

c) Choose the **two** foods from the table which are most unsuitable for slimmers. Explain your answers.

Food 1 _____

(1)

Explanation (2 lines) _____

(1)

Food 2 _____

(1)

Explanation (2 lines) _____

(1)

d) Suggest **two** reasons why soya is now replacing meat.

Reason 1 (2 lines) _____

(1)

Reason 2 (2 lines) _____

(1)

e) Various forms of single-cell protein (SCP) are now being made and used instead of more usual food materials. *Mycoprotein* is an example. It is made from a fungus which is grown on glucose solution. The fungus grows as fibres that smell faintly of mushrooms. The length and texture of the fibres depend on their growing time. Mycoprotein can be dried to a powder or made to look and taste like chicken, fish or beef. It contains all the nutrients in beef but more fibre.

i) Suggest **two** reasons why foods such as these are being made.

Reason 1 (2 lines) _____

(2)

Reason 2 (2 lines) _____

(2)

ii) Suggest **two** problems which the makers will have to overcome if such food substitutes are to be accepted..

Problem 1 (2 lines) _____

(1)

Problem 2 (2 lines) _____

(1)

(ULEAC)

QUESTION 13

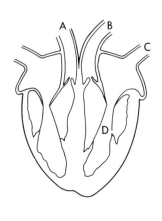

a) The figure alongside is a diagram of the heart.
Identify each of the four regions marked A, B, C and D.
i) left ventricle; ii) aorta; iii) pulmonary vein; iv) pulmonary artery.   *(2)*

b) *Underline* the correct word in the following statements:
i) Arteries carry blood to/from the heart.   *(1)*
ii) The blood vessels entering and leaving the heart on the right-hand side carry much/little oxygen.   *(1)*

c) Explain why arteries have thicker walls than veins. (2 lines available)   *(1)*

d) State the changes that take place in the blood as it passes through the lungs.
(4 lines available)   *(2)*

(WJEC)

QUESTION 14

A simplified diagram of the heart, lungs and circulation system is shown below. The arrows show the direction of circulation.

a) The three types of blood vessel labelled all vary in size, have different thickness of walls and in one case need valves along their length. With the help of diagrams, compare the blood vessels at points A, B and C.

A:

B:

C:

(6)

b) i) Using the previous diagram, explain how the heart works as a double pump to circulate blood round the body and also round the lungs. (4 lines available)

ii) Besides blood cells and plasma, what other materials would you expect to find in a sample of blood? (3 lines available)   *(7)*

c) Doctors in Britain are increasingly concerned by the number of deaths from heart disease.
i) How can exercise and a sensible diet help prevent heart disease? (5 lines available)
ii) Discuss the evidence which indicates cigarette smoking is harmful. (7 lines available)

(7)
(Total marks 20)
(ULEAC)

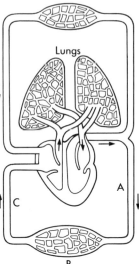

QUESTION 15

The graph shows a person's breathing rate and volume of breathing at the start of a race, during the race and after the race. The following questions relate to this graph.

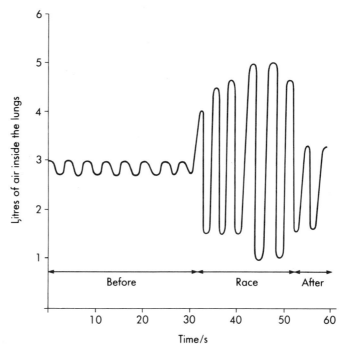

a) i) What was the maximum amount of air inside the athlete's lungs during the race?

(1)

   ii) What was the athlete's breathing rate per minute before the race started?

_____

(2)

Study the graph showing the pulse rates of a trained athlete, and of a person before and after starting to take regular exercise, and answer the questions that follow.

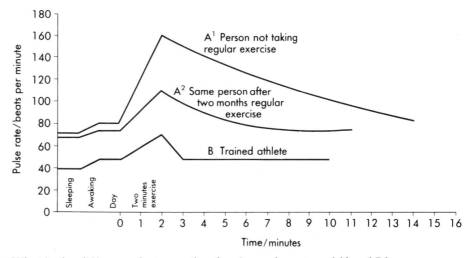

b) i) What is the difference between the sleeping pulse rates of Al and B?

_____

(1)

   ii) What is the difference between the recovery times of Al and A2?

_____

(2)

c) The illustration opposite shows two people who are very much overweight. They are said to be suffering from obesity.

   i) Give two dangers to health that might follow from obesity (4 lines available).

(2)

ii) State one precaution other than exercise which might be taken to avoid obesity
(2 lines available).

(1)
(NICCEA)

QUESTION 16

(Levels 4–6)

This is an example of a question requiring extended writing.

Explain how attention to diet, exercise and hygiene can keep your body healthy.
Marks will be given both for showing knowledge and understanding and for the
way in which your account is organised and expressed.

(8 marks and 20 lines are given for your answer)

(Co-ordinated Science ULEAC, NEAB, WJEC)

QUESTION 17

(Levels 6–8)

The diagram below shows some of the major organs in the human body.

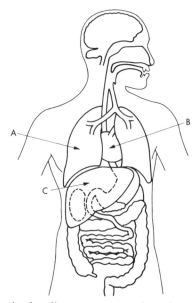

Use the information in the diagram to complete the table below.   *(6)*

Letter	Name of organ	The main function of the organ
A		
B		
C		

(SEG, Science Double Award)

ANSWERS TO EXAMINATION QUESTIONS

ANSWER 1

Key C. The vena cava brings blood from the body to the right atrium (2), and the blood is pumped to the lungs from the right ventricle (3), returning from the lungs via the left atrium (4) and then to the left ventricle (1).

ANSWER 2

Key E. Option D is a function of red blood cells. Option C, platelets, help to clot the blood.

ANSWER 3

Key A, the duodenum, the first part of the small intestine.

ANSWER 4

Key C, the stomach. The digestion of starch starts in the mouth, option A.

ANSWER 5

Key C. Be careful of option B, which is a function of the digestive system. Excretion is about removing waste produced by your body.

ANSWER 6

Key D, proteins. Option A, starch, and option B, fats, are used for energy.

ANSWER 7

Key B, diaphragm. Lungs have no muscle and do not contract, and ribs are moved by intercostal muscles.

ANSWER 8

a) i) sugar, (ii) starch,
b) i) to provide energy   ii) to build new cells for growth and repair
c) kilojoules
d) 11.7 mg
e) minerals
f) carbohydrate

ANSWER 9

a) lack of a balanced diet; all seven types of food must be eaten
b) protein
c) country Y

ANSWER 10

a) i)   scurvy   b) i)   vitamin C, citrus fruit
    ii) rickets   ii) vitamin D, green vegetables
    iii) anaemia   iii) iron, liver

ANSWER 11

a) starch
b) amylase
c) tube 2
d) tube 3
e) tube 1. Reason - the enzyme converted the starch to sugar after 10 minutes. Digestive enzymes work best at body temperature, 37°C.

ANSWER 12

a) i) butter
   ii) sugar
   iii) food - soya. Explanation - contains a proportion of all food types and is a good source of fat, protein, calcium and iron.
   iv) roughage
b) i) There is a general pattern which links the fat content and energy value of three of the four foods. The higher the fat, the greater the energy value. Butter has the highest amount of fat, and the highest energy value. Meat and soya have less than half the energy value of butter and only a quarter of the fat. Rice has less than half the energy value of butter and little fat.
   ii) Sugar has half the energy value of butter and contains no fat.
c) Food 1- sugar. Explanation - contains a lot of carbohydrate, which produces a lot of energy which has to be used up.
   Food 2 - butter. Explanation - contains a lot of fat, which is stored in the body if not used up.
d) Reason 1- soya is a plant, and it is more efficient to obtain food at the beginning of the food chain, as less energy has been lost.
   Reason 2 - soya is a better source of protein and calcium than meat, and many people are concerned about killing animals for meat.
e) i) Reason 1- to provide a good source of protein and fibre for many more people than could be supplied with meat.
   Reason 2 - the food can be stored more easily than meat, as it can be dried and made into different types of meat as necessary.
   ii) Problem 1- people will need to be convinced that the food substitute contains all the nutrients which were in meat.
   Problem 2 - the food will have to look and taste just like the meat it is replacing for it to be acceptable to meat eaters.

ANSWER 13

a) A pulmonary artery; B aorta; C pulmonary vein; D left ventricle.
b) i) Arteries carry blood *from* the heart.
   ii) The blood vessels entering and leaving the heart on the right side carry *little* oxygen.
c) The blood in arteries is under great pressure, so the artery walls are thicker.
d) The level of carbon dioxide in the blood is reduced as CO_2 diffuses into the air sacs. The level of oxygen in the blood is increased as O_2 diffuses into the blood.

ANSWER 14

a) A is an artery; B is a capillary; C is a vein.
b) i) The heart is divided by the septum, a thick wall which separates the blood going to the lungs from the blood going to the arteries. The ventricles on both sides contract at the same time. The right ventricle pumps blood to the lungs and the left ventricle pumps blood to the body.
   ii) water, salts, amino acids, urea, hormones, platelets.
c) i) exercise increases the efficiency of the heart in pumping blood around the body; a low fat diet reduces the risk of cholesterol building up and blocking the arteries.
   ii) Heavy smokers are more likely to die of heart disease than non-smokers, although the evidence is not conclusive; smoking reduces the oxygen-carrying capacity of the blood, and the heart has to work harder to pump the blood, so a heart attack is more likely.

ANSWER 15

a) i) 5 litres
   ii) 16 times per minute
b) i) 30
   ii) 6 minutes
c) i) 1 high blood pressure; 2 shorter life expectancy
   ii) balanced diet.

ANSWER 16

In this question you are told that marks are awarded for your knowledge and understanding, and for how you organise and express your answer. For example a maximum of 3 marks would be awarded for a coherent account using scientific language, showing a logical sequence. Only 1 mark would be awarded for an account using everyday language, showing little or no sequence.

You are asked to explain about how attention to diet, exercise and hygiene keep your body healthy, so try to include some facts about each of these in turn.

Some of the points you might include to gain the maximum 5 marks are:

Diet   eating a balanced diet (1)   with plenty of fibre (1)   not too much fat (1)

Exercise   regular exercise maintains a good circulation to the heart (1)
           fitness increases resistance to disease (1)

Hygiene   regular brushing of teeth removes food and reduces tooth decay (1)

ANSWER 17

A . . .   lung(s) (1)
           used for breathing / exchanging gases / taking in oxygen / air /
           getting rid of water (vapour) / carbon dioxide (1)   *(2)*

B . . .   heart (1)
           acts as a pump (for blood) (1)   *(2)*

C . . .   liver (1)
           stores some vitamins / produces heat / makes red blood cells (in a baby) /
           breaks down old red blood cells / makes bile / stores some minerals /
           makes chemicals which make blood clot / destroys poisons / bacteria /
           alcohol / deals with amino acids / deamination / keeps glucose level
           steady (1)   *(2)*

A STUDENT'S ANSWER WITH EXAMINER'S COMMENTS

66 Good, but include *to all cells* and *from cells* respectively. 99

66 Yes, but where? In coronary artery. 99

66 Good. 99

66 Yes, but also state arteries do not. 99

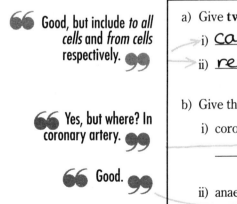

a) Give **two** functions of blood.

   i) carry oxygen

   ii) remove carbon dioxide

                                                                                 (2)

b) Give the cause of

   i) coronary thrombosis a blood clot

                                                                                 (1)

   ii) anaemia a lack of iron in the diet

                                                                                 (1)

c) Give **one** difference between a vein and an artery.

   veins have valves

                                                                                 (1)

The following results were obtained in an investigation to find the relationship between heartbeat and exercise.

Time in minutes	0	1	2	3	4	5	6	7	8
Number of beats per minute	60	60	80	100	100	88	76	65	60

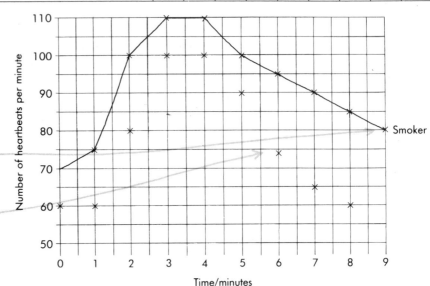

 **Good. This second graph is a line graph and you have followed the pattern of the first.**

 **Good.**

Error here. 73 should be 76.

d) On the graph paper above draw a *line graph* of the number of heartbeats per minute, plotted against time. *(2)*

e) Use your graph to answer the following questions.

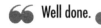 **Join points to show line.**

   i) Approximately when did the exercise start? between 1 and 2 minutes

   ii) Approximately when did the exercise stop? between 4 to 5 minutes

 Good answers.

   iii) What was the heartbeat rate after 2½ minutes?

   90 beats per minute

   (1½)

f) i) Draw a second graph using the same axes to show the results that you would expect from a person 50 years of age who had been a heavy smoker through life. *(1)*

   ii) Explain the graph you have drawn.

   The pulse rate is higher as the heart works harder.
   The pulse takes longer to get back to normal.

   (2)

Well done.

g) Explain why regular exercise is considered to be good for the heart.

   to keep the person fit

   (1)

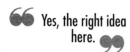 **A bit vague; exercise develops the hear muscle**

h) Quite often people with breathing difficulties as a result of a heart attack are given pure oxygen. Give **one** reason for this.

   to get more oxygen into the blood.

   (1)
   (WJEC)

Yes, the right idea here.

R E V I E W   S H E E T

At the end of each topic-based chapter you will find a review sheet, similar to this one. Try the questions yourself *before* looking back to the appropriate pages to check your answer.

Learning should be an active process. Even if you don't know an answer or make a mistake you will be learning as you check back to find the correct answer.

 What is the function of each of these cells?

    1. red blood cells _____

    2. nerve cells _____

 All cells have a nucleus except the _____ cells.

 Fill in the missing stages in the hierarchy of cells: → _____ → _____ → organ systems.

 The *circulatory system* is one of the seven main systems in your body. Name the other six.

    1. _____   3. _____   5. _____

    2. _____   4. _____   6. _____

 Why do we need each of the following in our diet? Suggest the food source in each case

    1. Carbohydrates _____   Source: _____

    2. Proteins _____   Source: _____

    3. Fats _____   Source: _____

    4. Roughage _____   Source: _____

 What do you understand by the word 'digestion'?

_____

 _____ is an enzyme in the saliva which breaks down large molecules of starch.

 Fill in as many of the labels on this diagram of the human digestive system as you can.

 Name the *substance used* and the outcome for a *positive result* in each of the following food tests

    Food   *Substance used*   *Positive result*

    1. Starch

    2. protein

    3. fat

    4. reducing sugar

 Complete the following chemical equation for respiration
food + oxygen →

 Blood flows in a series of tubes or blood vessels called _____ and _____ , which divide into very small blood vessels called _____ .

 Rank these foods in terms of energy value: milk; butter; cheese; apple.

✎ The function of *white* blood cells is _____

They can do this by producing _____

✎ The right atrium of the heart takes in _____ whereas the left atrium takes in _____

✎ The right ventricle pumps _____ to the lungs via the _____ artery; the left ventricle

pumps blood under great _____ around the body, via the _____, the thick-walled

main artery.

✎ Fill in as many of the labels on this
diagram of the human heart as you can.

✎ When breathing, the _____ muscles contract to pull your ribs up and out and the _____

muscle flattens so that your chest cavity is made larger. Air outside your chest cavity is at

_____ pressure than air inside your chest and this _____ in pressure causes air to rush

into your lungs.

✎ People who are fit generally have a _____ heart rate and therefore a _____ pulse rate
than people who are unfit.

✎ Aerobic respiration means _____

_____

The chemical equation for aerobic respiration is:
$C_6H_{12}O_6 + 6O_2 \rightarrow$

✎ Anaerobic respiration means _____

_____

✎ Athletes in sprint races usually use _____ respiration to release energy quickly.

✎ Name two functions of the skeleton

1. _____

2. _____

✎ Joints between the bones help with _____

✎ Muscles are attached to bones by _____

✎ Bones are held together by _____

PLANTS

GETTING STARTED

The process of photosynthesis, by which plants use energy from the Sun to make food, is essential to all other living things. Plants synthesise (make) carbohydrates from carbon dioxide and water, and these carbohydrates are converted into proteins and fats. Animals are dependent on plants to supply a never ending source of food.

Plants also use up large amounts of carbon dioxide from the atmosphere and release oxygen as a waste gas from the process of photosynthesis. People are sometimes confused about what happens with oxygen and carbon dioxide in plants. Plants *respire* (breathe) all the time, 24 hours a day, taking in oxygen and releasing carbon dioxide. During the daylight hours plants also *photosynthesise*, taking in carbon dioxide and releasing oxygen. The amount of carbon dioxide taken in is much greater than the amount produced during respiration, so the net effect is that plants reduce the amount of CO_2 in the atmosphere.

The destruction by burning of large areas of forest produces large amounts of CO_2; the trees are no longer able to remove CO_2 from the atmosphere, so the concentration increases, giving rise to the 'greenhouse effect'. CO_2 in the atmosphere traps heat energy from the Sun which should normally be reflected back into space. The temperature of the Earth then increases, leading to 'global warming', and a subsequent melting of ice caps in the polar regions causing a rise in sea level and possible flooding of coastal areas.

ESSENTIAL PRINCIPLES

Green plants convert carbon dioxide and water into carbohydrates and oxygen. This process is known as *photosynthesis*. An equation for photosynthesis is:

carbon dioxide and water   →   carbohydrates and oxygen

$$6CO_2 + 6H_2O \rightarrow C_6H_{12}O_6 + 6O_2$$

Energy from the Sun is absorbed by *chlorophyll* (the green pigment in plant leaves) and used to make sugars which are stored as *starch*. Oxygen is released as a waste product. You may have done experiments to show that light and carbon dioxide and water are necessary for photosynthesis.

The key facts to remember are that to show photosynthesis has occurred, a plant must be *destarched* by placing it in the dark for 2 days so that the stored starch is used up. The plant is then experimented on and the starch test can be carried out on a leaf to see if starch has been formed.

THE STARCH TESTS

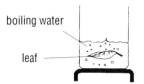

(a) Leaf is boiled in water (about 2 mins). (Purpose: to break down cell walls and to stop the action of enzymes within the leaf.)

(b) Leaf is warmed in ethanol (until leaf is colourless) CAUTION: ETHANOL IS INFLAMMABLE; NO FLAMES SHOULD BE USED AT THIS STAGE. (Purpose: to extract the chlorophyll, which would obstruct observations later. Chlorophyll dissolves in ethanol but not in water.)

> Testing for starch as evidence of photosynthesis

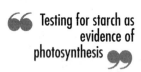

Fig 4.1 Testing a leaf for starch

(c) Leaf is dipped into the warm water (briefly) (Purpose: to soften the now brittle leaf.)

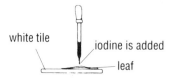

(d) leaf is placed on white tile and iodine added (Purpose: iodine shows the presence (blue–black) or absence (orange–brown) of starch; colours are shown against the white tile.)

To show that *chlorophyll* is necessary for photosynthesis, use a variegated leaf which has areas of green and white. Starch should be present in the green areas only (Figure 4.2).

> Testing for chlorophyll as a factor in photosynthesis

Fig 4.2 A variegated leaf before and after testing for starch

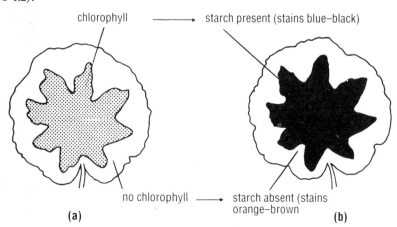

chlorophyll → starch present (stains blue–black)

no chlorophyll → starch absent (stains orange–brown

(a)   (b)

To show that *light* is necessary, a piece of foil is wrapped around part of the leaf to exclude the light. Starch should only be present in the areas exposed to light (Figure 4.3).

Testing for light as a factor in photosynthesis

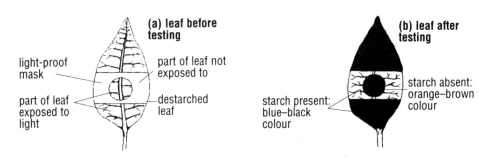

(a) leaf before testing

light-proof mask

part of leaf not exposed to

part of leaf exposed to light

destarched leaf

(b) leaf after testing

starch present: blue–black colour

starch absent: orange–brown colour

Fig 4.3 A partially covered leaf before and after testing for starch

To show that *carbon dioxide* is necessary, enclose part of the plant in a flask containing potassium hydroxide which absorbs the carbon dioxide. Starch should only be present in the leaves where carbon dioxide was available (Figure 4.4).

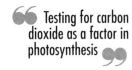
Testing for carbon dioxide as a factor in photosynthesis

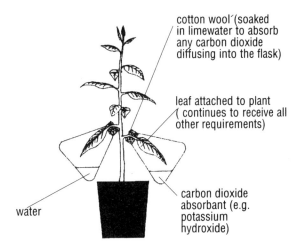

cotton wool (soaked in limewater to absorb any carbon dioxide diffusing into the flask)

leaf attached to plant (continues to receive all other requirements)

water

carbon dioxide absorbant (e.g. potassium hydroxide)

Fig 4.4 Apparatus to show that carbon dioxide is needed for photosynthesis

To show that *oxygen* is released during photosynthesis a plant can be trapped under a funnel, as shown in the diagram (Figure 4.5). The gas released can be tested with a glowing splint. The splint should relight showing the gas is oxygen. This experiment can also be used to study the rate of photosynthesis by measuring how many bubbles are produced per minute, given different intensities of light. The outcome is likely to be as shown in Figure 4.6.

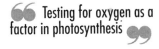
Testing for oxygen as a factor in photosynthesis

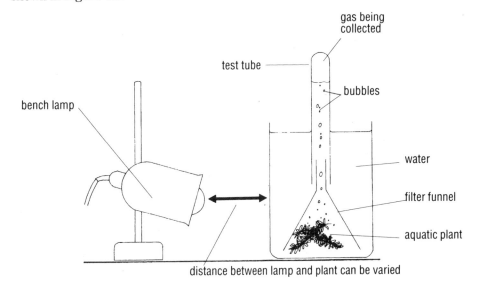

gas being collected

test tube

bubbles

bench lamp

water

filter funnel

aquatic plant

distance between lamp and plant can be varied

Fig 4.5 Experiment to demonstrate the effect of light intensity on the rate of photosynthesis

Limiting Factors

The rate of photosynthesis can be affected by factors such as light intensity and duration, concentration of carbon dioxide, and the amount of chlorophyll. If any of these factors is in short supply, it limits the rate of photosynthesis and is described as a *limiting factor*. For example, if the intensity of light is too low at dawn and dusk, then light becomes a limiting factor on the rate of photosynthesis.

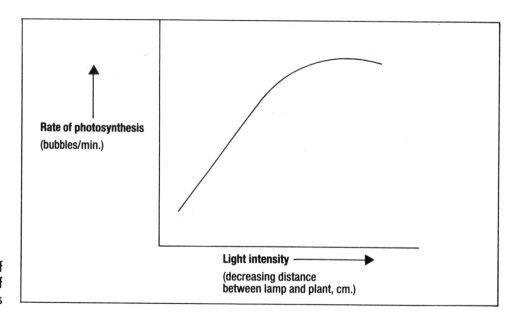

Fig 4.6 Graph to show the effect of light intensity on the rate of photosynthesis

Structure of leaves

Photosynthesis is carried out in the *chloroplasts* which contain chlorophyll (the green pigment). The cells which contain most chloroplasts are the *palisade* cells of the leaf. The leaf is very thin so that the light reaches these cells easily.

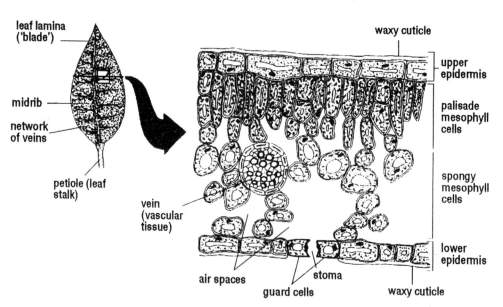

Fig 4.7 Structure of a typical leaf (vertical section; dicotyledonous leaf)

Mineral nutrition

Plants require *minerals* to help them manufacture proteins and other substances

The importance of minerals for plants

Mineral	needed for	symptom due to lack of mineral
Magnesium	to make chlorophyll	leaves turn yellow
Phosphorus	for enzyme systems	poor root growth, small leaves
Nitrogen	to make proteins	small leaves, thin weak stems

Active Transport

The movement of minerals into the root hair cells can take place by a process known as *active transport* which allows the plant to accumulate minerals above the concentration found in the soil (see 'Transport of Materials' below).

Food Storage

Plants store energy as starch, fats and oil so that they have sufficient energy to enable rapid growth in the spring. The potato that you eat is a stem tuber which stores starch. When these are planted, the 'eyes' of the tuber produce new shoots, using the food stored in the tuber.

The maize grain stores starch as the endosperm, so that when it germinates there is a supply of energy for the growth of the plumule and radicle until the new leaves are able to make food for the plant. Stored carbohydrates can be converted into protein, fat and chlorophyll.

2 > RESPIRATION

Respiration is a continuous process in plants whereas photosynthesis only occurs in green plants when there is sufficient light. The two processes can be thought of as opposite to each other as shown in the diagram.

$$\text{glucose + oxygen} \xrightleftharpoons[\text{photosynthesis}]{\text{respiration}} \text{carbon dioxide + water + energy}$$

In bright light the rate of photosynthesis is greater than the rate of respiration so there is a gain in materials required for growth.

Experiment to investigate the relative rates of photosynthesis and respiration

Four test tubes can be set up as shown in Fig. 4.8 with tubes C and D acting as controls without any leaves present. The bicarbonate indicator should appear red at the start of the experiment.

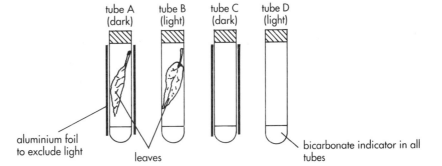

Fig 4.8 Experiment to investigate respiration and photosynthesis in leaves

TUBE	COLOUR OF INDICATOR AT END OF EXPERIMENT	CONCLUSION
A	Yellow	Carbon dioxide concentration is high; produced by respiration.
B	Purple	Carbon dioxide concentration is low; used in photosynthesis.
C	Red	Carbon dioxide concentration remains constant; no respiration or photosynthesis is occurring because no living tissue is present.
D	Red	

Carbon dioxide is produced as a result of respiration in tubes A and B, but in tube B photosynthesis is also occurring. As this process is more rapid than respiration in bright light the concentration of carbon dioxide is lowered.

3 > TRANSPORT OF MATERIALS

The arrangement of the *vascular tissues* in the stem and root of a dicotyledonous plant is shown in the diagram (Figure 4.9).

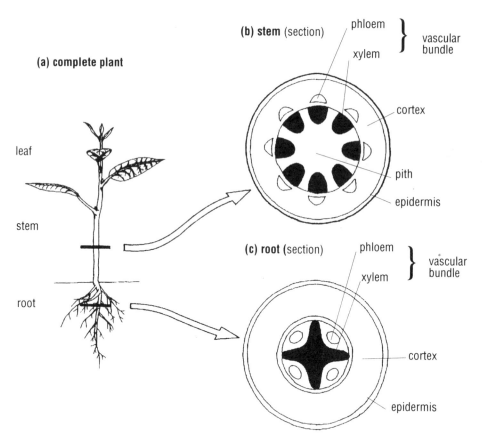

Fig 4.9 Distribution of vascular tissues in a dicotyledonous plant (vertical and transverse sections)

The *xylem tubes* carry water and mineral salts from the roots to the leaves. A stem placed in a red dye and then cut across after a few hours will show the red dye in the xylem tissues of the stem. The *phloem tubes* carry food such as dissolved sugars from one part of the plant to another.

Water is absorbed by *osmosis* through the root hairs which increase the surface area for absorption of water (Fig. 4.10). The solution inside the root hair cell is more concentrated than the water in the soil, so water moves in by osmosis. These cells are more dilute than the cells nearer the central part of the root, so a *concentration gradient* is set up and water is drawn into the xylem.

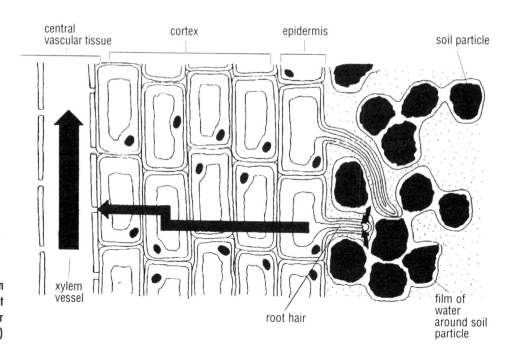

Fig 4.10 Absorption of water and minerals in the root (arrows show direction of water movement)

4 TRANSPIRATION

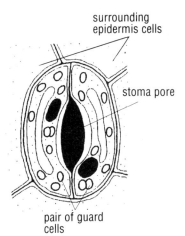

Fig. 4.11 A stoma showing two guard cells

Transpiration is the loss of water by evaporation from the leaves of plants. The water vapour moves out through the stomata (tiny pores) which cover the surface of the leaf. Each stoma has a pair of guard cells which regulate the size of the hole. When the cells take in water, they are described as *turgid* and the stoma opening becomes larger. When the cells lose water they become *flaccid* and the size of the pore is reduced (Fig. 4.11). This loss of water causes wilting. The closure of the stomata prevents excessive water loss by the plant. However the stomata needs to open from time to time to allow oxygen and carbon dioxide to enter or leave the plant by the processes of photosynthesis and respiration.

Transpiration rates

You may have investigated the *rate* of water loss from a plant by using a potometer. The potometer has a fine capillary tube containing water which has an air bubble. The rate of movement of the air bubble indicates the rate of transpiration from the leaves.

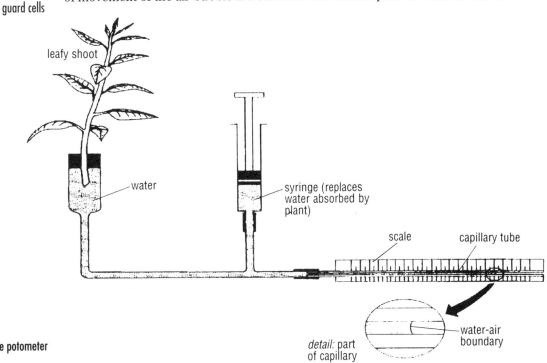

Fig 4.12 The potometer

Practical points to remember are to cut the plant and assemble the apparatus under water to prevent air bubbles entering the stem. The apparatus can be used to compare the rate of transpiration under different conditions. For example, by placing the potometer in the dark, or in the wind.

5 PLANT AND ANIMAL CELLS

The diagram (Figure 4.13) shows an example of a typical plant cell and a typical animal cell.

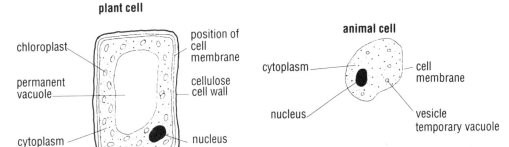

Fig 4.13 Generalised animal and plant cells

The chart lists the key differences between the two types of cells.

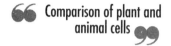
Comparison of plant and animal cells

Feature	Plant cell	Animal cell
cell wall	present	absent
cell vacuole	present as large permanent vacuole	present as small temporary vesicle
chloroplast	present	absent
shape of cell	regular	irregular

6 GERMINATION OF SEEDS

At the beginning of seed germination water is absorbed which activates enzymes to break down starch into smaller soluble molecules which release energy.

You may have studied the growth of a maize grain (Figure 4.14) shown in the diagram (Figure 4.15).

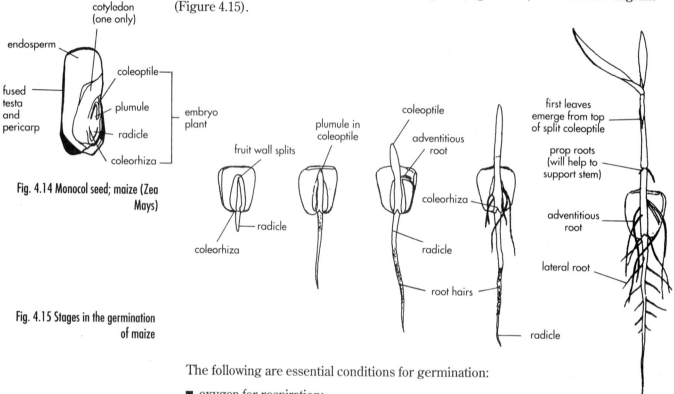

Fig. 4.14 Monocol seed; maize (Zea Mays)

Fig. 4.15 Stages in the germination of maize

The following are essential conditions for germination:

- oxygen for respiration;
- water for enzyme activity;
- a suitable temperature about 25°C.

Germination experiments to show that each of these conditions are necessary can be set up as follows.

Oxygen

To show whether *oxygen* is necessary for germination, use the apparatus shown in the diagram (Figure 4.16).

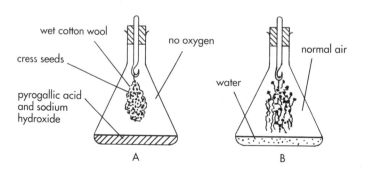

Fig. 4.16 To find out if oxygen is needed for germination

The pyrogallic acid and sodium hydroxide absorb oxygen from the air in the flask. The seeds in flask B will germinate because oxygen is present.

Water

To show whether *water* is necessary for germination use the apparatus shown in the diagram (Figure 4.17).

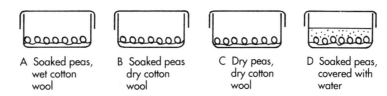

Fig. 4.17 Soaked peas covered with water

A Soaked peas, wet cotton wool

B Soaked peas dry cotton wool

C Dry peas, dry cotton wool

D Soaked peas, covered with water

Results

A germinate properly
B seeds shrivel up and die
C no germination
D seeds go mouldy and rot

Temperature

To investigate the effect of *temperature* on germination you can put three dishes of soaked seeds at different temperatures, eg. in a refrigerator at 4° C, in an incubator at 30° C and at room temperature at 20° C. Seeds usually have an optimum temperature for growth and the seeds at room temperature will usually germinate best.

7 ⟩ **GROWTH IN STEMS AND ROOTS**

Growth in plants occurs at the regions near the tip of the stem and root (Figure 4.18).

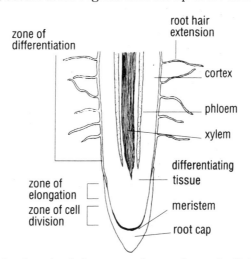

Fig 4.18 Growth in the root tip

zone of differentiation

root hair extension

cortex

phloem

xylem

differentiating tissue

zone of elongation

zone of cell division

meristem

root cap

Rapid cell division by mitosis increases the numbers of cells in the *zone of cell division*. In the *zone of elongation* the cells then become enlarged as the cell wall and vacuoles form. *Differentiation* into specialised cells such as xylem and phloem then occurs.

8 ⟩ **TROPIC RESPONSES**

Tropic responses are the way in which plants respond to factors such as gravity and light. The response is brought about by the action of hormones, such as *auxins*, which stimulate or inhibit growth in plants. The hormones are released in the shoot tip and root tip and can move through the plant by *diffusion*. They affect the zone of elongation just behind the shoot tip (plumule) and root tip (radicle).

Phototropism – response to light

Auxin hormones accumulate on the side of the shoot away from the light. The auxins stimulate the growth of the shoot so that the side away from the light,which has more auxins, grows more rapidly. This has the effect of bending the shoot *towards* the light so that more photosynthesis can take place – a *positive phototropic* response (towards light).

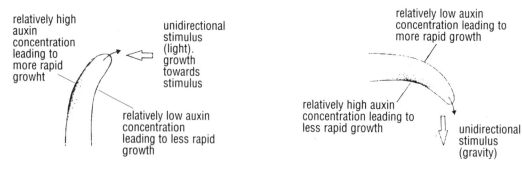

relatively high auxin concentration leading to more rapid growht

unidirectional stimulus (light). growth towards stimulus

relatively low auxin concentration leading to less rapid growth

Fig. 4.19 Positive phototropism in a shoot tip

relatively low auxin concentration leading to more rapid growth

relatively high auxin concentration leading to less rapid growth

unidirectional stimulus (gravity)

Fig. 4.20 Positive geotropism in a shoot tip

Geotropism – response to gravity

If the *root tip* is emerging from the seed horizontally, auxin hormones accumulate on the lower side of the root. Auxins in the root have the effect of inhibiting growth so that the side on top grows more rapidly. This has the effect of bending the root downwards *towards* water and mineral salts – a *positive geotropic* response (towards gravity), as in Figure 4.20.

If the *shoot tip* is emerging from the seed horizontally, the auxin has the opposite effect and stimulates the growth of the lower side of the shoot so that it curves upwards towards the light. This is described as a *negative geotropic* response (away from gravity).

The diagram (Figure 4.21) shows a *clinostat* used to investigate geotropism.

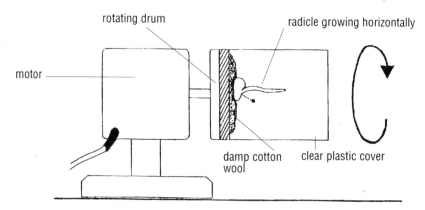

rotating drum

radicle growing horizontally

motor

damp cotton wool

clear plastic cover

Fig. 4.21 The clinostat

Applications of hormones

Artificially synthesised hormones are used to control growth and reproduction in plants by humans in many ways, for example:

to promote growth
- in the formation of fruit
- in stimulating root growth in cuttings
- in weed killers to disrupt growth patterns in weeds

9 ▶ REPRODUCTION IN PLANTS

The diagram shows a section through an insect pollinated flower (Figure 4.22).

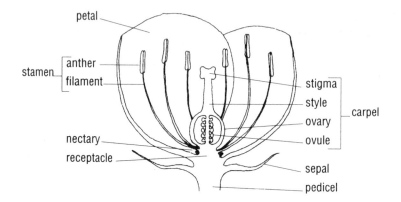

petal

stamen — anther
filament

stigma
style
ovary
ovule

carpel

nectary
receptacle

sepal
pedicel

Fig. 4.22 Structure of a generalised flower (vertical section)

The function of each part of the flower is as follows:

Part		Function
petal		to attract insects
nectary		to produce nectar to attract insect
sepal		to protect the petals
stamen	– anther	to produce pollen
	– filament	to support the anther
carpel	– stigma	to receive pollen
	– style	to hold up the stigma
	– ovary	contains the ovules
	– ovules	to form the seeds

Wind pollinated flowers have much smaller flowers and the reproductive parts usually hang outside the flower so that the very light pollen can be blown by the wind onto the stigma.

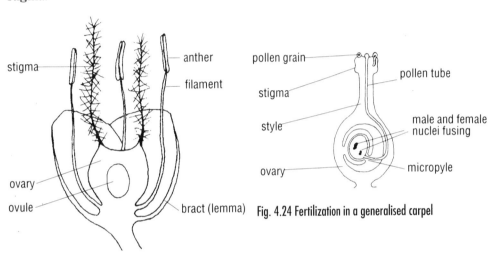

Fig. 4.23 Wind -pollinated flower: meadow grass (Poa spp.) (half flower)

Fig. 4.24 Fertilization in a generalised carpel

Pollination

Pollen is transferred either by insects or wind from the anthers (the male part of the flower) to the stigma (the female part of the flower).

Fertilisation

The pollen grains on the stigma grow a long tube through the style so that the nucleus of the pollen cell can travel down the tube and fuse with the nucleus of the ovum inside the ovule.

Development of fruit and seeds

The fertilised ovule develops into the seed. The ovary develops into the fruit which encloses the seeds and helps to disperse the seeds.

Fruit and seed dispersal

Dispersal is important so that seeds do not compete with the parent plant for resources such as light, space, and mineral salts. New areas can be colonised as seeds may be carried over long distances by animals, wind or water.

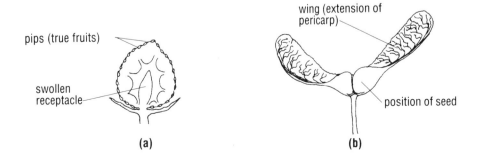

Fig. 4.25

(a)

(b)

EXAMINATION QUESTIONS AND ANSWERS

QUESTION 1

The diagram below (Figure 4.26) shows an apparatus used to investigate the production of heat by germinating seeds.

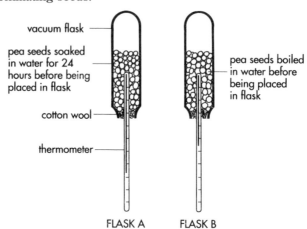

Fig. 4.26

FLASK A   FLASK B

The results of the experiment are shown in the tables below.

	temperature /°C	
day	flask **A**	flask **B**
1	19	19
2	21	19
3	24	19
4	24	19

a) Why were the seeds soaked in water before being placed in flask **A**?

b) Why were the seeds boiled in water before being placed in flask **B**?

c) Explain why the temperatures in flasks **A** and **B** are different.

d) The outer surfaces of all the seeds were sterilised before use (by washing them in a weak disinfectant) to kill any micro-organisms that might have been present. Suggest how the results might have been affected if this had NOT been done.

(4)

QUESTION 2

a) Compare the general features of an insect-pollinated flower with those of a wind-pollinated flower. Present your information in the form of a table, eg.:-

feature of insect-pollinated flowers	feature of wind-pollinated flowers
often scented	no scent
etc.	

(6)

b) The table below shows the results of an investigation into how sowing seeds at different times of the year affects the yield (mass of fruit produced per square metre).

time period for sowing seed	yield/kg per m^2
before March 1	0.8
March 1–14	1.5
March 15–31	2.3
April 1–14	2.9
April 15–30	2.5
May 1–14	2.2
May 15–31	1.3
June 1–14	0.7

    i) State the time period which results in
        a) the maximum yield
        b) the minimum yield.
   ii) If a farmer sowed seed in a plot with an area of two hectares
        (1 hectare = 10,000 m^2), calculate
        a) the maximum mass of fruit he could expect to obtain,
        b) the minimum mass of fruit he could expect to obtain   *(4)*

c) Explain why sowing seed at different times of the year can affect the yield of fruit.
                                                        (3)

d) Describe the sequence of events which occurs during the development of a NAMED fruit.   *(5)*

QUESTION 3

The diagram (Figure 4.27) shows the external features of a typical flowing plant. Label, on the diagram, features 1 to 5 using the words given in the list below.

    Stem   Terminal bud   Leaf   Side root   Axillary bud   *(5)*

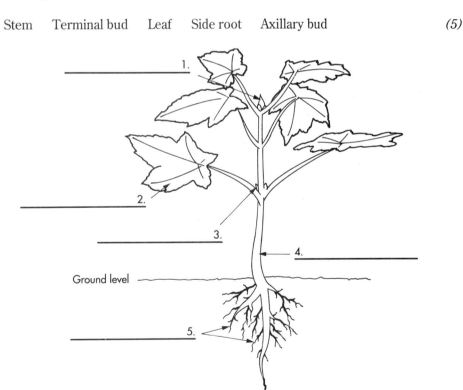

Fig. 4.27

QUESTION 4

The amount of water lost from the leaves of a sycamore shoot was measured at hourly intervals throughout a warm, dry, windless day. The results obtained are shown in the graph (Figure 4.28).

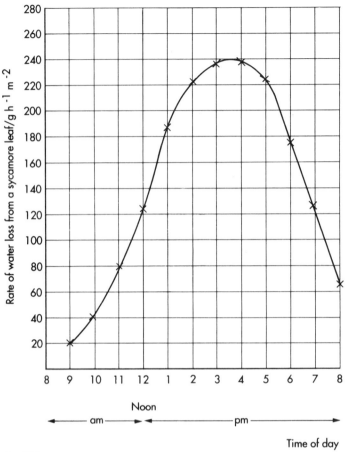

Fig. 4.28

a) Over which part of the day does the rate of water loss
   i) increase from 40 to 188 g h^{-1} m^{-2}
   ii) decrease from 240 to 68 g h^{-1} m^{-2}? *(4)*

b) i) At what time of day is the rate of water loss at a maximum?
   ii) Suggest TWO reasons for this. *(3)*

c) At what other time of day is the rate of water loss the same as it is at 12 noon? *(1)*

d) Would you expect the maximum rate of water loss to increase, decrease or stay the same if the measurements had been made on
   i) a warm, humid, windless day
   ii) a warm, dry, windy day?
   Give reasons for your choice of answer. *(6)*

e) i) At 2pm, how many grams of water are lost each hour from a leaf area of 1 m2?
   ii) How much heat is required to vaporize this mass of water?
      (Latent heat of vaporization of water = 2260 kJ/kg) *(4)*

f) Describe an experiment designed to show which surface of a leaf loses more water vapour. *(6)*

g) Give TWO reasons why transpiration is important to a plant. *(2)*

h) Explain how a high light intensity increases the transpiration rate. *(2)*

QUESTION 5

(Levels 4–6 Tier F)

The diagram shows a flowering plant.

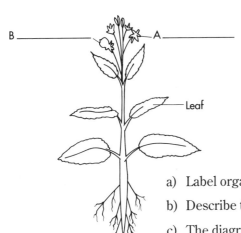

a) Label organs A and B on the diagram. *(2)*

b) Describe the functions of the root system. (3 lines available) *(3)*

c) The diagram below shows a cell taken from the root of a plant.

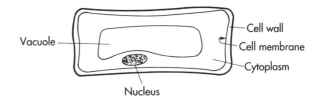

i) Give ONE difference between a typical leaf cell and this root cell. Explain the reason for this difference. (4 lines available) *(3)*

ii) Give ONE difference between this root cell and a typical animal cell. (2 lines available) *(1)*

(ULEAC, SEG Modular Science)

QUESTION 6

(Levels 6–8)

The picture below shows a plant known as the giant hogweed. It is an annual plant, which means that it grows from a seed each year. Its seeds germinate at the beginning of April and by the end of July the plants could have reached heights of over 2 metres.

a) Giant hogweed normally grows very quickly. Suggest **two** environmental conditions which would cause it to grow more slowly. *(2)*

Condition 1 _____

Condition 2 _____

b) In order to grow, green plants need to carry out photosynthesis. Give the name of a carbon compound which is made by a plant during photosynthesis. *(1)*

c) i) From the diagram, suggest and explain **two** ways in which the giant hogweed is well-adapted for photosynthesis. *(4)*

Suggestion 1 _____

Explanation 1 _____

_____

Suggestion 2 _____

Explanation 2 _____

_____

ii) Suggest and explain **one** reason why this plant has to photosynthesise at a rapid rate. *(2)*

Suggestion _____

Explanation _____

_____

d) A single giant hogweed produces many millions of seeds. Each seed is very light and feathery. Explain the advantage to the plant of the seeds being **light** and **feathery**. (4 lines available). *(3)*

(SEG, Science Double Award)

OUTLINE ANSWERS

ANSWER 1

a) water is needed for germination

b) to destroy the enzymes in the seeds and to stop any reactions

c) in flask **A** respiration is taking place and so heat is released. In flask **B** there is no respiration as the seeds have been killed, therefore no heat is released.

d) heat may have been released as micro-organisms cause the seeds to go mouldy.

ANSWER 2

a)

	insect pollinated	wind pollinated
1	large, coloured petals	small petals, not coloured
2	stamen and stigma enclosed in flower	stamen and stigma hang outside flower
3	large heavy pollen	small light pollen
4	nectar	no nectar

b) i) a) maximum yield April 1–14
   b) minimum yield June 1–14
   ii) a) 58,000 kg   b) 14,000 kg

c) – germination can depend on temperature
   – water must be available
   – some seed germination may coincide with outbreaks of pests

d) – ovule develops into the seed
   – ovary develops into fruit
   – the plumule, radicle and cotyledons develop inside the seed
   – the fruit wall becomes modified ready for dispersal

ANSWER 3

1 terminal bud
2 leaf
3 axillary bud
4 stem
5 side root

ANSWER 4

a) i) from 10 a.m. to 1 p.m.
    ii) from 4 p.m. to 8 p.m.

b) i) between 2 p.m. and 3 p.m.
    ii) hottest part of the day, increased transpiration takes places

c) 7 p.m.

d) i) decrease – transpiration reduced if humid and no wind;
    ii) increase – transpiration increased by dry, moving air.

e) i) 224 g
    ii) 506 kJ

f) fix small squares of cobalt chloride paper to each surface of leaf and compare time taken for paper to change from blue (when dry) to pink (when moist)

g) – allows water and mineral salts to be drawn up to leaves;
    – possible cooling effect of evaporation of water

h) the stomata open to allow more rapid evaporation.

ANSWER 5

a) On the diagram, A is the flower (1), B is the fruit (1)

b) the root system holds/anchors the plant in the ground (1)
    obtains water (1) and minerals (1) for the plant
    stores food (1)

c) i) make it clear which cell you are referring to.
       Note you are asked to explain the reason for the difference

       a typical leaf cell contains chlorophyll/choroplasts (1)
       which are needed to absorb light (1)
       to enable the leaf to carry out photosynthesis (1)

    ii) the root cell has a cell wall and a vacuole (1)
        whereas the animal cell does not

ANSWER 6

a) ANY **TWO** FROM:

    lack of water / drought / (1 mark)
    lack of food / fertiliser / minerals (1 mark)
    lack of sun (shine) (1 mark)
    lack of heat (1 mark)
    poor soil   (2)

    NOTE: each condition **must** be qualified.

b) carbohydrate / glucose / sugar / starch
    or any other correct carbohydrate   (1)

c) i) leaves flat / large (surface area) /
        not under one another (1 mark)
        pick up max / lots sunlight (1 mark)   (2)

        tall stems (1 mark)
        hold leaves above competitors (1 mark)   (2)

    ii) needs to get tall / large /
        quickly (1 mark)
        needs a lot of energy / protein
        for this (1 mark)   (2)

d) LIGHT
    easily carried by the wind (1 mark)

    FEATHERY
    large surface area (1 mark)

    CONSEQUENCE
    get carried a long way (1 mark)   (3)

Total 12 marks

R E V I E W   S H E E T

✎ Photosynthesis is the process by which green plants convert _____
The chemical equation for photosynthesis is:

      carbon dioxide and water →   (in words)

          $6CO_2 + 6H_2O$ →   (in symbols)

✎ Energy from the sun is absorbed by _____ in green plants and used to make sugars
which are stored as _____

✎ Describe a starch test to show that *light* is necessary for photosynthesis.

_____

_____

_____

_____

✎ List two 'limiting factors' on the rate of photosynthesis

1. _____   2. _____

✎ Complete this chart, showing why plants need minerals.

Mineral	needed for	symptom due to lack of mineral
Magnesium		
Phosphorus		
Nitrogen		

✎ Complete both sides of this diagram, showing how respiration and photogynthesis can be thought of as opposite processes.

    respiration

    ⇌

    photosynthesis

✎ Four test tubes are set as shown in the diagram. Tubes C and D are set up as controls without any leaves present. Bicarbonate indicator is used in this experiment to investigate the relative rates of photosynthesis and respiration. The bicarbonate indicator is red at the start of the experiment.

    Fill in the conclusions

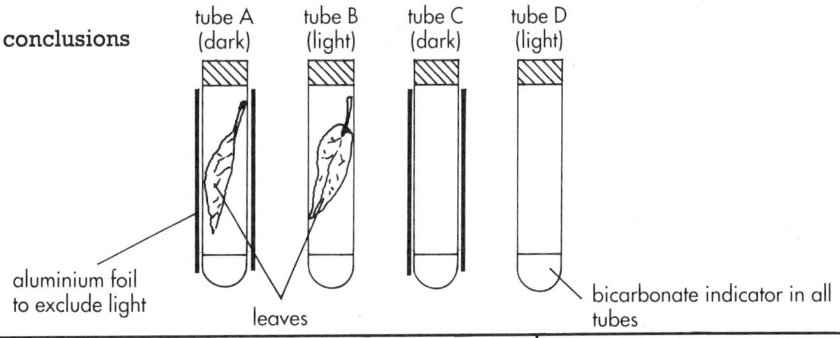

tube A (dark)   tube B (light)   tube C (dark)   tube D (light)

aluminium foil to exclude light   leaves   bicarbonate indicator in all tubes

TUBE	COLOUR OF INDICATOR AT END OF EXPERIMENT	CONCLUSION
A	Yellow	
B	Purple	
C	Red	
D	Red	

✎ The *xylem tubes* carry _____ from the roots of plants to the leaves. The *phloem tubes* carry _____ from one part of the plant to another.

✎ Water is absorbed by _____ through the root hairs of the plant.

✎ *Transpiration* is the _____

_____

✎ _____ responses are the way in which plants respond to factors such as gravity and light.

Hormones, such as _____ , help to bring about such responses.

✎ *Phototropism* means the response to _____

✎ *Geotropism* means the response to _____ . We can investigate geotropism by using an instrument called a _____

✎ Fill in this table listing the functions of each part of the flower.

Part	Function
petal nectary sepal stamen – anther – filament carpel – stigma – style – ovary – ovules	

Dispersal is important because it means that fruits and seeds do not _____

_____

✎ Fill in as many of the label lines on this vertical section of a flower as you can.

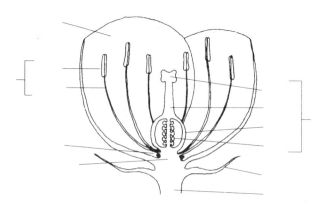

VARIATION, INHERITANCE AND EVOLUTION

GETTING STARTED

This chapter is all about 'changes' - and in today's world change is something we must all come to terms with; *new* models of familiar things appear every day! New cars, personal stereo players, compact discs and cameras keep appearing in the shops, all different in some way to those we have already, and tempting us to part with our money. It is now quite possible to imagine a machine which would behave much like a human, taking in energy, moving about and having enough artificial intelligence to make simple decisions and react appropriately to stimuli. What this machine, and the others listed above, would *not* be able to do is to *reproduce* - this is a unique characteristic of living things and so sets them apart from the machines we make.

Even more amazing is the way in which each generation of living things may be *different* from its parent generation. As we begin to understand the mechanisms of inheritance, this is no longer such a mystery, as we recognise that differences may simply be due to the reshuffling of *existing* genes and the creation of *new* ones by mutation. We think we can now explain how some 200 million different species of plants and animals have come into being on the Earth; according to the *theory of evolution*, organisms changed gradually from one generation to the next and, over many generations, new species have formed. To understand the *processes* that bring about evolution, it is essential to have an understanding of how living things *reproduce*, since this is the key to change.

E S S E N T I A L   P R I N C I P L E S

1 ＞REPRODUCTION

Reproduction is a characteristic of all living things. It may occur once, or many times, in an organism's lifetime. All life exists because previous generations have reproduced and the new individuals that survived have also reproduced. Because living things vary, they are not all equally well adapted to survive, so not all organisms which are born live long enough to reproduce. There seem to be many different *ways* of reproducing, but if we remove the details there are only two basic methods: *asexual* and *sexual*.

ASEXUAL REPRODUCTION

Asexual reproduction only involves one parent. This can be an advantage in that an isolated individual can reproduce on its own and produce offspring which are exact copies of the parent. If the parent is successful in coping with its environment, then it is important for the survival of the offspring that the parent's characteristics are passed on exactly. (Plants which are genetically identical are described as *clones*.) However, a lack of variation can cause problems if there is a sudden *change* in the environment - it may then be that none of the offspring will survive. A disease could destroy the whole population because there would be no resistant varieties.

> " All the offspring are the same "

Bacteria, yeasts and other single-celled organisms reproduce asexually by growing to a maximum size and then *dividing* into two smaller individuals. A single disease-causing bacterium could do this every twenty minutes, so that in only twenty-four hours some 4000 million bacteria would be produced, which could make you very ill indeed. Many different species of plants are able to reproduce asexually, and can also reproduce sexually, using whichever method is most advantageous for survival of the species.

Asexual reproduction in plants usually involves part of the plant becoming separated from the parent and developing into a new individual. Weeds in the garden do this when the gardener uses a mechanical cultivator, chopping up and replanting the weeds, thus accidentally increasing the weed problem. Gardeners are also able to grow new plants from their old favourites by taking cuttings, and to be sure that the new plants will be just like the original.

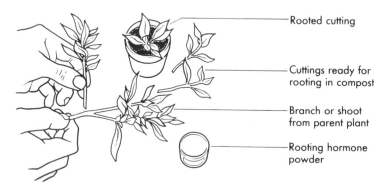

Rooted cutting

Cuttings ready for rooting in compost

Branch or shoot from parent plant

Rooting hormone powder

Fig. 5.1 Cuttings being taken.

SEXUAL REPRODUCTION

> " The offspring all differ from each other "

Sexual reproduction usually involves two parents, although there are many organisms which have both female and male sex organs. Such plants and animals are called *hermaphrodites* and can make both male and female sex cells - these organisms usually exchange gametes with others of the same species. Common hermaphrodites include earthworms and buttercups.

Sexual reproduction always involves the fusion of two *gametes* - one male sex cell (sperm) and one female sex cell (egg). The new cell produced, the *zygote,* divides many times to form an *embryo* and eventually grows to become the young organism.

The first problem to be solved by organisms reproducing in this way is how to find a member of the opposite sex, and the second is how to get the sperm and egg together – both have been solved in many ways. In humans, fertilisation is *internal,* so the egg and sperm fuse inside the female's body. In frogs, fertilisation is *external,* with the sperm being shed over the eggs, which are laid in water. Usually offspring which are produced by internal fertilisation are better protected, as they develop either in an egg with a tough shell, or inside the mother, as in humans. The main advantage of sexual reproduction, as compared with asexual reproduction, is that the offspring will *vary* from each other and from the parents - variety can mean the difference between success or extinction for the species in a constantly changing environment.

2 ▷ GAMETES

These special sex cells are *not* the result of the sort of cell division we call *mitosis*, like ordinary body cells. Cells produced by mitosis are identical to the parent cells, having exactly the same chromosomes.

" Gametes are sex cells "

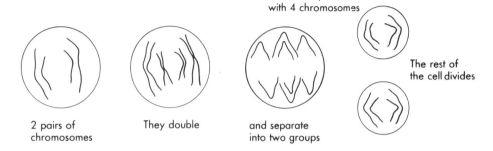

Fig. 5.2 Mitosis in a cell with four chromosomes.

2 pairs of chromosomes   They double   and separate into two groups

2 new cells, each with 4 chromosomes

The rest of the cell divides

Gametes are produced by *meiosis*, or reduction division, which only happens in the sex organs. These new cells have *half* the number of chromosomes of the parent cell and so half of the information content. Two of these must fuse at fertilisation to produce the first normal cell of the offspring, one male and one female gamete. Female gametes are produced in the ovary, male gametes in a testis or stamen.

" A zygote is a fertilised egg "

At fertilisation, each gamete carries only one of each type of chromosome. When fusion has taken place the zygote has two full sets of chromosomes, which is normal for an ordinary body cell. An interesting outcome of meiosis is that all the gametes produced are different, but you would need to know much more about both meiosis and chromosomes to understand why.

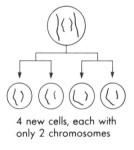

4 new cells, each with only 2 chromosomes

Fig. 5.3 Meiosis in a cell with four chromosomes.

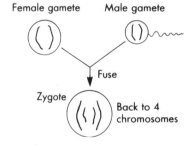

Female gamete   Male gamete

Fuse

Zygote

Back to 4 chromosomes

Fig. 5.4 Fertilisation.

3 ▷ HUMAN REPRODUCTION

Male and female reproductive organs fit together during sexual intercourse in order to place the *sperm* (male gametes) well inside the female's body. Sperm are made in the testes and pass out of the male's body in a fluid (semen) through the penis during ejaculation. The sperm have only a short distance to swim to enter the uterus. They move across the uterus and travel along the fallopian tubes towards the ovaries. If there is an egg in the fallopian tube, *fertilisation* may take place. The fertilised egg travels to the uterus and embeds itself in the lining (endometrium). If fertilisation does not take place, the endometrium breaks down and is lost as part of the monthly menstrual cycle. Pregnancy (*gestation*) in humans is about 9 months; after birth, human offspring require a great deal of parental care and attention.

" Sperm and egg join together to make a zygote "

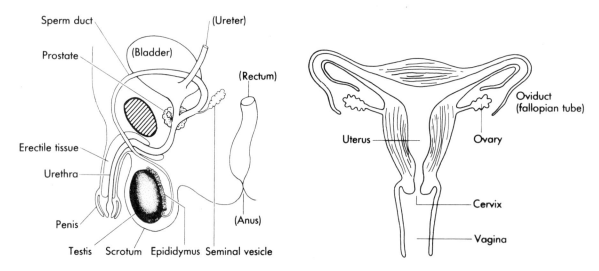

Fig. 5.5 The human male reproductive system.

Fig. 5.6 The human female reproductive system.

During gestation (pregnancy) the fertilised egg divides rapidly by mitosis and develops into a ball of cells known as the *embryo*. After about 8 weeks the *embryo* begins to show distinct human features and forms the *foetus*. The foetus is joined to its mother by the *placenta* which allows substances to diffuse from the mother's blood to the blood of the foetus and vice versa. The blood supply never mixes, thereby protecting the foetus from the higher blood pressure of the mother's blood. The foetus is connected to the placenta by an *umbilical cord* and supported by *amniotic fluid* which acts as a shock absorber.

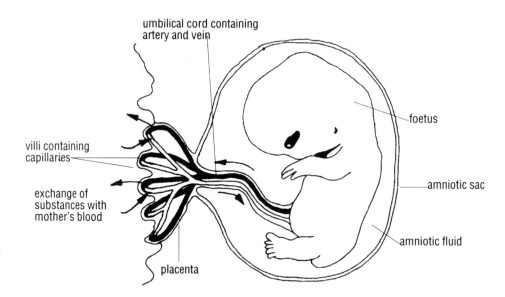

Fig 5.7 Exchange of substances at the placenta

After about 40 weeks the baby's head is normally positioned above the cervix and is pushed out of the uterus by rhythmic contractions of the uterus muscles during 'labour'. The placenta is also pushed out of the uterus after the baby is born. The sudden drop in temperature causes a reflex response which makes the baby breathe.

Soon after birth, the mammary glands of the mother begin to produce milk which contains all the necessary nutrients for the baby until the baby is weaned on to solid food.

The menstrual cycle

This is a periodic change which occurs in a woman's body about every 28 days. During the first few days of the cycle the extra lining of the uterus breaks down and is released from the body. During the next 10 days an egg ripens in the ovary and the uterus lining thickens again. On about the 14th day the egg is released from the ovary during ovulation, and this is when fertilisation can occur. If there is no fertilisation then the uterus lining breaks down and is released on about the 28th day.

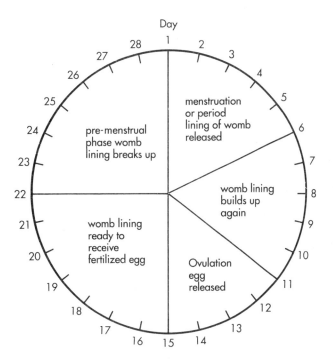

Fig 5.8 The Menstrual cycle

Contraception

The table below provides a useful review of the various methods of contraception.

METHOD	HOW IT WORKS	ADVANTAGES	DISADVANTAGES
Contraceptive pill	Contains hormones which prevent ovulation.	Very effective.	Possible side effects; possible to forget.
Cap (diaphragm)	Blocks path of sperm at cervix.	Simple, effective if used with spermicidal cream.	May be incorrectly fitted.
Intra-uterine device (IUD) (coil)	Fitted in uterus; prevents implantation.	Once fitted, does not require frequent attention.	May cause pain or heavy bleeding.
Condom (sheath)	Rubber sleeve, fits over erect penis; retains semen.	Simple, effective; may prevent sexually transmitted diseases e.g. AIDS	May be damaged; may not be carefully removed.
Withdrawal	Penis withdrawn from vagina before ejaculation.	Does not require any preparation.	Semen may be released before ejaculation.

66 **Chromosomes carry hundreds of genes** 99

Normal human body cells have 23 pairs of chromosomes in the nucleus, and every 23 pairs carries instructions for the whole human body. Each chromosome holds the information for many chemical reactions and is made of complex molecules of DNA (deoxyribonucleic acid). DNA carries genetic information in the form of a code determined by the particular sequence of four bases. The sequence of this code directs the correct sequence in which amino acids are assembled to build specific proteins such as a particular enzyme. It is thought that one gene is responsible for making one protein. We believe, for instance, that the instructions for making the enzyme salivary amylase and the Rhesus blood antigens are part of the *same* chromosome.

The instructions for a particular characteristic, or trait, are called a *gene*. There are genes for all our characteristics such as eye colour, hair colour and blood type. Each chromosome carries many genes, each a certain length of DNA. We have two copies of each gene in every normal human body cell, one in each of a pair of chromosomes because we inherit one gene of each type - one from our father and one from our mother. These genes may be identical or have slightly different effects. For instance, we all have two genes for eye colour, if one is for blue eyes and one for brown eyes you will have brown eyes. We can't see genes, but their effects have been observed and patterns of inheritance discovered by scientists. A gene is described as a *dominant* gene if it is expressed in the appearance of an individual when both genes are present. For example a *heterozygous* person for eye colour has the dominant gene for brown eyes and the recessive gene for blue eyes so the eyes appear brown. A *homozygous* person for eye colour who has both recessive genes will appear to have blue eyes.

The *phenotype* is the outward appearance of an individual and is determined by the interaction of the genetic constitution and the environment. The *genotype* is the genetic constitution of an individual. In the example in Fig. 5.9 there are two possible phenotypes and three genotypes (here B = black, b= brown).

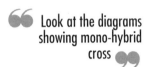

Genotype	Phenotype	Description
BB	black	homozygous dominant
Bb	black	heterozygous
bb	brown	homozygous recessive

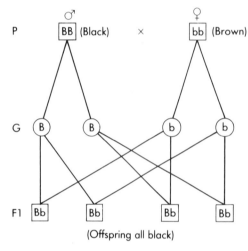
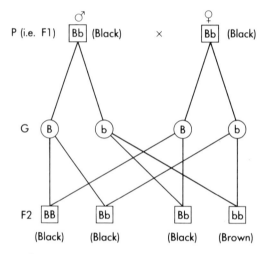

Fig. 5.9 A typical monohybrid cross for two generations.

♂ = male
B = dominant (black) allele
b = recessive (brown) allele
P = parents

♀ = female
× = crossing (mating)
G = gametes
F1 = offspring in first generation ('first filial')
F2 = offspring in second generation

Over the 100 years or so since an Austrian monk, Gregor Mendel, established the basic laws of inheritance, the science of genetics has become well established. Our understanding of genetics has developed to a point where we can now create new organisms by genetic engineering, that is by transferring genes from one organism to another.

Sex determination

In humans, the sex of an individual is determined by a small pair of chromosomes called the sex chromosomes. In a human female these chromosomes are homologous (identical) and are described as X chromosomes. In the male, one of the pair is smaller and is called the Y chromosome.

A female individual results from having two X chromosomes and a male from having an X and a Y chromosome. At meiosis all the female gametes carry an X chromosome whereas half of the male gametes carry an X chromosome and half carry a Y chromosome. If an X bearing sperm fertilises the ovum then the zygote is XX and develops into a girl. If a Y bearing sperm fertilises the ovum the zygote is XY and develops into a boy. The expected ratio of female to male is therefore 1:1.

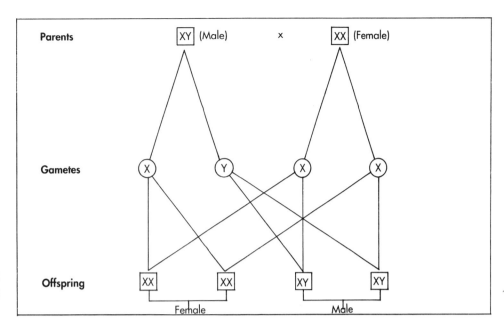

Fig 5.10 Inheritance of sex in humans

5 > MUTATIONS

When chromosomes are copied during mitosis and meiosis there is a possibility for mistakes to be made. These mistakes are known as *mutations* and can affect either single genes or whole chromosomes. Exposure to radiation and chemicals, such as mustard gas or LSD, can increase the rate of mutation. Mutation in body cells may result in cancer. Gene mutations are usually *harmful* and may cause genetic diseases. An example would be the albino gene; this mutation prevents the formation of the dark skin pigment melanin which protects against the sun's ultra-violet rays. Albino animals, therefore, are not protected. Some mutant genes are however *helpful* and can improve an organism's chance of survival. For instance, the sickle-cell gene, which affects the red blood cells in humans causing sickle-cell anaemia, can give some immunity to malaria. Other mutations seem to have no effect and are termed *neutral* - they appear not to affect survival.

The sickle-cell gene can however be harmful if a child gets it from *both* parents. This is one of some three thousand known genetic diseases, and we now have genetic counsellors to help affected people. About 5% of children admitted to UK hospitals are suffering from genetic diseases.

Chromosome mutations can also occur when chromosomes are altered during meiosis. Bits may be broken off or added to chromosomes, and sometimes whole chromosomes may be lost or gained. The faulty gametes which are produced may be fertilised and produce zygotes with *damaged* chromosomes, or *too few* or *too many* chromosomes. An extra number 21 chromosome in humans produces a Down's Syndrome child with a low mental age and very characteristic facial features which led to the previous name for this genetic disorder - *mongolism*. You may indeed know of a Down's person who has developed useful skills through special training and is a happy member of a family. Such diseases can now be detected in the early stages of pregnancy by taking a sample of fluid from the amniotic fluid in the womb and by examining some of the embryo's cells.

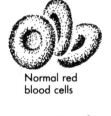

Normal red blood cells

'Sickle' cells

Fig. 5.11 Sickle cells compared with normal red blood cells.

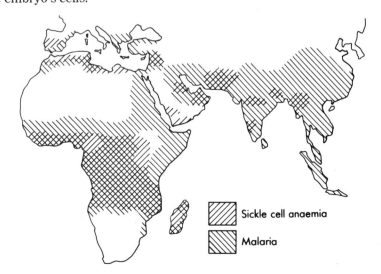

Sickle cell anaemia

Malaria

Fig. 5.12 Distribution of sickle cell anaemia and malaria.

6 > HYBRIDS

If two different varieties of animals or plants are allowed to breed together, the offspring are known as *hybrids* and will possess the characteristics of both the varieties that were cross-bred. The technique of cross-breeding has been used to great advantage in producing disease-resistant plants and high-yielding crop plants. Hybrids such as varieties of corn were introduced to America in the 1930s and resulted in increased yields of up to 50%. You will find that seeds of hybrid flowers and vegetables are very expensive.

7 > VARIATION

Organisms vary even within the same family. The variations are the result of new genes (mutations) and new mixtures of genes (sexual reproduction). There are two *types of variation* between individuals of the same species:

1 *Discontinuous variation.* This enables us to separate individuals into distinct groups; one of the most used examples is blood grouping. We all belong to one of the four main groups. The groups are A, B, AB and O; there are no in-between groupings such as AO. The information in the genes accounts for most of this form of variation, and the environment affects it very little.

2 *Continuous variation.* This refers to characteristics that do not allow us to separate individuals into distinct groups. Your height and weight are good examples of this sort of characteristic. Many genes may influence height and weight, but the environment can be important also. In any large population you would get a whole range of heights and weights.

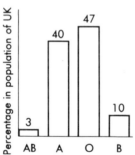

Fig. 5.13 Discontinuous variation in human blood groups.

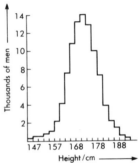

Fig. 5.14 Continuous variation in humans: height.

SPECIES

This is the word we use to describe organisms that are related closely enough to breed successfully, which means that the offspring must be able to reproduce themselves when they mature. It is possible for horses and donkeys to mate and produce offspring called mules, but these are sterile and cannot breed. Of all the groups that we use to classify living things, the species, or breeding group, is the smallest.

8 > NATURAL SELECTION

Think about these carefully

Natural selection is the theory we use to explain evolution. Darwin's voyage around the world in the 1830s aboard HMS Beagle provided the key for him to develop and refine his theory in the years that followed. Darwin's observations were that:

■ organisms produce large numbers of offspring;

■ the offspring vary considerably;

■ many offspring die before adulthood;

■ many offspring do not survive to breed;

■ they die because they can't overcome problems - starving, being eaten by predators, being fatally injured, suffering disease, etc.

The struggle for existence

Darwin described this as a *struggle for survival* against a harsh environment. Scientists today term the difficulties 'selection pressures'. It is these pressures that determine which individuals survive. Those best adapted survive to pass their genes on to the next generation. Hares that can run fastest will escape the fox, and so genes for powerful leg muscles will be 'selected' and over many generations the performance of the species will be enhanced.

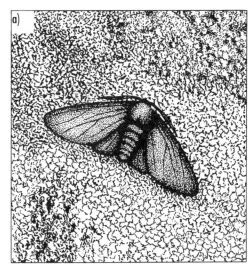 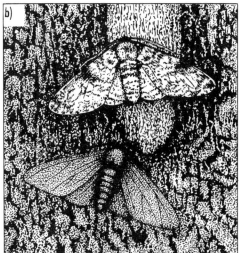

Fig. 5.15 Pale and dark forms of the peppered moth:
a) Lichen covered tree in unpolluted area.
b) blackened tree in polluted area.

	Percentage of each form	
Year	Dark	Pale
1848	1	99
1894	99	1

Fig. 5.16 Increase in relative numbers of the dark form of the peppered moth in an industrial area.

If the environment changes, the process of natural selection allows the species to adapt to the new situation, the most advantageous variations surviving to breed. Without variation, a species is very likely to become extinct. The Peppered Moth is a good example in that the colour of the moths has changed in recent times, the darker mutant ones becoming more common in industrial areas as the Industrial Revolution blackened the environment. However, they were still rare in the countryside where the lighter form was dominant. Camouflage is the key to understanding this; predators could easily find lightcoloured moths in sooty cities, and so selection favoured the dark genes. In the countryside the reverse was true. Now that industrial pollution is less severe the situation should change again.

9 > ARTIFICIAL SELECTION

This is selective breeding, and humans have taken many species from the wild and controlled their evolution, with amazing results. All the different varieties of dog have been produced by artificial selection of the wolf, a single wild species. Our domesticated cattle breeds, poultry, sheep and cereal crops have all been bred from wild species by generations of farmers. Plant and animal breeding is now big business, and so breeders are always on the look-out for wild varieties that could be useful.

Genetic Engineering

Genetic engineering involves the transfer of a section of DNA from one organism to the DNA of another organism of a different species. For example the gene determining production of the hormone insulin can be inserted into the DNA of bacteria or yeast cells. The transferred gene continues to produce insulin which can be used in the treatment of diabetes. This process is now carried out on an industrial scale to manufacture large quantities of the hormone.

Genes can also be transferred into the cells of animals or plants at an early stage so that they develop certain beneficial characteristics such as resistance to disease. It is also possible to produce genetically identical organisms by a process known as tissue culture, using small groups of cells from a part of a plant to grow a new plant, genetically identical to the parent. There are obvious benefits in agricultural terms to being able to produce many identical plants say with high resistance to drought or high yields of fruit. However all the plants produced in this way from one parent could be affected by the same disease or insect pest as they are all the same. In animals, cells from a developing embryo can be split apart and each can develop into a new, genetically identical organism.

Genetic engineering raises many social and ethical issues; for example how far should it be used to produce genetically identical human beings?; should research be carried out using potentially viable human embryos which may later have to be destroyed? Guidance on these issues is being developed in the medical profession.

On medical grounds, genetic engineering could be used to help treat diseases such as cystic fibrosis and muscular dystrophy. It could therefore help people who have a defect in their immune system and are unable to make a particular protein. The missing gene could be inserted into some white blood cells and the person would then be able to lead a normal life.

EXAMINATION QUESTIONS

MULTIPLE CHOICE

QUESTION 1

In a species of pea plant, red flowers were dominant to white flowers.

Pure-breeding, red-flowered pea plants are crossed with pure-breeding, white-flowered pea plants. What proportion of red- and white-coloured plants will be produced in the F_1 generation?

A all white-flowered plants
B equal numbers of white-flowered plants and red-flowered plants
C a 3:1 ratio of red-flowered plants to white-flowered plants
D a 3:1 ratio of white-flowered plants to red-flowered plants
E all red-flowered plants

QUESTION 2

Which one of the following organs in the body forms gametes?

A the brain   D the uterus
B the penis   E the vagina
C the testes

QUESTION 3

How many sperm are needed to fertilise a human egg cell?
A 1; B 10; C 100; D 1000; E 1000 000

QUESTION 4

Which one of the following is an example of discontinuous variation?

A blood group   D shoe size
B headsize   E weight
C height

QUESTION 5

Which one of the following processes takes place when the sperm fuses with an egg?

A fertilisation   D menstruation
B intercourse   E selection
C ovulation

STRUCTURED QUESTIONS

QUESTION 6

a) In sexual reproduction, new offspring are formed after fusion (fertilisation) of eggs and sperms.

   i) In the space below, draw diagrams of an egg and sperm and then show what happens during fertilisation:

   egg   *sperm*   *fertilisation*

   (3)

   ii) Explain, in words or diagrams, how:
      1 non-identical twins are formed   *(2)*
      2 identical twins are formed   *(2)*

b) A boy had two rabbits. The male was grey and the female was white. He allowed them to mate so that he could make some money from selling baby rabbits. **ALL** the baby rabbits were grey.

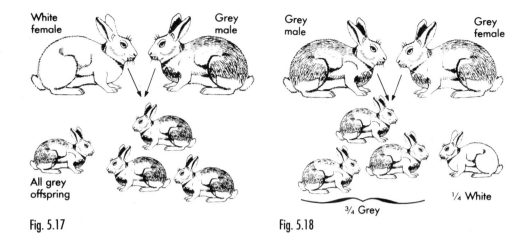

White female Grey male   Grey male   Grey female

All grey offspring

¾ Grey   ¼ White

Fig. 5.17   Fig. 5.18

When the baby grey rabbits had grown he let two of them mate several times. One quarter of their babies turned out to be white.

i) Which coat colour was dominant?

ii) Explain why:

    1 the first two rabbits (shown in Fig. 5.17) did not have any white babies;   *(2)*

    2 the grey offspring were able to have white babies (see Fig. 5.18).   *(2)*

iii) White rabbits are easier to sell, and fetch a higher price than grey rabbits. Suggest how the boy could arrange mating so that only white babies were produced. (4 lines available)   *(2)*

c) i) In vegetative (asexual) reproduction, new plants can be made from just one parent. Choose from the examples in Fig. 5.19 (or any other examples you may know about) and describe how you could produce **two** identical plants from one parent.

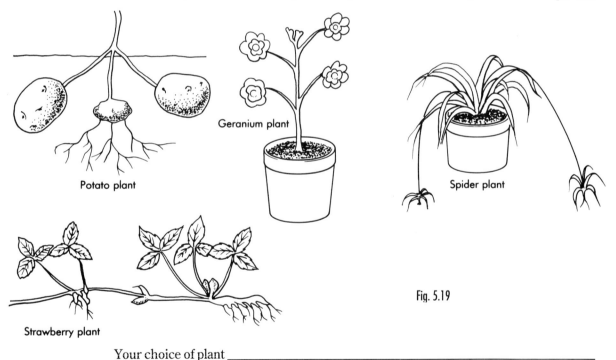

Geranium plant

Potato plant

Spider plant

Fig. 5.19

Strawberry plant

Your choice of plant _____

Method (4 lines available *and* space for optional diagram)

    (2)

ii) Plant growers use methods based on **asexual** reproduction to produce many beautiful plants for sale to the public. Give two reasons why they prefer to use these methods rather than the normal sexual reproduction (pollination – seeds – growth).

    1 _____

    2 _____

    (2)

(Total marks 18)

(ULEAC)

QUESTION 7

a) It is believed, from fossil evidence, that the horse evolved from a small, dog-sized organism into a large, strong organism.

Examine Figure A showing the evolution of the horse and then answer the questions which follow.

Explain the environmental factors that may have led to the changes in the horse in Fig. 5.20. (6 lines available) *(4)*

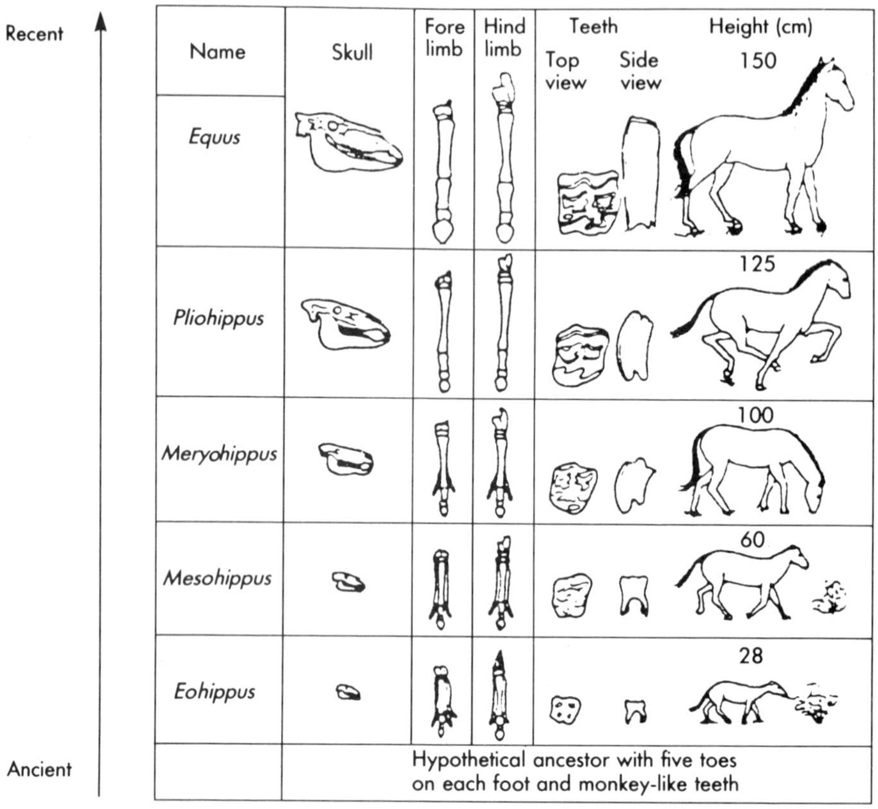

Fig. 5.20

b) Table 1 below shows some external characteristics of two organisms which look very similar.

	Honey Bee	Hoverfly
Body	3 segments	3 segments
Legs	3 pairs	3 pairs
Wings	2 pairs	1 pair
Colour	yellow and black strips	yellow and black stripes
Length	1.5 cm	2 cm
Sting	present	absent

Table 1

A predator of insects will not eat either of these organisms, even though the hoverfly is harmless.

   i) Explain the reason for the predator's behaviour. *(3)*

   ii) What is the meaning of the term 'genetic mutation'? *(1)*

   iii) Explain how genetic mutations in the ancestors of the hoverfly account for the similarities between it and the bee. (3 lines available) *(2)*

   iv) Mutations in disease-causing bacteria are a serious medical problem. Suggest a reason for this. *(1)*

c) In 1884, in the Manchester area, a very dark variety of the peppered moth was found. Usually this moth is greyish-white in colour with black dots. By 1895 about 95% of the peppered moths in the same area were of the very dark form.

   i) Explain very carefully how it is possible to have had only one very dark peppered moth in 1884, but for 95% of the population to be very dark in 1895. (5 lines available) *(3)*

ii) Nowadays, pollution is being removed from the environment. Explain very carefully what effect the removal of pollution would have on the population of peppered moths in Manchester. *(4)*

(Total marks 18)

(ULEAC)

QUESTION 8
Levels 6–8 (Tier 1) and 8–10 (Tier H)

This question is common to both Tiers I and H with the exception of (a) (iv) which is for levels 8–10 only.

Fig. 5.21 is a diagram of a sweetcorn plant, which has both male and female flowers. The plant is pollinated by the wind. Once the female flowers have been fertilised, they grow into corn cobs which are made up of fruits.

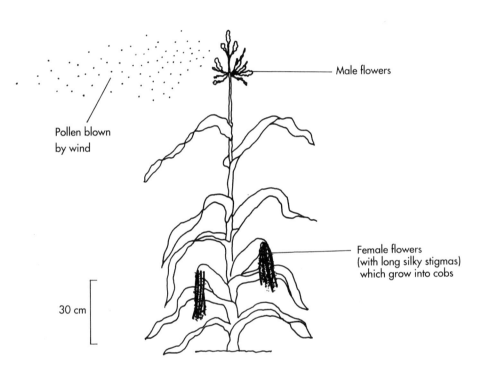

Fig. 5.21

a) i) Explain the advantage to the plant in having the male flowers at the top of the stem. (3 lines available) *(2)*

   ii) Explain the advantage to the plant in having long, silky stigmas. (3 lines available) *(2)*

   iii) When growing sweetcorn plants, many gardeners group them together in a rectangle pattern rather than in a long, single row.
Explain the advantage of this. (3 lines available) *(3)*

   iv) Describe what happens inside the female flower after pollination has taken place. (3 lines available) *(3)*

b) A pure-breeding sweetcorn plant with starchy fruits was crossed with a pure-breeding sweetcorn plant with non-starchy fruits.
Their offspring (F1 generation) produced cobs containing only starchy fruits.
One of the F1 plants was then self-pollinated. Its cobs (F2 generation) were found to have both starchy and non-starchy fruits.
These crosses are shown in the diagram.

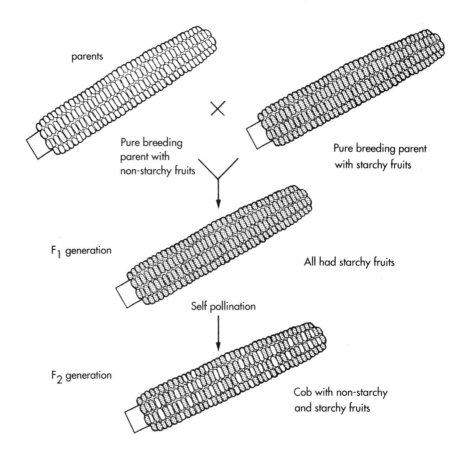

i) Count the number of sweet fruits which can be seen on the self-pollinated (F2 generation) cob.
Number of sweet fruits _____
(1)

ii) 120 starchy fruits can be seen on the self-pollinated cob.
What is the ratio of starchy fruits to non-starchy fruits?
Show your working. (3 lines available)
(2)

c) Two alleles 'starchy' and 'non-starchy' determine the type of fruit produced by sweetcorn.
Which of the two alleles is dominant?

_____

Give a reason for your answer. (3 lines available)
(2)

d) Using suitable symbols, show in the box below the cross between the two pure-breeding parents that produced the F1 generation.

Symbol for dominant allele = _____

Symbol for recessive allele = _____

gametes		

(Modular Science, ULEAC, SEG)

QUESTION 9
(Levels 6–8)

Cystic fibrosis is a serious disease of humans in which the lungs clog with mucous. The disease is inherited and involves a single gene. This gene exists as two alleles.

Two healthy parents had three children. The third child was found to have cystic fibrosis although the other two children were normal.

a) Is the allele that causes cystic fibrosis dominant or recessive?

_____

Explain the reason for your answer.

_____

_____ *(1)*

b) What is the genotype of the parents?

_____ *(1)*

c) i) What is the chance of a fourth child having the disease?

_____ *(1)*

ii) By means of a genetic diagram explain your answer. *(3)*

[Co-ordinated Science, ULEAC, WJEC, NEAB Level 8–10]

QUESTION 10
(Levels 8–10)

This question gives you some stimulus information in a table to help you think about your answers. Part (b) is an example of extended writing where you may find it helpful to draft some key points before writing your answer.

Genetic engineering has recently played an important part in farming, and some applications are listed below.

PROPERTIES OF PRODUCT	EXAMPLES
Improved yields	More corn on each cob
Improved nutrient value	Leaner meat
Improved physical properties	Shorter stems in winter wheat
Improved disease resistance	Less black spot in potatoes

i) Which part of the living cell is changed in genetic engineering? Give reasons for your answer. (3 lines available) *(2)*

ii) Discuss THREE of the concerns that people have about the widespread use of genetic engineering. (40 lines available) *(8)*

[Co-ordinated Science, ULEAC, WJEC]

ANSWERS TO EXAMINATION QUESTIONS

MULTIPLE CHOICE

ANSWER 1

Key E, all red-flowered plants. The red colour is dominant to white, so option A is wrong. The parents are both pure-breeding, so the recessive gene is not present in the red-flowered parent; this invalidates options B, C and D.

ANSWER 2

Key C, the testes. The uterus and vagina are involved in reproduction but not in formation of sex cells.

ANSWER 3

Key A, one sperm. Although millions are produced, only one fertilises the egg.

ANSWER 4

Key A, blood groups. All the others show a gradual change and are therefore continuous variation.

ANSWER 5

Key A, fertilisation. Option C, ovulation, is when an egg is released, and option D, menstruation, is the release of the extra lining of the womb.

STRUCTURED QUESTIONS

ANSWER 6

a) i)

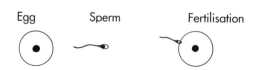

Egg   Sperm   Fertilisation

    ii) 1 Two different sperm fertilise two ova at the same time to produce non-identical twins.
        2 When a sperm has fertilised the ovum or egg, the fertilised egg then divides and forms two zygotes. A new individual is formed from each zygote, each having identical chromosomes, so the twins are identical.

b) i) grey
    ii) 1 The grey gene was dominant over the white gene. The male carried two dominant grey genes and was homozygous, or pure-bred.
        2 Each offspring carried one dominant grey gene and one recessive white gene, so when they mated the recessive white genes combined to produce a white offspring.
    iii) He could only breed from white rabbits.

c) i) Geranium
      Take two or more small cuttings from part of the geranium stem where there are side shoots, and put them into some soil.
    ii) 1 Plants are produced which are identical to the parent
        2 The process is quicker than using seeds.

ANSWER 7

a) There may have been a change in availability of food, so that the horses with better adapted teeth would survive.
    A change in the type of predator may have favoured larger horses which could run more quickly.

b) i) The hoverfly mimics the bee, which has a sting. The predators have learnt that the bee has a sting and therefore avoid another insect with the same warning colours.
    ii) A genetic mutation occurs when there is a mistake in the way in which the genes are copied in the nucleus, so the number or type of genes is different to the parent.
    iii) The hoverflies which may have been produced as mutations with the yellow and black stripes of the bee survived, and those which did not look like the bee were eaten. The genes from the successful hoverflies would be passed on to the next generation.
    iv) Bacteria can become resistant to antibiotics and other drugs used to kill bacteria. Mutations are produced at a rapid rate and pass on their resistance to the next generation.

c) i) The dark-coloured moth survived against the dark-coloured bark of the polluted trees. This moth passed on its chromosomes to the next generation, so more dark-coloured moths were produced. The light-coloured moths were eaten as they showed up on the bark.

ii) As the bark of the trees becomes lighter, the dark moths will show up and be eaten. Any light-coloured moths will have an advantage and will survive, so the population may change back to that of 1884.

ANSWER 8

Note the use of the word of instruction 'explain' in many of these questions.

a) i) the male flowers produce pollen *(1)*
        it is easier for the wind to release the pollen from the male flowers at the top of the stem *(1)*
    ii) the long silky stigmas have a large surface area *(1)*
         so it is easier to collect the pollen *(1)*
    iii) there is more chance of the pollen being blown across a female flower *(1)*
         in a single row the pollen would be wasted *(1)*
         more cobs will be produced *(1)*
    iv) Levels 8–10 only
         a pollen tube grows from the pollen grain *(1)*
         from the stigma to the ovary/ovule *(1)*
         the male nucleus fuses/fertilises the female nucleus *(1)*
         a seed/zygote is formed *(1)*

b) i) 'sweet' in the question refers to non-starchy.
        count the number of unshaded fruits on the F2 diagram = 40
    ii) the ratio is 120:40 *(1)* = 3.1 *(1)*

c) the starchy allele is dominant *(1)*
    as all the F1 generation have starchy fruit *(1)*

d) choose an appropriate letter for which it is easy to see the difference between the capital and small letter, e.g. B, b; note the parents are pure breeding so the gametes will be identical for one parent (homozygous)
    all the F1 will be identical Bb (heterozygous)
    Symbol for dominant allele B *(1)*
    Symbol for recessive allele b *(1)*

gametes	B	B	*(1)*
b	Bb	Bb	*(1)*
b	Bb	Bb	*(1)*

ANSWER 9

a) the allele is recessive
    both parents were healthy but one child had the disease *(1)*

b) choose an appropriate letter here to represent the heterozygous parents e.g. Ff *(1)*

c) i) 1 in 4 chance *(1)*
    ii) think about setting out your answer as a genetic diagram so that you show the genotypes of the parents, gametes *(1)* and children *(1)* and state the phenotypes of the children *(1)*

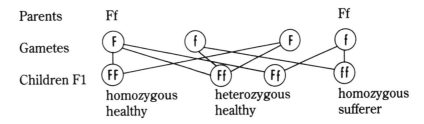

Parents   Ff   Ff
Gametes   F   f   F   f
Children F1 FF   Ff   Ff   ff
           homozygous   heterozygous   homozygous
           healthy   healthy   sufferer

ANSWER 10

i) a gene or section of DNA on a chromosome in the nucleus *(1)*
a new section of DNA is transferred from one organism to another of a different species during genetic engineering *(1)*

ii) the 8 marks here are allocated for a well argued account some of the points you could make should include reference to medical, ethical and social concerns:

the uses of genetic engineering in treating people who have a defective immune system *(1)*
and are unable to make a particular protein *(1)*
and suffer from diseases such as cystic fibrosis and muscular dystrophy *(1)*
these people could be helped to live a normal life *(1)*
human individuals need to act as 'guinea pigs' while these techniques are developed *(1)*

the ethical concerns about using human embryos which are later destroyed *(1)*
these embryos could have developed into normal individuals *(1)*

the social concerns that genes could be inserted into reproductive cells *(1)*
to improve on characteristics such as eye colour or height *(1)*

A STUDENT'S ANSWER WITH EXAMINER'S COMMENTS

a) Use has been made of knowledge of genetics and inheritance to breed plants and animals suited to our needs.

i) What do we call this process?

artifical selection

(1)

ii) Explain how a farmer could use this knowledge to breed cows which produce a lot of milk.

The farmer only breeds from the cows which produce the most milk.

(2)

66 Good, correct answers. 99

b) Genes are units of inheritance found on chromosomes in cells.

i) How many chromosomes are found in a human embryo cell?

46

(1)

ii) How many chromosomes are found in a human egg or sperm cell?

23

(1)

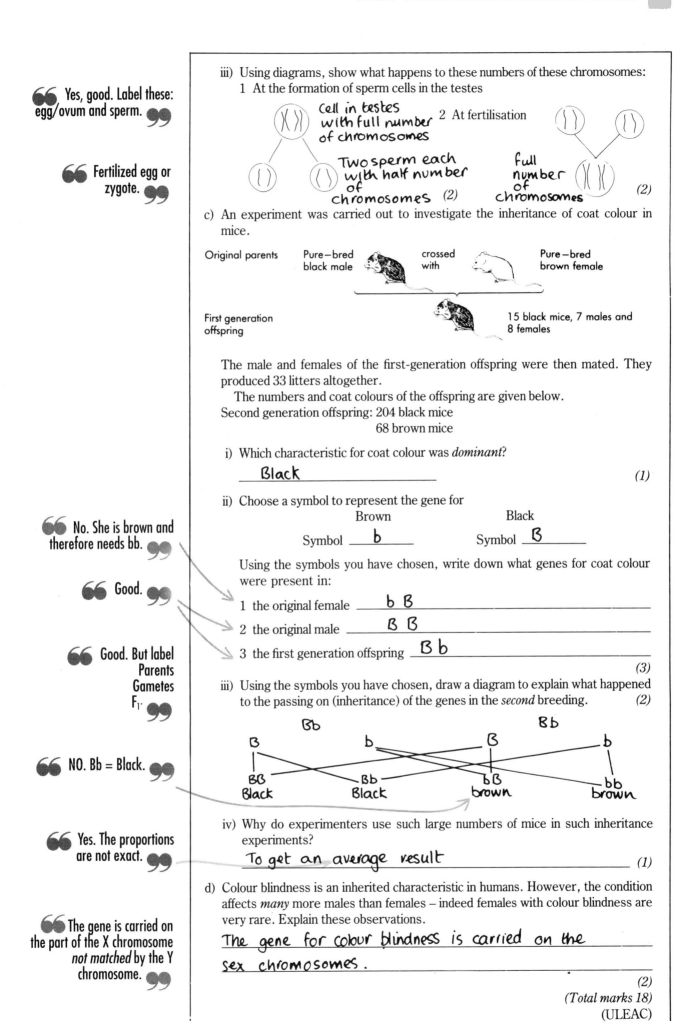

66 Yes, good. Label these: egg/ovum and sperm. 99

66 Fertilized egg or zygote. 99

iii) Using diagrams, show what happens to these numbers of these chromosomes:
1 At the formation of sperm cells in the testes

Cell in testes with full number of chromosomes

2 At fertilisation

Two sperm each with half number of chromosomes (2)

full number of chromosomes (2)

c) An experiment was carried out to investigate the inheritance of coat colour in mice.

Original parents   Pure-bred black male   crossed with   Pure-bred brown female

First generation offspring   15 black mice, 7 males and 8 females

The male and females of the first-generation offspring were then mated. They produced 33 litters altogether.

The numbers and coat colours of the offspring are given below.

Second generation offspring: 204 black mice
68 brown mice

i) Which characteristic for coat colour was *dominant*?

__Black__ (1)

ii) Choose a symbol to represent the gene for

Brown   Black

Symbol __b__   Symbol __B__

66 No. She is brown and therefore needs bb. 99

66 Good. 99

66 Good. But label
Parents
Gametes
F₁. 99

66 NO. Bb = Black. 99

Using the symbols you have chosen, write down what genes for coat colour were present in:

1 the original female __b B__

2 the original male __B B__

3 the first generation offspring __B b__

(3)

iii) Using the symbols you have chosen, draw a diagram to explain what happened to the passing on (inheritance) of the genes in the *second* breeding. (2)

Bb   Bb

B   b   B   b

BB   Bb   bB   bb
Black   Black   brown   brown

66 Yes. The proportions are not exact. 99

iv) Why do experimenters use such large numbers of mice in such inheritance experiments?

__To get an average result__ (1)

66 The gene is carried on the part of the X chromosome *not matched* by the Y chromosome. 99

d) Colour blindness is an inherited characteristic in humans. However, the condition affects *many* more males than females – indeed females with colour blindness are very rare. Explain these observations.

__The gene for colour blindness is carried on the__
__sex chromosomes.__

(2)

(Total marks 18)
(ULEAC)

R E V I E W   S H E E T

✎ When only one parent is involved, we call it _____ reproduction.

✎ Name one *advantage* of this type of reproduction.

_____

✎ Name one *disadvantage* of this type of reproduction.

_____

✎ Organisms with both male and female sex organs are called _____

✎ We call the male sex cell the _____ and the female sex cell the _____ . The

new cell produced is the _____ and this divides many times to form an _____

✎ Name an important advantage of sexual reproduction over asexual reproduction

_____

✎ Gametes are sex cells produced by the sort of cell division we call _____ , or reduction

division. These new cells have _____ the number of chromosomes of the parent cell.

✎ At fertilisation each gamete carries _____ of each type of chromosome. After fertilisation

the fertilized egg (i.e. the _____) has _____ of each type of chromosome.

✎ Fill in the stages of the menstrual cycle in each *segment* of this diagram.

Menstrual cycle

✎ Normal human body cells have _____ pairs of chromosomes in the nucleus. Each

chromosome carries many _____ , which provide instructions for a particular characteristic.

✎ Fill in the boxes and state which boxes will represent boys and which girls in the following
diagram.

Parents   XY (Male)   ×   XX (Female)

Gametes   X   Y   X   X

Offspring

✎ We call organisms that are related closely enough to breed _____ .

✎ Name two types of variation between individuals of the same species.

1. _____   2. _____

✎ Mistakes made in the copying of chromosomes during mitosis and meiosis are known as

_____ .

✎ An extra number 21 chromosome in humans produces a _____ child.

✎ If two different varieties of animals or plants breed together, the offspring are known as

_____ .

✎ Fill in the missing labels on these diagrams of the human reproductive system.

✎ Suggest advantages and disadvantages for each form of contraception.

METHOD	HOW IT WORKS	ADVANTAGES	DISADVANTAGES
Contraceptive pill	Contains hormones which prevent ovulation.		
Cap (diaphragm)	Blocks path of sperm at cervix.		
Intra-uterine device (IUD) (coil)	Fitted in uterus; prevents implantation.		
Condom (sheath)	Rubber sleeve, fits over erect penis; retains semen.		
Withdrawal	Penis withdrawn from vagina before ejaculation.		

ECOLOGY

GETTING STARTED

Ecology is the study of the relationships between the living and non-living factors in the environment. The living factors, the plants and animals, are sometimes called the *biotic* factors; the non-living factors, such as climate, soil, and the circulation of carbon, nitrogen and water, are the *abiotic* factors. These living and non-living factors make up the basic unit in ecology, the *ecosystem*.

You may have started this topic by studying the feeding relationships between plants and animals in a habitat near your school, and then used the information you obtained to draw a *food chain*, or a more complex *food web*, to show what was feeding on what.

You may have identified the *producers* or *green plants*, which obtain energy from the sun by *photosynthesis*. Feeding on the producers will be the *herbivores* or *primary consumers*, and feeding on those will be the *carnivores* or *secondary consumers*. In this way energy flows from the producers to the consumers at the top of the food chain or web. Some energy is lost at each link in the chain, and this means that there are always fewer carnivores than herbivores.

Chemical pesticides, used to control insect pests, may affect other animals in the ecosystem because the chemicals may become more concentrated in animals which are higher up the food web.

ESSENTIAL PRINCIPLES

> 66 **Use information from your own field studies where possible** 99

You may have been out of school on a 'field trip' as part of your science course, in order to study an *ecosystem* such as a woodland, a rocky shore, or a pond. You may have just done some field work in the immediate area around your school, and looked at a rotting log, or a hedgerow. During your studies you will probably have noted the living (biotic) and nonliving (abiotic) factors which made up the ecosystem which you were studying.

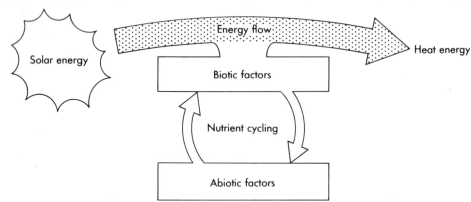

Fig. 6.1 How the biotic and abiotic factors interact in an ecosystem.

For any ecosystem the non-living (abiotic) factors will include rainfall, temperature, wind and light intensity, as well as factors which affect the soil, such as the presence of minerals, air and humus.

The living (biotic) factors will include the community of animals and plants which are found in the ecosystem. You may have counted the numbers in a population of just one species of animal or plant. You may also have noticed how different populations are not always competing for food, space, light, etc., and are therefore able to live together in the same ecosystem.

COLONISATION

> 66 **A mature woodland is a 'climax' community** 99

Part of your own study about ecology may have involved finding out how a community of plants and animals becomes established within a particular habitat by the process of succession. Succession happens when different species move into a new area and begin to be established. For example, dandelion seeds are sometimes blown on to an area of bare soil, where they become established very quickly. Each plant or animal which settles in a new area helps to stabilise the soil and release nutrients, and may help to provide a habitat for other species. Gradually the numbers of different plants and animals which occupy the area increase, until a stable and balanced community of animals and plants is reached. This is known as a climax community. Figure 6.2 shows how the numbers of species increase with time.

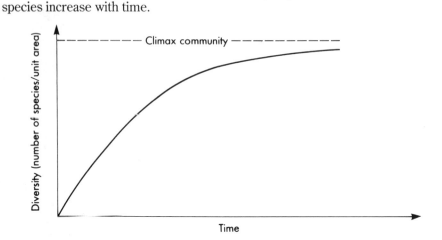

Fig. 6.2 The number of species increases over a period of time.

When you studied an ecosystem, you were probably able to identify the main species of plants and animals, and to find out what was feeding on what. A *food chain* simply shows how an animal obtains its food directly from another animal or plant. The arrows show the *direction* of transfer of energy.

Producer	Primary consumer	Secondary consumer	Tertiary consumer
Oak (leaves) ⟶	Caterpillar ⟶	Shrew ⟶	Owl

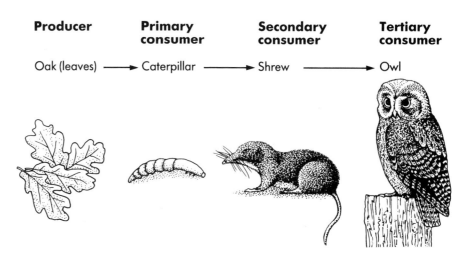

Fig. 6.3 A simple food chain. The arrow shows the direction of energy transfer.

Food webs are more complicated, as they show how one animal may be feeding on several others to obtain food, or how one plant may have several different animals feeding on it.

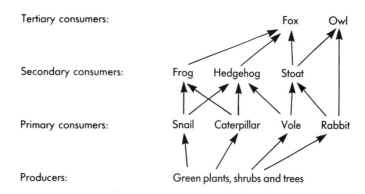

Fig. 6.4 In a food web one animal feeds on more than one source of food.

PRODUCERS

Learn these definitions

At the start of all food chains and webs are the green plants, called the *producers*. Green plants make their own food by using solar energy from the sun in the process of *photosynthesis*. Plants convert carbon dioxide and water into carbohydrates, which are then converted into plant protein, oils and fats.

CONSUMERS

These are all the animals in the food chain, and can be divided into herbivores and carnivores. The *herbivores* are the *primary consumers*, which feed directly on the plants or producers. The *carnivores*, which obtain their energy by feeding on the herbivores, are the *secondary consumers*. Some carnivores obtain their energy from *other* carnivores, and these are described as *tertiary* or *third level consumers*; for example, a hawk or fox which feeds on other carnivores in the food chain. Some animals feed on a *mixed diet* of plants and animals, and these are described as *omnivores*. They feed at more than one level in the food chain.

DECOMPOSERS

When plants and animals die, all the nutrients which are stored in their bodies are recycled by *decomposers*, such as bacteria and fungi. These organisms break down the bodies of dead animals and plants, and release nutrients such as nitrogen into the soil.

3 ⟩ PYRAMIDS

PYRAMID OF NUMBERS

Figure 6.5 shows how energy is *lost* at each stage of the food chain. This means that there is a decrease in the number of organisms at each stage of the food chain, as there is less energy available. The *pyramid of numbers* in Figure 6.5 indicates how the number of producers supports fewer herbivores, which in turn support fewer carnivores, supporting still fewer tertiary consumers. However the pyramid of numbers can also look like Figure 6.6!

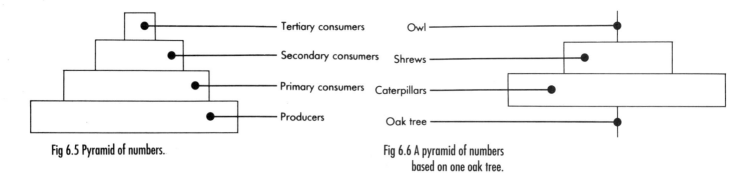

Fig 6.5 Pyramid of numbers.

Fig 6.6 A pyramid of numbers based on one oak tree.

This shows how *one organism*, an oak tree, provides energy for many caterpillars, which provide energy for a few shrews, which in turn provide energy for just one owl.

PYRAMID OF MASS

The total mass or biomass of organisms in a population decreases along the food chain, because less energy is available at each stage. The *pyramid of biomass* may look like Figure 6.7.

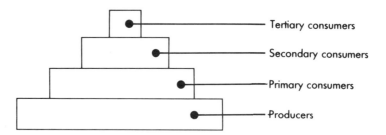

Fig. 6.7 Pyramid of biomass.

<table>
<tr><td>4</td><td>ENERGY
TRANSFER</td></tr>
</table>

66 Long food chains are inefficient! **99**

Energy is *transferred* at each stage of the food chain, from the plant producer to the herbivores and then to the carnivores. Only about 10% of the available energy is transferred at each stage of a food chain (Fig. 6.8). The other 90% is lost by life processes such as respiration, excretion and movement. The amount of living material or *biomass* is therefore reduced at each stage of the food chain.

For example, when a cow eats grass, the cow excretes about 60% of the energy taken in from the grass. Another 30% is used up by the cow in respiration, growth and movement. When the cow is eaten by man, only about 10% of the energy originally taken in by the cow is available for food.

Figure 6.9 shows how one hectare of land can produce either enough food for cows to feed 10 people, or enough grain to feed 100 people. It is evidently much more efficient for man to obtain food from *producers* instead of from *consumers* who have wasted so much energy.

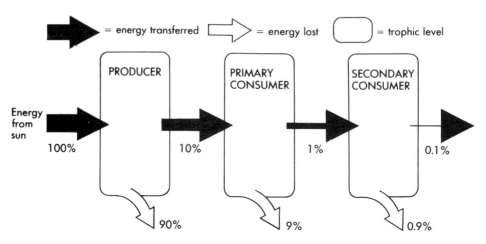

Fig. 6.8 Energy is lost at each stage of the food chain.

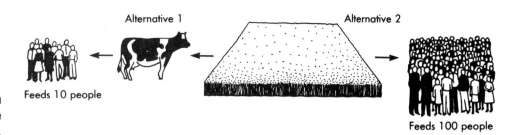

Alternative 1   Alternative 2

Feeds 10 people

Feeds 100 people

Fig. 6.9 The alternative ways in which the corn produced by one hectare of land could be used.

5 ▷ PEST CONTROL

CHEMICAL PESTICIDES

Gardeners and farmers often use chemical pesticides to control insects which are damaging crops and other plants. The advantage of using chemical pesticides is that they are very effective and fast-working. Herbicides are also used to kill unwanted plants which otherwise affect the yield of crops. Although these chemicals may be used only in very small quantities, the concentration of chemical may build up at each stage of the food chain, and accumulate in the top carnivore: for example, a bird of prey such as an owl or hawk. The chemicals would affect each organism in the food chain, but the top carnivore, which receives the highest concentration, would be affected the most, and may even be killed or have very low rates of reproduction.

> ❝ Chemical pesticides can build up in the food chain ❞

BIOLOGICAL CONTROL

> ❝ Biological methods of control are safer but slower ❞

An alternative method of controlling pests without the use of chemicals is to introduce another animal into the food chain which will feed on the pest. This method avoids pollution, but it is much slower in its effects than using chemical pesticides. Also the 'new species' which has been introduced can itself become a pest if it starts to feed on another animal or plant in the chain.

A common insect pest in greenhouses is a tiny red spider which damages plants. Instead of spraying with insecticide, gardeners can introduce another insect which is a predator on the red spider and which eats about 20 red spiders a day! An advantage of using such *biological control* is that no dangerous chemicals have to be used and strains of insects that are resistant to chemicals do not develop.

6 ▷ SAMPLING POPULATIONS

When you studied an ecosystem you may have been involved in estimating the *population* of a particular species of animal or plant. One of the techniques which you may have used is *random sampling*, as outlined below.

RANDOM SAMPLING

1 Measure the whole area of study.
2 Use a quadrat of known size, eg 0.25m x 0.25m = $\frac{1}{16}$ m^2.
3 Place the quadrat at random.
4 Count the numbers of a particular species of animal, or assess the proportion of the quadrat which is covered by a particular plant.
5 Record your result.
6 Repeat stages 3, 4 and 5 until data has been collected
7 Find the average numbers of the species, or average percentage cover of a plant per square metre.
8 Multiply by the total number of square metres to find the total population of the area.

> ❝ Refer to your own field work here ❞

Quadrat

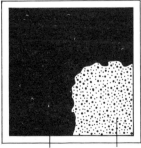

Species A   Species B

Fig. 6.10 Using a quadrat to estimate percentage cover.

MARK-RELEASE-RECAPTURE

Another commonly used method of counting a population is mark-release-recapture. This method could be used to count a population of snails, for example, and would involve using a special non-toxic paint or marker pen.

1 Capture, count and mark a representative sample of a population.
2 Release the animals in the same area.
3 At a later stage, when the marked animals have mixed with the rest of the population, recapture and count the numbers of animals, and record how many of the marked animals are in the second sample.

4   Use the formula below to estimate the total population:

$$\frac{\text{number in first sample x number in second sample}}{\text{number of marked animals recaptured}}$$

Your own studies of the abundance and distribution of species in a particular habitat or locality should indicate to you that the numbers and types of animals and plants vary from place to place. Different species live and grow where, and when, conditions are most suitable for them. The following physical factors which vary from place to place and at the time of the year will affect organisms:

- temperature
- light
- water
- availability of oxygen
- concentration of carbon dioxide
- nutrients

<table>
<tr><td>**7**</td><td>**GROWTH OF POPULATIONS**</td></tr>
</table>

Simple ecological methods can be used to study how populations change in size. Figure 6.11 shows a typical growth curve for a population.

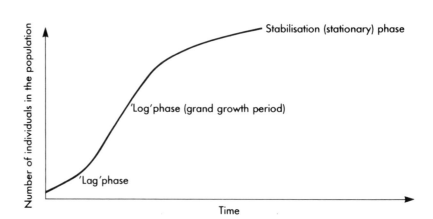

Fig 6.11 The graph shows a typical growth curve for a population.

As you can see, a new population starts with very low numbers in the 'lag' phase, and then shows a very rapid increase in number in the 'log' phase. When resources limit growth, then a *stabilisation* phase is reached and the population remains fairly constant. This continues until there is a *change* in one of the limiting factors, such as availability of food, space or disease. Remember that a population is *all* the members of the *same species* in an area.

Human populations may also be affected by the following factors:

- the extent to which the number of births is controlled
- how well diseases are prevented and cured
- natural disasters such as flooding, drought and earthquakes

COMPETITION

When two organisms both require the same resource, such as food, space, light and water, they can be said to be *competing* with each other. Sometimes competition occurs between members of the same species, and sometimes between members of different species. Figure 6.12 shows how the population of a *predator* increases and decreases as the population of the *prey* goes up and down. As the population of a *prey* increases, more food is available for the predators and so their population increases. However as the population of the *predators* increases, more food is needed and the population of the prey therefore decreases, and so on.

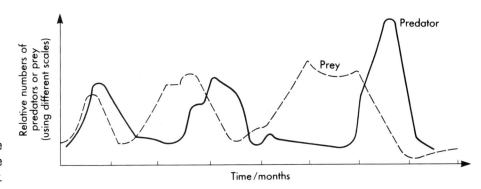

Fig 6.12 The population of the prey affects the numbers of the predator.

8 ▷ NUTRIENT CYCLES

Many natural substances such as animal and plant waste are described as biodegradable as they are broken down by the action of bacteria and fungi. Many of the nutrients contained in the waste are returned to the soil and recycled. The recycling of nitrogen, carbon and water forms an essential link between the living and non-living factors in the ecosystem.

THE NITROGEN CYCLE

> **Trace the cyclical path taken by each substance in the three cycles**

Plants such as peas, beans and clover are able to absorb nitrogen gas from the air through special lumps on their roots called *nodules*. These nodules contain nitrogen-fixing bacteria which take in or 'fix' the nitrogen as nitrates. The nitrates are then used by plants to make proteins. The proteins are taken in by animals when they eat the plants, and are returned to the soil when animals and plants are decomposed by bacteria and fungi which live in the soil. The decomposers form ammonium compounds, which are converted into nitrates by nitrifying bacteria.

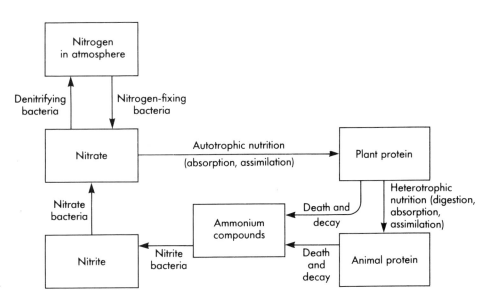

Fig 6.13 The Nitrogen cycle.

> **Beans and clover add nitrogen to soil**

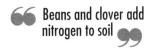

Farmers often plant peas, beans or clover to help increase the amount of nitrates in the soil, instead of adding nitrogen in the form of nitrate fertilisers. The peas, beans and clover can then be ploughed back into the soil, and the nitrates can be used by other plants to make proteins.

Some nitrates are lost from the soil when denitrifying bacteria convert the nitrates into nitrogen gas, which is released into the air. However some nitrates are added to the soil when lightning converts nitrogen, oxygen and water in the air to acids in rain.

Plant nutrients can be lost from the soil when animals or plants are removed for food, for example, during harvesting. This means that fertilisers or compost must be added to the soil to replace the lost nutrients.

THE CARBON CYCLE

Carbon is breathed out, as carbon dioxide, by all animals and plants. Whenever fossil fuels, such as coal, oil or gas, are burnt, carbon dioxide is also released into the atmosphere.

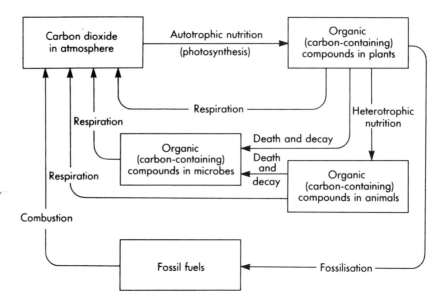

Fig. 6.14 The Carbon cycle.

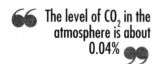
The level of CO_2 in the atmosphere is about 0.04%

Green plants take in carbon dioxide during the daytime, and combine the carbon dioxide with water to make carbohydrates. This process is known as photosynthesis, and it releases oxygen as a waste product.

The plants are eaten by animals, and the carbon, in the form of carbohydrates, proteins and fats, is used to make the cells of the animals. As the animals respire, the carbohydrates are broken down to form carbon dioxide and water. The carbon is released as carbon dioxide into the atmosphere.

THE WATER CYCLE

See Chapter 13 – 'clouds'

Water in the ocean is continuously being evaporated by the heat of the sun, and this vapour condenses to form clouds. When the clouds are blown over hills and mountains, they release the condensation as rain. Some of the water drains through the ground and back to the sea by rivers, and some of it is absorbed through the roots of plants, and is evaporated from the leaves in the process of *transpiration*. Rain also dissolves some of the poisonous gases in the air, such as sulphur dioxide, and forms dilute sulphuric acid, which falls as acid ram.

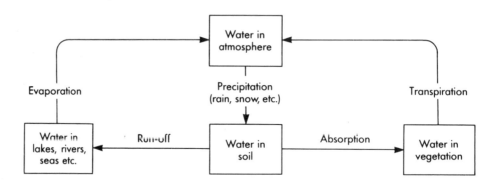

Fig. 6.15 The Water cycle.

9 **HUMAN INFLUENCE ON THE ENVIRONMENT**

Since 1900 the world population has roughly doubled in number. By the year 2000 it is estimated that there will be over 6 billion people on Earth. This rapid increase in world population has increased the demand for raw materials, including non-renewable energy resources, and has increased the amount of waste produced. One of the main effects of human activity on the environment has been the increase in pollution of water, land and air as described below:

■ pollution of water by sewage;
   this can cause rapid growth of water plants; when these plants die they are broken down by microbes which use up the dissolved oxygen in the water and lead to suffocation of fish and other animals.

■ pollution of water by chemical waste from factories, farms, waste dumps and oil spills;
   chemical wastes are usually poisonous (toxic) and are discharged into rivers and lakes, often ending up in the ocean where they affect the food chains and can be harmful to marine life; the chemicals are not broken down by the cells of living organisms and become concentrated within the food chain

Types of pollution

■ pollution of land by fertilisers, pesticides and rubbish dumps;
   for example, pesticides accumulate in predators which have eaten prey treated with pesticides

■ pollution of air by waste gases produced by power stations, factories and vehicle exhausts;
   for example, lead from car exhaust fumes can cause brain damage in children; see also Acid Rain, Chapter (11); the Greenhouse Effect, Chapter (13); the Ozone Layer Chapter (13).

Deforestation and desertification

Deforestation is the large scale removal and destruction of natural forests. It can result in the extinction of many plant and animal species and has reduced the rate at which carbon dioxide is removed from the atmosphere during photosynthesis. The burning of large areas of forests has also resulted in increased carbon dioxide levels.

One of the reasons for deforestation is to clear land in order to grow crops and to raise cattle. These activities generate more income to a farmer than large areas of impenetrable forest. However when the tree cover is removed erosion of the topsoil by wind and water takes place and as a result very little vegetation is able to grow. The over exploitation of the land by clearing of vegetation, over cultivation and overgrazing results in a poor environment and *desertification* occurs when the land gradually changes into a desert. Desertification means the land produces less food, sustains fewer livestock and feeds less people. It is almost impossible to reverse this process and create good agricultural land from the desert. Desertification threatens 35% of the Earth's land surface and 20% of the world population.

Food production

It is estimated that about 30% of the world's land area can be cultivated; the rest is either too dry, too steep or otherwise unsuitable. Of the land being cultivated about half is used for growing crops, the rest is used for pasture or forest. Due to the increasing world population, yields of food from the land and sea have to be increased. In the developed world, agricultural yields are improved through the following techniques:

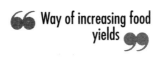

Way of increasing food yields

■ use of fertilisers to increase grain yields
■ the use of pesticides to control predators and disease
■ use of herbicides to reduce competition from weeds
■ use of selective breeding and genetic engineering to produce disease resistant high yielding strains
■ use of irrigation to increase yields

These techniques are usually expensive and usually not available to farmers in developing countries.

In the harvesting of animals it is essential that quotas are agreed as to how many organisms are removed each year to allow a breeding population to remain in order to build up numbers for the following year. The oceans offer vast food resources, especially fish which are an excellent form of protein but in large scale fishing in the sea, a minimum mesh size for fishing nets allows smaller fish to escape. If too many organisms are removed at the same time the population declines rapidly and consequently less are available for another year.

EXAMINATION QUESTIONS

MULTIPLE CHOICE

QUESTION 1

The diagram below shows a food web.

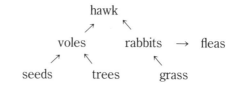

Which of the following is a primary consumer?

A   fleas   D   seeds
B   grass   E   voles
C   hawks

QUESTION 2

Look at the following simple food chain.

     oak tree → caterpillars → small birds → buzzard

Which of the following diagrams shows the pyramid of mass for this food chain?

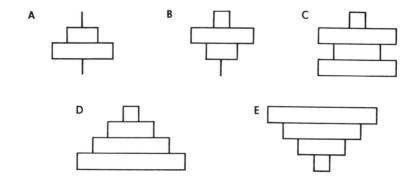

Fig. 6.16.

QUESTION 3

What are the organisms called which first occupy a newly formed sand dune?

A   colonisers   D   herbivores
B   consumers   E   predators
C   decomposers

STRUCTURED QUESTIONS

QUESTION 4

Below is drawn part of the carbon cycle.

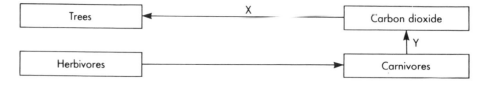

a)   Name the processes represented by X and Y.

     X is _____   Y is _____

                                                                       (2)

b)   Could fungi be used instead of trees? Give one reason for your answer. (2 lines)

                                                                       (1)
                                                                        (WJEC)

QUESTION 5

a) The curves below show how the population of rabbits and foxes changes over a two-year cycle. Use the curves to answer the questions which follow.

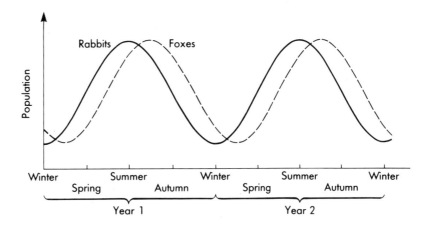

   i) At what time of year is the rabbit population lowest?

   _____

   (1)

   ii) At what time of year does the rabbit population rise most rapidly?

   _____

   (1)

   iii) Why do you think that the fox population falls each year?

   _____

   (1)

b) Use the information given in the simple food web below to answer the questions which follow.

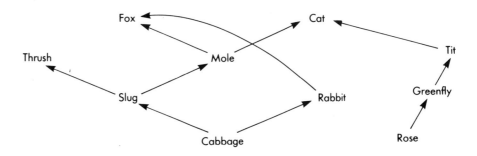

   Name:

   i) a major predator _____

   (1)

   ii) a herbivore _____

   (1)

   iii) a carnivore _____

   (1)

   iv) a producer _____

   (1)

c) Complete the following food chain.

   cabbage → rabbit → _____

   (1)

d) What would be the effects of removing the foxes? (2 lines)   *(3)*

e) Many rosegrowers need to protect their crops from greenfly attack. Suggest **two** ways of controlling greenfly.

1 _____

(1)

2 _____

(1)

(MEG)

QUESTION 6

The diagram below shows how different living things depend on others.

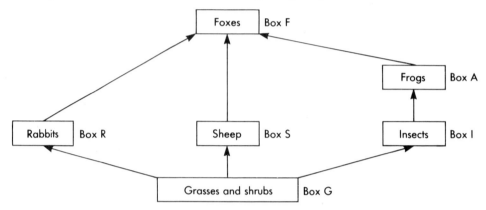

After each group or 'box' there is a code letter. Use this code letter to answer some of the questions where indicated.

a) What is the name or term given to this type of diagram?   *(1)*

b) Which group or 'box' would contain
   i) the *smallest number* of individual living things?
   ii) the *greatest total weight* of living things?   *(2)*

c) i) Which box contains the primary producers?
   ii) Where do these primary producers get their energy from?   *(2)*

d) If the rabbit population was killed off by disease, what two effects could this have on sheep-farming in the area?

i) _____

_____

ii) _____

_____

(2)

(WJEC)

QUESTION 7

The diagram shows the energy pathway through a simple food chain.

a) i) In the diagram, **X** and **Y** represent energy losses from living organisms. Suggest **one** process for each which could illustrate the loss.   *(2)*
   ii) Calculate the percentage of the Sun's energy absorbed by plants.   *(2)*

b) i) What happens to most of the Sun's energy falling on grassland?   *(1)*
   ii) Explain why it is more efficient for man to obtain his energy from grassland (eg wheat) rather than meat (eg cow).   *(2)*

c) In the Arctic, human communities have difficulty in growing food crops.
   i) Suggest **two** factors that are mainly responsible for this.   *(2)*
   ii) What would be the probable effect of lack of food on the size of the human communities?   *(1)*

(MEG)

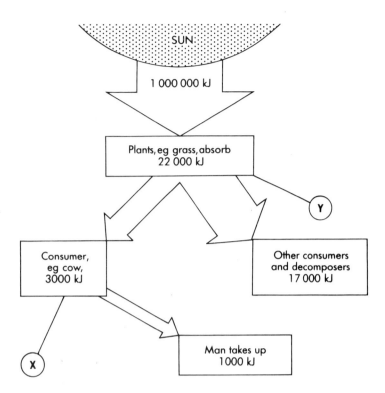

QUESTION 8

The diagram below shows the position of a sewage outflow pipe at a local beach.

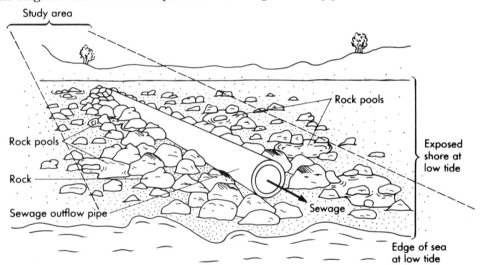

The whole beach is covered in different types of seaweeds, growing on rocks and in rock pools. The main species of animals are snails, crabs, mussels, barnacles, limpets and fish. The animals live in the rock pools.

There is concern that the animals and plants are being affected by the sewage from the pipe.

You and a group of friends decide to investigate the situation by collecting some information about the different types of animals and plants.

a) Describe how you would measure the size of the population of **one** of the types of animals found in the study area on the beach. *(4)*

b) Describe how you would compare the seaweeds growing in the study area on this beach with those growing on a beach where there was no sewage pipe. *(4)*

c) Suggest three factors, other than the presence of the sewage pipe, which could affect the types of plants and animals found on the two beaches. *(3)*

QUESTION 9

Beans are important in the diet of many people in the world. In addition, growing bean crops helps improve the soil fertility. This can be very important in parts of the world where farmers cannot afford expensive fertilisers.

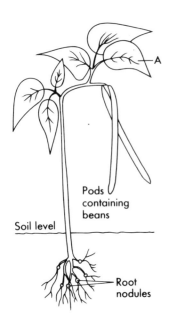

Soil level

Pods containing beans

Root nodules

a) i) Name the structures at **A** through which the plants lose water to the atmosphere.

_____ *(1)*

ii) Name the process by which plants lose water to the atmosphere.

_____ *(1)*

b) i) What kind of living organism lives inside the bean root nodules?

_____ *(1)*

ii) What important element is obtained for the plant through the root nodules?

_____ *(1)*

iii) Explain how the organisms in the root nodules help the plant to obtain this element. (2 lines) *(1)*

iv) After harvesting the beans, farmers dig in the roots of beans. They do not remove them. Explain why they do this. (2 lines) *(1)*

v) Explain how growing beans can help to improve soil fertility. (2 lines) *(2)*

c) Write a paragraph to explain why in some underdeveloped countries beans may be an important part of the diet of the people. (4 lines) *(3)*

(ULEAC)

QUESTION 10

(Levels 6–8)

This is typical of a question which presents you with unusual or novel information and asks you to use your scientific knowledge. In this question you are given diagrams of an animal you may never have seen. Look carefully at the diagrams and think about the habitat this animal lives in, namely a fast flowing stream.

The diagrams below (Fig. 1) show an animal which lives in fast-flowing streams.

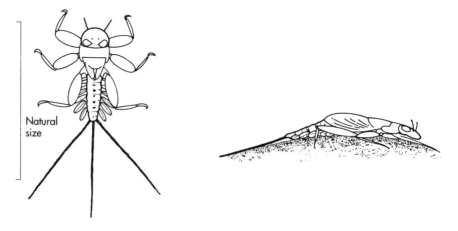

Natural size

Using ONLY the information shown in the diagrams, explain THREE ways in which the animal is adapted for life in running water.

1 _____

_____ *(2)*

2 _____

_____ *(2)*

3 _____

_____ *(2)*

[Co-ordinated Science NEAB, ULEAC, WJEC]

QUESTION 11

(Levels 8–10)

This question presents you with data in the form of a table. Parts (a) and (c) are aimed at level 8 whereas (b) is aimed at level 9

The table below shows a number of features of the population of six countries in 1980.

COUNTRY	POPULATION (Millions)	BIRTH RATE (per 1000)	DEATH RATE (per 1000)	INFANT MORTALITY RATE (per 1000)	LIFE EXPECTANCY (years)	POPULATION UNDER 15 years (%)	ESTIMATED POPULATION BY YEAR 2000 (millions)
Canada	24.1	16	6	16	74	30	32.6
France	54.1	16	9	12	73	25	62.9
Egypt	40.2	41	17	100	54	43	65.6
Angola	7.2	51	28	203	41	42	12.9
Turkey	42.3	40	14	119	57	44	73.0
Japan	115.4	20	7	11	75	26	134.7

a) The world mean life expectancy in 1980 was 61 years.
   How many of these countries had a life expectancy greater than this?

_____ *(1)*

b) i) Which country is estimated to have the largest increase in population by the year 2000?

_____ *(1)*

   ii) Suggest TWO reasons why the population of this country is estimated to rise so much.

   1 _____

   _____

   2 _____

   _____ *(2)*

c) Suggest TWO possible reasons for the high infant mortality rate in Angola.

   1 _____

   _____

   2 _____

   _____ *(2)*

[Co-ordinated Science NEAB, ULEAC, WJEC]

ANSWERS TO EXAMINATION QUESTIONS

MULTIPLE CHOICE

ANSWER 1

Key E, voles; remember primary consumers are herbivores which feed from the green plants or producers in the food chain. The hawks and fleas are secondary consumers.

ANSWER 2

Key D; remember pyramid of mass means the amount of biomass in a food chain, not the number of organisms. Option A shows a pyramid of number for this food chain, one oak tree and one buzzard, represented by a single line, with many caterpillars and fewer small birds.

ANSWER 3

Key A, colonisers; the other options are all organisms involved in food chains but not in colonisation of a new area.

STRUCTURED QUESTIONS

ANSWER 4

a) X is photosynthesis, Y is respiration.

b) No, because green plants are needed in the carbon cycle to carry out photosynthesis and to make carbohydrates. Fungi are not green plants as they do not have chlorophyll. They obtain their energy from decaying animals and plants.

ANSWER 5

a) i) in the winter (note the rabbit population is the solid line).
   ii) in the spring
   iii) The foxes feed on the rabbits. When there are fewer rabbits the number of foxes declines.

b) i) fox (or cat)
   ii) slug, rabbit or greenfly (all acceptable)
   iii) mole, tit, thrush, fox, cat (all acceptable)
   iv) cabbage (or rose)

c) cabbage → rabbit → *fox*

d) The numbers of rabbits and moles would increase, the numbers of cabbages and slugs may decrease.

e) 1 putting more ladybirds on the rose bush to eat the greenfly
   2 adding chemical pesticide to the rose bush to kill the greenfly.

ANSWER 6

a) food web

b) i) box F
   ii) box G

c) i) box G
   ii) the Sun

d) i) more grasses and shrubs available for the sheep, so the numbers of sheep could increase
   ii) the foxes may eat more sheep as they cannot feed on rabbits, so the numbers of sheep may decrease.

ANSWER 7

a)   i)   Energy loss X could be excretion and respiration.
         Energy loss Y could be reflection and transpiration.
    ii) 2.2%

b)   i)   Most of the energy is reflected, some is used to evaporate water, some goes into the soil.
    ii) Energy is wasted at each level of the food chain, so it is more efficient for man to obtain energy as close to the start of the food chain as possible.

c)   i)   low temperatures, short growing season, poor soil
    ii) population size may be reduced in number.

ANSWER 8

a)   1 Measure the total area of the beach to be studied.
    2 Using a $\frac{1}{4}$ m^2 quadrat, place the quadrat at random and count the numbers of individuals in that small area.
    3 Record results and repeat until 10 quadrats have been sampled.
    4 Add all results together; divide by 10 to find average result.
    5 Multiply by total area of beach to find total population.

b)   Using random quadrats, sample the proportion of a particular species of seaweed on the two different areas of beach. Repeat for different species. Observe differences in colour, size, etc., of seaweeds of the same species on the two different beaches.

c)   1 exposure of the beach to strong waves and wind.
    2 amount of human interference on the beach, eg tourism, boating, etc.
    3 different types of pollution such as oil and other chemicals in the seawater.

ANSWER 9

a)   i)   stomata
    ii) transpiration

b)   i)   bacteria
    ii) nitrogen (as nitrates)
    iii) bacteria in the nodules absorb the nitrogen from the air in the soil, and combine it with other elements.
    iv) the bacteria can live freely in the soil to fix nitrogen
    v) beans increase the nitrogen content of the soil. Nitrogen is required by plants to make plant protein.

c)   Beans provide a good source of proteins, minerals and vitamins. They are at the beginning of the food chain, so it is a more efficient use of the total energy which is available, rather than having cattle grazing on the land and converting the plants into meat.

ANSWER 10

Remember to only use information shown in the diagrams, and to explain rather than just describe three ways the animal is adapted for life in running water. You would probably only obtain 3 marks for description instead of the 6 available.

Your answers could include:

the shape of the animal is very flat (1)
which offers little resistance to the flow of water (1)

the animal has strong well developed legs (1)
to enable it to swim against the current (1)

the animal has hooks at the end of its legs (1)
so that it can cling to rocks (1)

ANSWER 11

a)   Look for the countries where life expectancy is above 61 years
    Answer = 3 (1)

b) i) Look for the country where the figure for estimated population and actual population show the greatest difference. You can roughly work out that the biggest differences are for Turkey and Egypt, and then work out the accurate increase. Turkey has an increase of 30.7 millions whereas Egypt is only 25.4 millions.

Answer = Turkey (1)

ii) The word of instruction asks you to 'suggest' so any reasonable scientific answer will obtain the mark. For example: immunisations have reduced infant mortality (1) birth control may not be widely used (1)

c) Again you are only asked to suggest reasons, you do not have to know the correct answer, and there may not be one correct answer. Possible answers include: lack of immunisation / lack of basic health care facilities (1) poor nutrition (1)

A STUDENT'S ANSWER WITH EXAMINER'S COMMENTS

1 The diagram below shows part of a food web.

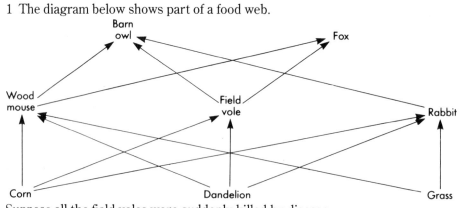

Suppose all the field voles were suddenly killed by disease.

a) Why would the number of dandelions be likely to increase?

not being eaten by voles

(2)

b) Why would the number of foxes be likely to decrease?

 Good.

less voles to eat

owls may eat more mice so less for fox

(2)

The label below shows the chemical composition of a rose fertiliser.

Analysis	
COMPOUND FERTILIZER	10.5-7.5-10.5
NITROGEN (N) Total	10.5%
PHOSPHORUS PENTOXIDE	
(P_2O_5) Total	7.5%
of which Soluble in water	4.5%
Insoluble in water	3.0%
POTASSIUM OXIDE	
(K_2O) Total	10.5% (K8.7%)
MAGNESIUM (Mg)	2.7%
	1.2 kg 2.65 Ib.

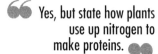 Yes, but state how plants use up nitrogen to make proteins.

c) Why is it necessary to put substances such as nitrogen back into the soil?

It is lost from the soil

(2)

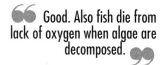 Good. Also fish die from lack of oxygen when algae are decomposed.

d) Explain briefly the dangers to the environment of fertilisers which are readily soluble in water..

They are washed into lakes and cause algae to grow.

(3)

(NICCEA)

R E V I E W   S H E E T

✎ A woodland, a rocky shore and a pond are all examples of _____ . This is made up of living or _____ factors and non-living or _____ factors.

✎ The process of _____ occurs when different species move into a new area and begin to be established.

✎ When a stable and balanced community of plants and animals is reached we say that there is now a _____ community.

✎ Fill in the boxes in the diagram below. Each box tells you the *stages* in a food chain.

Oak (leaves) ⟶ Caterpillar ⟶ Shrew ⟶ Owl

✎ A more complicated diagram showing, for example, how one animal is feeding on several others to obtain food, is called a _____

✎ When plants and animals die, all the nutrients which are stored in their bodies are recycled by _____ . Two examples of these are _____ and _____ .

✎ The following diagram is a _____ showing how energy is lost at each stage of the food chain.
   Label each line in this diagram

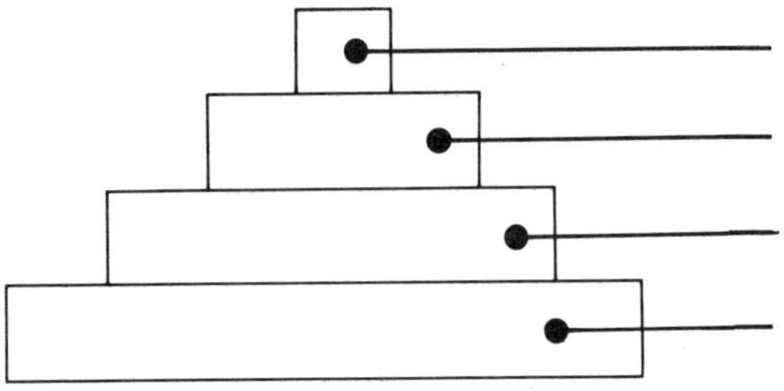

✎ It can save energy if people obtain food from _____ instead of from _____ who have wasted so much energy.

✎ The build up of chemical pesticides will have its largest effect on the _____ in the food chain.

✎ Name one advantage and one disadvantage of biological control.

advantage _____

disadvantage _____

✎ Give an example of the use of biological control.

_____

List 6 physical factors which will affect **the abundance and distribution of species in a particular habitat**

1. _____   4. _____

2. _____   5. _____

3. _____   6. _____

Which of these curves represents the *prey* and which the *predator*?

Explain your reasoning

_____

_____

Why do farmers often plant peas, beans **or clover in the soil?**

_____

Plants use nitrates to make _____

Green plants take in _____ during **the daytime and combine the carbon dioxide to make**

_____ . This happens during the **process called** _____

Fill in the boxes in this diagram of the **water cycle.**

Name three different types of pollution

1. pollution of _____

2. pollution of _____

3. pollution of _____

Name two problems associated with **deforestation**

1. _____

2. _____

Suggest four techniques or ways of increasing **agricultural yields from farmland**

_____

FEEDBACK AND CONTROL

GETTING STARTED

Biological, physical and chemical systems usually need to be in a state of *homeostasis,* that is stable and controlled. If our biological systems become unstable, we become ill and may die unless control is regained and stability restored. Electronic, mechanical and chemical systems will break down and cease to function if control is lacking.

Stability is important in all sorts of situations. For example, if you are riding a bicycle you use information from your sense organs to calculate your stability on two wheels; as you become off balance, your brain sends messages to muscles which contract or relax to return you to a balanced position. Such minute adjustments occur at a rate of many times per second so that you can ride safely.

Your deep freeze, your goldfish pond and many other systems may need to remain stable. Each consists of a large number of factors that vary as time passes and which need to be controlled if the system is to remain stable. At least three components are necessary to keep a system stable:

1 A *receptor* or *sensor* which detects any change from the normal or set value.
2 A *control mechanism* or *comparator* which initiates the corrective measures.
3 An *effector* or *actuator* to bring about the corrective measures.

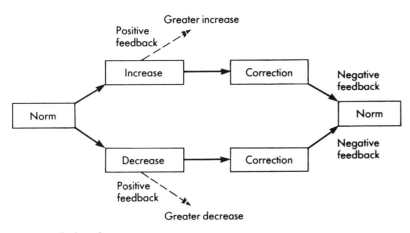

Fig. 7.1 Feedback mechanisms.

ESSENTIAL PRINCIPLES

1 PRINCIPLES OF FEEDBACK SYSTEMS

This idea is easier to understand if we look at an example. Whenever we use energy we need to control it. If we don't, then the results are often disastrous. Heat energy, released from the elements in an electric oven, needs to be very carefully controlled if a burnt cake is to be avoided. All systems that we want to control will consist of inputs and outputs. In this system the *input* is the amount of electricity and the *output* is a constant oven temperature. To *control* this system we can use information about the output - the temperature of the oven - in order to control the input of electrical energy. By reading a thermometer and adjusting the amount of electricity being used, we could control the system ourselves by turning up the electrical supply when the temperature dropped, and turning it down when the temperature rose too high. To save us time and trouble, modern ovens are fitted with simple control devices called *thermostats* which can be set at the desired temperature and left to do the adjustment automatically.

66 Feedback in the kitchen! 99

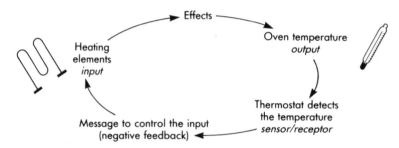

Fig. 7.2 How negative feedback controls an oven.

In the oven the thermostat acts as both sensor and comparator; the actuator is the heating element that can bring the level of the output back to the set point. The actuator needs to be linked to the sensor so that appropriate action is taken. Information about the temperature of the oven is linked to the amount of current flowing to the heating element. This information is known as **feedback.**

Feedback can be either **positive** or **negative**. Positive feedback can lead to systems going out of control, so it is not useful in maintaining homeostasis. The example above illustrates how negative feedback can be used to maintain a steady state.

Feedback carries simple messages that are often in code. The messages being transmitted in the oven example were of two types, each reversing the direction of the temperature change taking place. This is why we use the term 'negative' feedback. The two messages were:

1 'The oven is too hot, *reduce* the current to the heating elements.'
2 'The oven is too cold, *increase* the flow of current.'

If the message had been 'The oven is too hot, increase the flow of current to the heating elements', this 'positive' feedback would have resulted in a very burnt cake! A good example of positive feedback is the chain reaction which occurs in a nuclear reactor out of control.

2 BIOLOGICAL SYSTEMS

Body temperature and *water content* need to be automatically controlled and monitored in mammals, and provide two good examples to remember.

CONTROL OF BODY TEMPERATURE

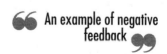
66 An example of negative feedback 99

In mammals, a part of the brain, the *hypothalamus,* responds to temperature changes both inside and outside the body. The temperature of the blood flowing through the brain is monitored by the hypothalamus. Information about external temperature comes from special *thermoreceptors* in the skin which are connected by nerves to the hypothalamus. The brain initiates responses appropriate to the information received. If the temperature is *too high*:

1 the body is cooled by sweating;
2 the hair lies flat against the skin;

3 blood is pumped to capillaries just below the skin surface;
4 there is a general lowering of the body's metabolic rate.

A *fall* in temperature would cause the *opposite* responses plus shivering to raise the temperature by producing heat in the muscles. Mammals are very sensitive to temperature change and humans soon die if the body core temperature is too high or too low. Human body temperature is maintained at about 37°C.

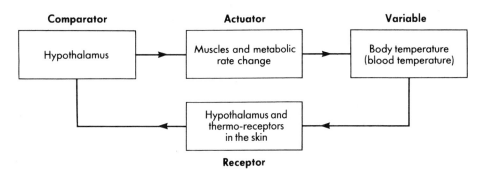

Fig. 7.3 Temperature control in a mammal.

THE SKIN

The skin is basically in two layers:

outer epidermis, consisting mostly of dead cells;
inner dermis, a living layer of cells including sensory cells.

The sensory cells can detect touch, pressure, pain and temperature.
The diagram (Figure 7.4) shows the position of the sensory receptors in the human skin.

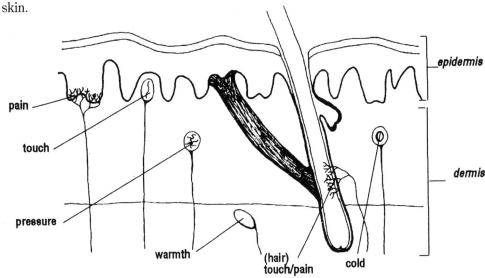

Fig 7.4 Receptors in the human skin (vertical section)

 The skin helps with temperature regulation

The skin has an important role in temperature regulation. When the temperature either inside or outside the body is too high, then the capillaries just under the skin dilate or widen. The person looks flushed or red and heat is lost from the blood, with the result that the person cools down. This is known as *vasodilation* (See Figure 7.5).

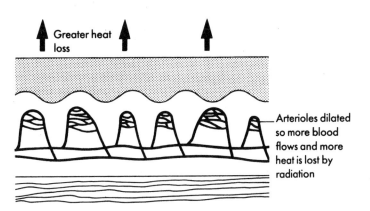

Fig. 7.5 Vasodilation

If the person is too cool then *vasoconstriction* occurs and the blood vessels become narrower, with the result that heat is retained in the body (See Figure 7.6).

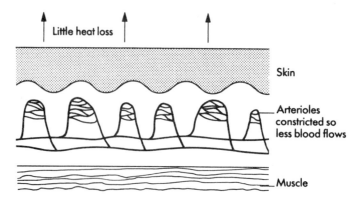

Fig. 7.6 Vasoconstriction

CONTROL OF WATER CONTENT - OSMOREGULATION

The average adult human body is some 58% water, and it is vital that the amount remains constant. If we drink too much our body fluids become dilute; if we lose too much water they become too concentrated. Either way, cells would cease to function properly. *Osmoregulation* is the term we use to describe the process of maintaining the correct fluid balance in our bodies.

The organ which controls the amount of water leaving the body is the kidney, which works with the hypothalamus and anti-diuretic hormone (ADH) to achieve homeostasis, as shown in Figure 7.7.

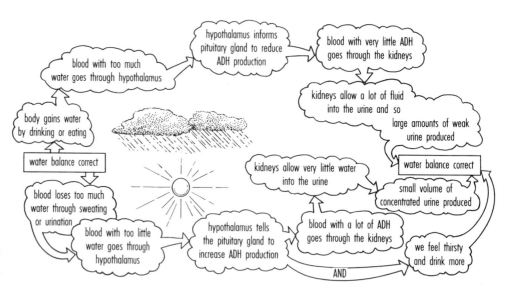

Fig. 7.7 How fluid level is controlled in mammals

THE KIDNEYS

The kidneys are organs of excretion and osmoregulation. Remember excretion is the removal of waste metabolic products from the body.

The diagram (Figure 7.8) shows the structure of the kidney.

> ❝ The kidneys remove waste and maintain correct fluid balance ❞

The *medulla* is the region where water, salts and urea are passed from the blood into the urine (See Figure 7.9).

The *renal artery* carries blood containing urea, water and salts to the kidney. Molecules such as glucose, water, salts, amino acids and urea are small enough to be forced under pressure into the *tubule*. About 99% of this fluid is reabsorbed into the blood, i.e. most of the water, all of the glucose and some of the salts are replaced into the blood supply. The *renal vein* transports the blood from which the urea has now been removed away from the kidney. The urine is carried by the ureter to the bladder, and then to outside the body by the urethra.

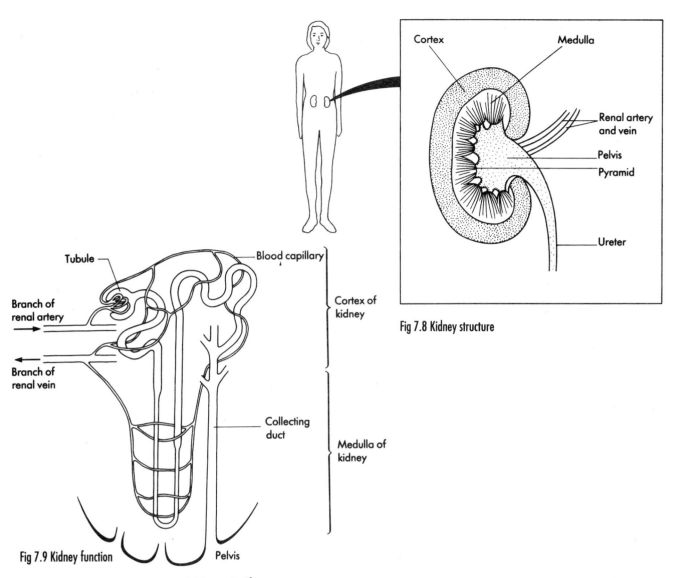

Fig 7.8 Kidney structure

Fig 7.9 Kidney function

Kidney Failure

Artificial kidney

A person who suffers from kidney failure due to disease can sometimes receive treatment on a kidney machine (dialysis machine). This machine, also known as the artificial kidney carries out some of the functions of a normal kidney and needs to be used for several hours every 2–3 days. Blood from an artery in the patients arm is diverted through a dialyser where the small molecules of urea and salts are removed from the blood by diffusing through a partially permeable membrane. Useful substances such as glucose, amino acids, some salts and water are retained in the blood which is returned to a vein in the arm.

Kidney Transplant

An alternative to an artificial kidney may be a kidney transplant, providing that a suitable donor can be found, such as a road accident victim or someone related to the patient who can continue living with one kidney. The tissues of the patient and donor must match to avoid rejection of the new kidney by the body's immune system. There are usually insufficient people able to donate kidneys to meet the demand for transplants.

THE REFLEX ARC

The *reflex arc* is the functional unit of the nervous system eand demonstrates how homeostasis may be achieved automatically. The reflex arc shown in Figure 7.10 is the direct pathway from a receptor to an effector, via the central nervous system (CNS). Sensory and motor nerve cells (neurones) may connect directly, although more often they do so through an intermediate neurone. There are **two** main sorts of reflex pathway:

Two types of reflex

1 the simple reflex;
2 the conditioned reflex.

Simple reflexes consist only of a reflex arc, and result in a very fast and automatic response to a stimulus. They are instinctive and usually increase an animal's chance of survival. Examples are coughing, blinking and eye-focusing, withdrawing a limb from a source of pain, and the well known knee jerk reflex, as shown in Figure 7.11. The sequence of events is labelled 1-7.

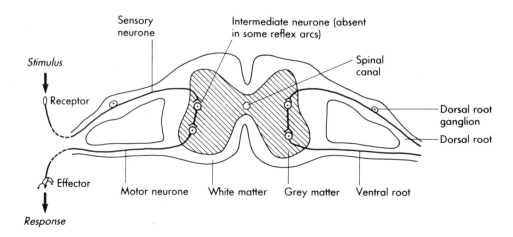

Fig. 7.10 The reflex arc.

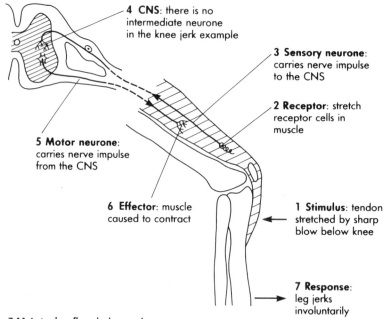

Fig. 7.11 A simple reflex: the knee jerk.

Conditioned reflexes involve learning and memory, and they allow us to ride bicycles and drive cars without too much conscious thought.

HORMONES

Hormones are chemical substances produced in very small amounts by special glands in the body called *endocrine glands*. Hormones are carried from the gland where they are produced via the blood stream to the target organ where they have their effect. The diagram (Figure 7.12) shows the position of the main endocrine organs in the body.

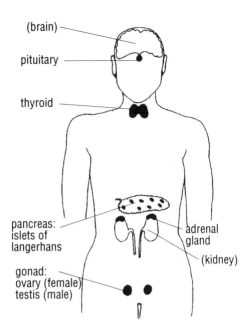

Fig 7.12 Position of the main endocrine glands in humans (the relative position of some other organs is also shown)

The table shows the names of the major hormones and their effects in the body.

Gland	Hormone	Effects
Pituitary	Trophic hormones	Cause other endocrine glands, e.g. thyroid, adrenal and gonads, to release their hormones.
	ADH vasopressin	Increases water reabsorption in **nephrons** of the **kidney**.
	Oxytocin	Causes contraction of the **uterus** during birth.
	Prolactin	Stimulates milk production from breasts.
Thyroid	Thyroxine	Increases the general rate of **metabolism** (chemical reactions in the body) and stimulates **growth**.
Adrenal gland	Adrenalin	Sometimes called the **fight, flight or fright hormones;** prepares the body for potentially difficult or dangerous situations, for instance by increasing **heart rate**, efficiency of **muscles** and **breathing rate**. Adrenalin also raises the *blood glucose* level.
Pancreas (islets of Langerhans)	Insulin	Causes the conversion of glucose to glycogen.
	Glucagon	Causes the conversion of glycogen to glucose.
Gonads: ovary	Oestrogen	Promotes the development of female secondary sexual characteristics.
	Progesterone	Maintains the uterus during pregnancy.
Testis	Testosterone	Promotes the development of male secondary sexual characteristics.

Summary of some of the main hormones in humans

CONTROL OF BLOOD SUGAR

In humans the concentration of glucose in the blood is controlled within narrow limits and maintained at around 90 mg of glucose per 100 cm^3 of blood. Two hormones produced by the pancreas, namely insulin and glucagon, are involved. Insulin is released when the concentration of glucose is increased, for example after a meal. The effect of insulin is to decrease glucose concentration by converting it to glycogen. Glucagon is released when the concentration of blood glucose is decreased, for example during exercise. Its effect is to convert glycogen, stored in the liver, to glucose.

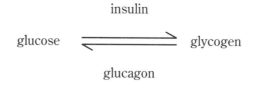

DIABETES

Diabetes is caused by lack of sufficient insulin and this results in an increase in the glucose concentration in the blood. The kidneys are unable to reabsorb all the glucose and some appears in the urine. Diabetics can control the condition through low-sugar diets and by regular injections of insulin.

The following table presents a comparison of the nervous and hormonal control systems.

Aspect of comparison	Nervous control	Hormonal control
message	nerve impulse	hormone
route	nervous system	blood system
transmission	rapid	slow
origin of message	receptor	endocrine gland
destination of message	effector	target organ(s)
speed and duration of effect	immediate, brief	delayed, prolonged

3 ▶ MECHANICAL SYSTEMS

Automatic *mechanical* systems are very common. For example, a household central heating system contains many automatic control devices, such as ballcocks (Figure 7.13), radiator thermostats, flame-out protectors on the gas boiler, etc. *Bimetallic* strips are often used in thermostats. These are made up from two *dissimilar* metals joined together. When heated, the metals expand at different rates and cause the strip to bend. This bending movement can be used to switch various devices on or off; this device is found in domestic irons (Figure 7.14).

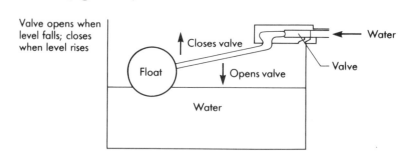

Fig. 7.13 Automatic water control – a ballcock.

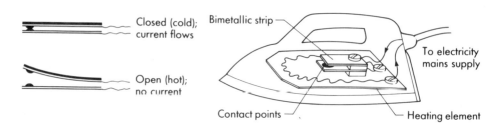

Fig. 7.14 Bimetallic strip thermostat in an iron.

4 ▶ ELECTRONIC SYSTEMS

Many *electronic* circuits employ feedback mechanisms in their control applications. Both positive and negative feedback systems are used; the former for *latching*, and the latter to maintain *stable* situations, as in temperature control. Professional electronics engineers apply a *systems approach* to solving problems and do not usually deal with single components, as you did when you studied current electricity. Integrated circuits contain *many* components in a single microchip.

As described in the introduction 'Getting Started' at the beginning of this chapter, electronic systems have the following features:

■ Input sensors to detect any changes from the normal environment.
Examples are : thermistors which detect changes in temperature, light dependent resistors (LDRs) which detect changes in light, switches which respond to pressure or magnetic fields

■ A processor which decides what corrective action is needed.
These are electronic logic gates in a circuit such as AND, OR, NOT

Check Ch. 16 for standard symbols.

■ An output device, controlled by the processor, which brings about the corrective action
Examples are : buzzers which produce sound, lamps and light emitting diodes (LEDs) which produce light, heaters which produce heat and motors which produce movement

5 ▷ DIGITAL SYSTEMS

The voltage signals applied to a system are either analogue or digital; the former can have any voltage input or output value, but the digital systems respond only to one of two signals, high or low. These are usually described as *logic level 1* and *logic level 0*. This idea can be best illustrated using a normal switch, as in Figure 7.15.

*Digital systems can be either **on** or **off***

The common way of showing how circuits behave is to produce a *truth table*, which is a summary of what the circuit can do. The circuit in Figure 7.15 has its switch either on or off and its lamp is also either on or off. If 1 = ON and O = OFF, Figure 7.16 will be the truth table for the circuit.

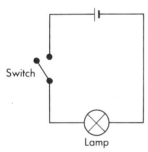

Fig. 7.15 On/Off logic.

Switch	Lamp
0	0
1	1

Fig. 7.16 Truth table for circuit in Fig. 7.15

The working of the more complicated circuit shown in Figure 7.17 can also be summarised in a truth table. Look at the truth table in Figure 7.18 and check it through.

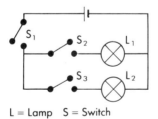

L = Lamp   S = Switch

Fig. 7.17 A more complicated circuit.

Switch			Lamp	
S_1	S_2	S_3	L_1	L_2
0	0	0	0	0
1	0	0	0	0
1	1	0	1	0
1	0	1	0	1
1	1	1	1	1

Fig 7.18 Truth table for a more complicated circuit.

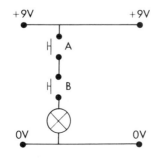

Fig. 7.19 Series logic with two switches.

Switch		Lamp
A	B	
0	0	0
1	0	0
0	1	0
1	1	1

Fig. 7.20 Truth table for circuit in Fig. 7.19.

As systems get more complicated they can be simplified by removal of the supply, with just two lines drawn to represent the positive (+) and negative (-) sides of the circuit. In these logic circuits the sswitch can be left on or off so that all possible connections can be made; Figure 7.19 is such a circuit.

A truth table can be produced, as before, to summarise possibilities for the circuit, as in Figure 7.20.

6 LOGIC GATES

These are electronic 'gates' in a circuit which only allow an output signal in response to particular input situations. They are termed *gates* because they are either open (logic 1) or closed (logic 0). A gate is a piece of electronic circuitry which is described by the way its output will become logic HIGH = 1 when its input is changed. Three common gates are the 'NOT', the 'AND' and the 'OR'.

1 The NOT-gate is sometimes called an *inverter* because it does just that: a high = 1 input causes a low = 0 output and vice versa. Its symbol and truth table are shown in Figure 7.21.

2 The AND-gate has an output that goes high if both inputs are also high. A simple circuit, as in Figure 7.22, shows this: the lamp will only light when both switches are on.

The symbol of the AND-gate and its truth tables are shown in Figure 7.23. Any system that gives this output is called AND. Remember, the output is high if both one input AND the other are high.

3 The OR-gate is called an 'OR' because the output goes high if *either* of the inputs goes high, as shown in Figure 7.24.

Input	Output
0	1
1	0

Fig. 7.21 NOT-gate symbol and truth table.

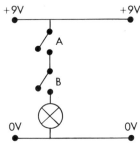

Fig. 7.22 A simple AND-gate.

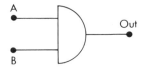

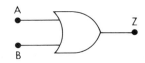

Input		Output
A	B	Z
0	0	0
1	0	0
0	1	0
1	1	1

Fig. 7.23 AND-gate symbol and truth table.

Input		Output
A	B	Z
0	0	0
1	0	1
0	1	1
1	1	1

Fig. 7.24 OR-gate symbol and truth table.

Two other gates often used are the NAND and the NOR (Figure 7.25).

Name of gate	Symbol	Truth table			Description
NAND		0	0	1	Opposite of *AND* gate
		0	1	1	
		1	0	1	
		1	1	0	
NOR		0	0	1	Opposite of *OR* gate. Output high if neither A *NOR* B is high
		0	1	0	
		1	0	0	
		1	1	0	

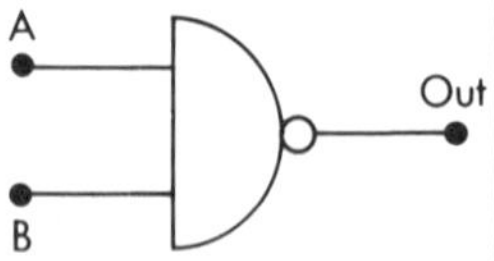

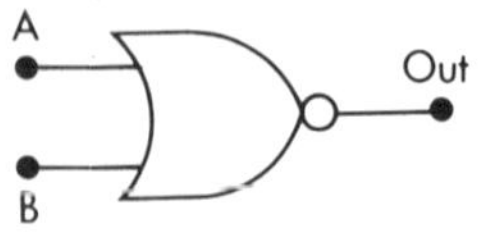

Fig. 7.25 NAND and NOR-gates.

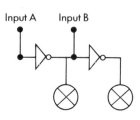

Fig. 7.26 Two NOT-gates.

Once the function of a logic gate is known, it can be built into a circuit with others and be of practical use in electronics .

BISTABLE CIRCUITS

These may be built in a number of ways and their main feature is that whatever happens to the input, the output has only one of two stable states, which are achieved by feedback. In Figure 7.26, if input A is logic high and input B not connected, then indicator A is off and the B input is at logic 0. Similarly if input A is not connected and B is at logic 1, the output of B is at logic 0 and the input A is at logic 0.

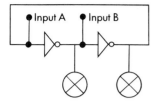

Fig. 7.27 A bistable system.

In these circuits a connection between output and input *reinforces* information. If the output of B is fed back to the input of A, a *bistable* system is created (Figure 7.27). Input A goes high, input B is not yet connected: output A goes low, output B goes high and reinforces (feedback) the high input to A. If the original connection to A is removed, the message is retained: the system has a memory.

Two NOR-gates can be used to produce a bistable latch (circuit inside the dashed box, Figure 7.28), which could be used as a burglar alarm activated by the burglar's flashlight beam. In this example only one of the two outputs is in use. If the switch is in the position shown, there is no output, whether the light dependent resistor (LDR) is illuminated or not. When the switch is up, the bell is activated when the light shines on the LDR and remains sounding until the switch is moved again. This is a 'latch' system. keeping one steady desired state.

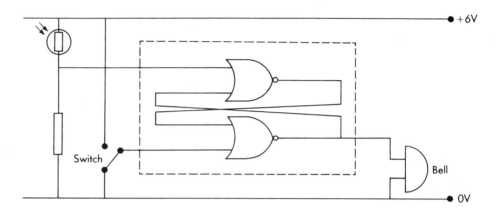

Fig. 7.28 A bistable latch burglar alarm.

EXAMINATION QUESTIONS

QUESTION 1

Which part of the control system in an electric oven is the actuator?
A   the control knobs   C   the thermostat
B   the on/off switch   D   the heating element

QUESTION 2

Which part of the body detects the temperature of the blood?
A   the brain   C   the kidneys
B   the heart   D   the skin

QUESTION 3

The diagram below shows a circuit activated by low light intensity.

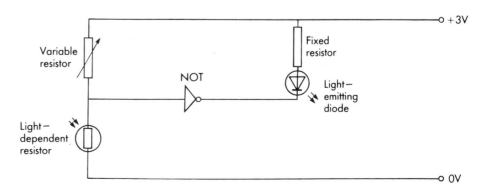

Which component detects a change in light intensity?
A light dependent resistor   C NOT-gate
B light emitting diode   D variable resistor

QUESTION 4

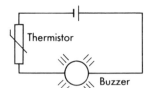

The diagram below shows a thermistor in a circuit.

Which of the following describes the purpose of this circuit?
A to switch on the buzzer if the temperature falls
B to switch on the buzzer if the light intensity increases
C to switch on the buzzer if the temperature rises
D to make the buzzer go on and off

STRUCTURED QUESTIONS

QUESTION 5

An alarm system, installed near a nuclear reactor, is set off if the light intensity or temperature increases above a certain level. The system used is shown below.

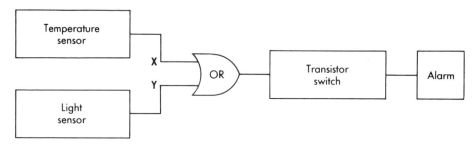

a) Name **one** electronic device which may be used in this system to sense a change in

   i) temperature _____

                                                             (1)

   ii) light intensity _____

                                                             (1)

b) Complete the truth table for the OR-gate.

Inputs		Output
X	**Y**	
0	**0**	
0	**1**	
1	**0**	
1	**1**	

(3)
(MEG)

QUESTION 6

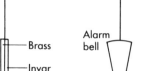

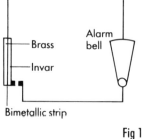

Fig 1

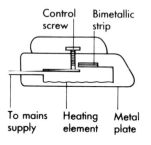

a) A thermostat can be used to control a system. Figure 1 shows how a bimetallic strip can be used in a simple fire alarm.

   i) Explain fully how a fire would cause the alarm to sound. (5 lines available) *(4)*

   ii) State **two** ways in which the thermostat could be altered to sound the alarm at a lower temperature.

     1 _____

                                                     (1)

     2 _____

                                                     (1)

b) In an electric iron it is important to be able to set the temperature of the iron, which should then remain constant.

   Describe how the working temperature of the iron is:

   i) set _____

                                                             (2)

ii) kept constant _____

(2)

c) The graph shows the temperature of an iron varied with time after the iron is switched on.

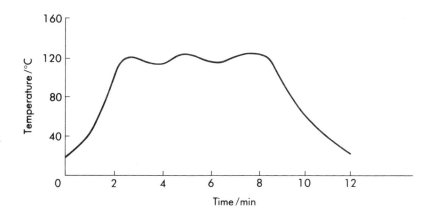

i) What was the room temperature? _____

(1)

ii) To what temperature was the iron set? _____

(1)

iii) Explain why the temperature of the iron does not remain exactly constant. (2 lines)

(2)

(Total marks 14)

QUESTION 7

a) The circuit in Figure (a) contains two switches, A and B, which can be either open or closed. Figure (b) is a truth table for the circuit. It shows what will happen to the lamp when the switches are in different positions.
   i) Complete the truth table for the circuit.
   ii) State in words the condition for the lamp to be lit. (1 line)

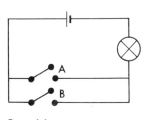

Figure (a)

Switch A	Switch B	Lamp ON or OFF
Open	Open	
Closed	Open	
Open	Closed	
Closed	Closed	

Figure (b)

b) The truth table in Figure (c) refers to a certain two-input logic gate.

Figure (c)

Input		Output
A	B	Z
0	0	0
0	1	1
1	0	1
1	1	1

i) What logic gate is indicated by this table?
ii) Draw a symbol representing this logic gate.

c) A circuit is to be designed so that a bell will ring if a push switch is operated, but only if there is also an input from a light sensor, a heat sensor, or both. These requirements can be summarised in the table in Figure (d).

Figure (d)

Push Switch	Light sensor	Heat sensor	Output
0	0	0	0
0			0
0			0
0			0
1	0	0	0
1			
1			
1			

i) Complete the table.

ii) This result can be achieved by using two two-input logic gates between the switch and sensors and the bell. Show how this can be done completing the lines below.

From push switch _____

From light sensor _____ to bell.

From heat sensor _____

(NICCEA)

QUESTION 8
(Levels 6–8 and 8–10)

This question is common to levels 6–8 and 8–10 with the exception of part (c) which is for level 8–10 only.

Graph 1 shows the glucose and insulin content and graph 2 shows the glucose and glucagon content of a person's blood.

The person's blood was tested over a period of one hour on two separate occasions.

On one occasion the person ate glucose tablets at the start of the test. On the other occasion the person was injected with insulin at the start of the test.

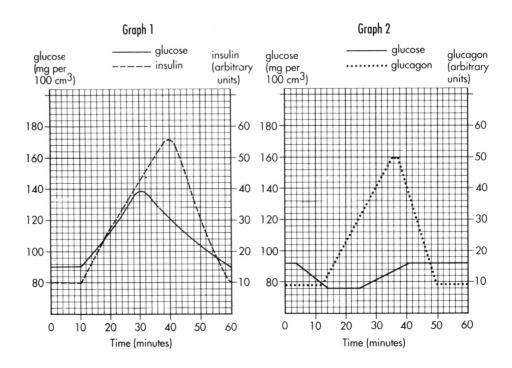

Use the information in the graphs and your own knowledge to answer the following questions.

a) Which graph shows the effects of the insulin injection?
    Give a reason for your answer.

    _____
    (1)

b) i) What evidence is there that glucose stimulates the production of insulin?

    _____
    (1)

    ii) Which organ produces insulin?

    _____
    (1)

    iii) At which times was the insulin level 30 arbitrary units?

    _____
    (1)

    iv) Describe the effects of insulin in the body (4 lines).

    _____
    (3)

c) Explain how a fall in the level of glucagon in graph 2 is an example of homeostasis
    and negative feedback. (4 lines)   *(3)*

    (Total 10 marks)
    [ULEAC Combined Science, Levels 6–8 and 8–10]

ANSWERS TO EXAMINATION QUESTIONS

MULTIPLE CHOICE

ANSWER 1

Key D. The actuator is the part of the control system which brings about the correction; in this example it is the heating element.

ANSWER 2

Key A, the brain, detects the temperature of the blood. The skin detects the external temperature.

ANSWER 3

Key A, the LDR. The resistance of the LDR falls as more light falls on it.

ANSWER 4

Key C. The resistance of the thermistor falls as the temperature rises and so switches on the buzzer.

STRUCTURED QUESTIONS

ANSWER 5

a) i) a thermistor
    ii) a light dependent resistor
b) the output should be 0
                          1
                          1
                          1

ANSWER 6

a) i) When the bimetal strip becomes hot the brass expands about twenty times as much as the invar, so the strip bends and pushes the strip towards the two contacts. When the contacts close the current flows to the alarm bell, which rings.

ii) 1 Make the contacts closer together   2 Use thinner metal in the bimetallic strip

b) i) The control screw closes the circuit and adjusts the position of the contacts so that when the iron reaches the required temperature the bimetallic strip bends away from the contact and breaks the circuit.

ii) The strip now cools and straightens and so the circuit is closed again.

c) i) 20°C

ii) 120°C

iii) When the iron reaches just above its required temperature, the bimetal strip bends and breaks the circuit. The iron cools down to just below the set temperature before the strip makes contact again.

ANSWER 7

a) i) See Figure (i).

Switch A	Switch B	Lamp ON or OFF
Open	Open	Off
Closed	Open	On
Open	Closed	On
Closed	Closed	On

Figure (i)

ii) The lamp is ON if either A or B or both are closed (an OR-gate).

b) i) The table represents an OR-gate.

ii) See Figure (ii).

A
B   Output

Figure (ii)

c) i) See Figure (iii).

ii) See Figure (iv). The system needs to link the heat and light sensors with an OR-gate. The output combines with the push through an AND-gate.

Push Switch	Light sensor	Heat sensor	Output
0	0	0	0
0	1	0	0
0	0	1	0
0	1	1	0
1	0	0	0
1	1	0	1
1	0	1	1
1	1	1	1

Figure (iii)

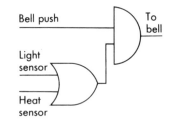

Figure (iv)

ANSWER 8

a) graph 2 because the glucose level (shown by the solid line) falls after a few minutes (1)

b) i) in graph 1 the insulin level (dotted line) rises after the glucose level rises (1)

ii) pancreas (1)

iii) take care here to read the insulin level of 30 units from the right hand vertical axis of graph 1; two readings are required 22 and 55 minutes (1)

iv) reduces glucose concentration in blood (1)

converts glucose to glycogen (1)

in liver (1) and muscle (1)

more glucose can be absorbed by cells (1)

cell membranes are more permeable to glucose (1)

c) (level 8–10 only)

the fall in the level of glucagon (dotted line)

is an example of homeostasis because the glucose level has returned to normal (1)
it also shows negative feedback because when the level of blood glucose is decreased (1)
more glucagon is secreted (1)
which increases level of glucose (1)

A STUDENT'S ANSWER WITH EXAMINER'S COMMENTS

Figure 1 is a diagram of a kidney tubule (nephron) and surrounding blood vessels.

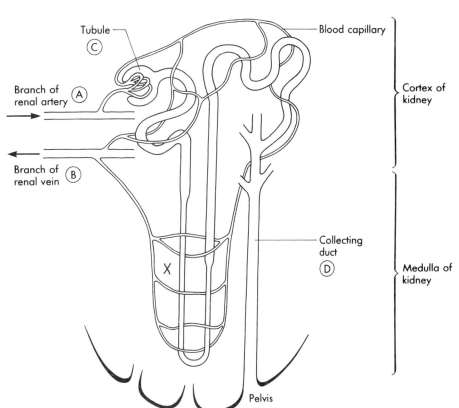

> Anti-diuretic hormone (ADH) affects the kidney tubule.

Figure 1

Adapted from *Biology – A course to 16+* by G. Jones and M.Jones (1984), by kind permission of Cambridge University Press.

a) Samples of fluids were taken from **A**, **B**, **C** and **D** shown in the diagram above. Table 1 shows the relative amounts of protein, glucose, salt, water, oxygen and carbon found in each sample.

Table 1

Sample No.	Water	Protein	Glucose	Salt	Oxygen	Carbon dioxide
1	70%	High	High	High	High	Low
2	95%	None	None	Medium	Very low	Very low
3	70%	High	High	High	Low	High
4	98%	None	High	High	Very low	Very low

i) Identify which sample came from each of the points **A**, **B**, **C** and **D**.

Sample 1 came from point __A__ ✓

Sample 2 came from point __D__ ✓

Sample 3 came from point __B__ ✓

Sample 4 came from point __C__ ✓

(4)

ii) On the diagram, label a point X where the hormone ADH acts to control water balance. (1)

b) Sara's kidneys do not work. She has to go on a 'kidney dialysis' machine twice a week. This machine does a job similar to normal kidneys.

i) Explain why it is important in between dialysis sessions that she:

1 does not drink a lot of water

the kidneys filter a lot of water normally so if they don't work she shouldn't drink.

2 eats no added salt

the kidneys normally reabsorb salt into the blood.

3 does not eat a lot of protein

the kidneys remove protein from the blood as urea.

(6)

ii) Why is she able to eat as many salty things as she likes while she is on the machine?

because the machine does the work of the kidney.

(1)

c) The kidney is an example of a control system.

Explain how **feedback** is used in the control of water balance in the human body. (You may draw diagrams.)

The brain detects the water in the blood and sends a message to a gland to realease ADH. If the blood does not have much water in it then a lot of ADH is produced so the kidneys remove only a little water from the blood. If there is a lot of water in the blood then less ADH is produced and more water is removed.

BRAIN ⟶ GLAND ADH ⟶ KIDNEY ⟶ VARIABLE WATER IN BLOOD

FEEDBACK

(5)
(17 marks)
(ULEAC)

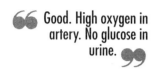

Good. High oxygen in artery. No glucose in urine.

Good. This is quite a difficult point.

Yes. They remove urea not protein.

Good. The brain is the sensor. The pituitary gland is the actuator.

Good.

REVIEW SHEET

✎ _____ refers to a state that is stable and controlled.

✎ We can use a _____ to detect any change from the normal value.

✎ Corrective mechanisms can be introduced by a _____ and carried out by an _____.

✎ The thermostat provides an example of _____ feedback.

✎ _____ feedback can lead to a situation going out of control.

✎ The _____ is part of the brain in mammals which responds to temperature changes.

✎ List four ways in which the body can be cooled if its temperature is too high

    1. _____   3. _____

    2. _____   4. _____

✎ Human body temperature is maintained at around _____ °C.

✎ _____ is a technical word used to describe the process of maintaining the correct fluid balances in our bodies.

✎ The _____ is the organ which controls the amount of water leaving the body.

✎ Fill in as many of the labels as you can in this diagram of the kidney.

✎ The _____ carries blood containing urea, water and salts to the kidney.

✎ Name two sorts of reflex.

    1. _____   2. _____

✎ Give one example of each type of reflex

    1. _____   2. _____

✎ The _____ glands produce hormones.

✎ Which gland produces the hormone insulin?

_____

✎ Complete this chemical equation.

$$\boxed{} \underset{\text{glucogen}}{\overset{\text{insulin}}{\rightleftarrows}} \boxed{\text{glycogen}}$$

✎ _____ and _____ are two hormones produced by the pancreas.

✎ Diabetes is caused by a lack of _____ .

✎ Bimetallic strips are often used in _____ . We call these strips bimetallic because

_____ .

✎ _____ systems respond only to one of two signals, high or low, which are usually described as logic level _____ and logic level _____ .

✎ If, in the following circuit, 1 = ON and O = OFF, complete the truth table.

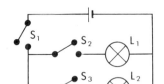

L = Lamp   S = Switch

Switch			Lamp	
S_1	S_2	S_3	L_1	L_2
0	0	0		
1	0	0		
1	1	0		
1	0	1		
1	1	1		

✎ The NOT – gate is sometimes called an _____ , since a high = 1 input causes a _____ output.

✎ The AND-gate has an output that goes _____ if both inputs are high.

✎ The OR-gate has an output that goes high if either of the inputs goes _____ .

✎ Complete the following truth table for the OR-gate

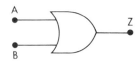

Input		Output
A	B	Z
0	0	
1	0	
0	1	
1	1	

✎ A _____ circuit has the feature that whatever happens to the input, the output has only one of two stable states, which are achieved by feedback.

MATTER AND PARTICLES

GETTING STARTED

Chapters 8 to 13 of this book will take you through the main topics and points needed to cover Attainment Target 3: Materials and their properties.

Materials can be grouped in a variety of ways for different purposes:

- solid/liquid/gas;
- metals/non-metals;
- element/compound/mixture;
- ionic/covalent.

Each form of classification has its uses. However if we want to understand why materials are placed in one group or another and why materials have the properties they do, then we need to understand something about the internal structure of matter.

The kinetic theory is a model (an idea) that takes the view that:

- all substances are made of particles;
- these particles have energy and are constantly moving - they have **kinetic energy**.

This idea can help us understand and explain many properties, such as expansion, melting, evaporation, diffusion, osmosis.

Atomic structure. Another useful idea is to imagine that atoms are themselves made of particles, which are found in the nucleus (centre) and as electrons orbiting the nucleus.

- A knowledge of the nucleus helps us understand radioactivity.
- A knowledge of the electrons and how they fit into an atom helps us understand how and why chemical reactions take place.

E S S E N T I A L   P R I N C I P L E S

1 ▷ THE KINETIC THEORY

All matter can be classified as either **solid**, **liquid**, or **gas**. These are called the three *states of matter*. The view that matter (solid, liquid or gas) is made up of particles which are in constant motion is called the *kinetic theory*. This idea can help us explain several properties of solids, liquids and gases.

The particles in a *gas* are moving very fast (they have a lot of kinetic energy) and are a great distance apart. The particles in a *liquid* are moving more slowly and are closer together. In a *solid* the particles are very close together and are 'vibrating' rather than moving freely. This idea is often shown by a piece of equipment similar to that in Figure 8.1. The motor turning very fast (providing a lot of energy) makes the metal spheres imitate a gas, but when it is moving more slowly (providing less energy) the spheres imitate a liquid.

❝ Make sure you read this carefully and try to understand these ideas ❞

BROWNIAN MOTION

Brownian motion was first seen by a scientist called Robert Brown. He noticed that when he looked at pollen grains in water through a microscope they were 'jiggling' around in a random way. This was explained in later years by another scientist, who said that the strange movement was due to the very much smaller water particles (water molecules) hitting the pollen grains and making them move. This can also be seen in a 'smoke cell', where the particles of smoke are being moved by the air molecules striking them. The water or air molecules cannot be seen, even with the most powerful microscope; they are far too small, but the effect they have on the much, much larger pollen grains or smoke particles is very obvious.

This odd movement could only be explained by assuming that air (gas) and water (liquid) were made of particles and that these particles were moving.

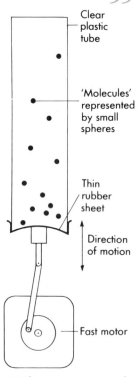

Fig. 8.1 This equipment imitates the movement of particles.

2 ▷ DIFFUSION

Diffusion means *mixing*; gases, liquids and even solids can mix together or *diffuse* if left alone (even without anyone stirring them!). Diffusion provides *evidence* for the kinetic theory.

DIFFUSION IN GASES

a) When the top is removed from a bottle containing ammonia solution, you can smell the ammonia (which is a *gas*) even if you are some distance away. The ammonia has mixed with the air and spread out.

b) When the equipment in Figure 8.2 is set up and left for a short time, a white ring appears in the tube. This white substance is ammonium chloride, which is formed when the gas ammonia meets the gas hydrogen chloride. This could only happen if the gas particles had *kinetic energy* and were able to spread out and mix. Notice the white ring where the gases meet is *not* in the centre. Which gas spreads out the faster? Does this tell you which has the lighter particles?

❝ Ammonia molecules are moving faster than hydrogen chloride ❞

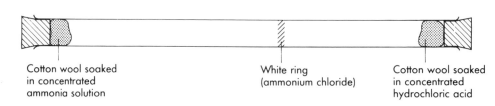

Cotton wool soaked in concentrated ammonia solution

White ring (ammonium chloride)

Cotton wool soaked in concentrated hydrochloric acid

Fig 8.2 Diffusion in gases.

DIFFUSION IN LIQUIDS

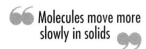 *Molecules move more slowly in solids*

Diffusion can also occur in *liquids*, eg between ink and water. This can be shown by leaving a layer of water in contact with a layer of ink (see Figure 8.3a). The diffusion takes place more slowly than between gases because the particles have less energy. They are moving more slowly and are closer together.

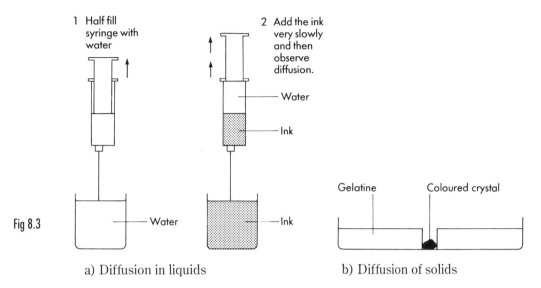

Fig 8.3

a) Diffusion in liquids   b) Diffusion of solids

DIFFUSION BETWEEN SOLIDS

Diffusion can take place between *solids*, although this takes place even more slowly. In Figure 8.3b a coloured crystal is placed in some gelatine; after a day or two the colour has spread throughout the gelatine.

The only way to explain these results is to assume that substances are made of *particles* and that these particles have kinetic energy (are moving).

Diffusion in action

Gas exchange in the alveoli of the lungs takes place by diffusion (see Figure 8.4). Diffusion of particles takes place from where there is a higher concentration to where there is a lower concentration. Particles will diffuse until they are evenly distributed.

Diffusion can also be a nuisance; it is because of diffusion that pollutant gases, eg from car exhausts, power stations and aerosols, can spread throughout the atmosphere.

	Concentration of gas in blood flowing to alveoli	*Concentration of gas in air in alveoli*
oxygen	low	high
carbon dioxide	high	low

Fig. 8.4 Concentration of gases in the lung.

3 ⟩ EXPANSION

In general, when matter is heated it expands, though some substances expand more than others. Again, this can be understood if we imagine all substances to be made of particles. In Figure 8.5 we see that heating transfers energy to the substance, increasing the kinetic energy of its particles.

A common mistake is to say that the particles themselves get bigger; this is not so, it is the **gaps** between the particles that increase.

Expansion can be seen in action in many ways. For example:

Check up here with Chapter 7 on feedback and control

1 *Bimetallic strip*: this consists of two metals with different expansion rates (*coefficients of expansion*) stuck together. When heated, the strip bends. Bimetallic strips are often used in thermostats as a switching device, as well as for flashing light bulbs.
2 *Gaps* are left between the end joints of rails on railways to allow for expansion.

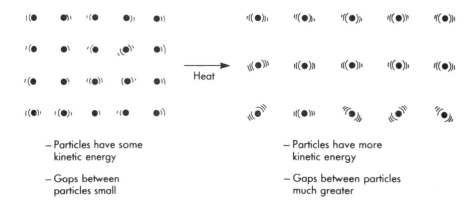

- Particles have some
  kinetic energy

- Gaps between
  particles small

- Particles have more
  kinetic energy

- Gaps between particles
  much greater

Fig 8.5 Expansion is caused by
increased kinetic energy of particles.

COMPARING SOLIDS, LIQUIDS AND GASES

In figure 8.6 we see the relationships between the particles in solids, liquids and gases.

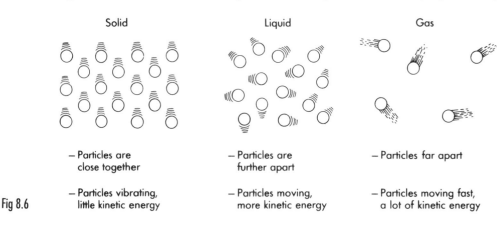

Solid

Liquid

Gas

- Particles are
  close together

- Particles vibrating,
  little kinetic energy

- Particles are
  further apart

- Particles moving,
  more kinetic energy

- Particles far apart

- Particles moving fast,
  a lot of kinetic energy

Fig 8.6

By adding more energy to the system (by *heating)*, we can change a **solid** to a **liquid**
to a **gas**. Similarly, by taking energy away from the system (by *cooling)*, we can change
a **gas** to a **liquid** to a **solid.**

MORE ABOUT GASES

The particles in a *gas* are moving very fast. When these particles hit something they
exert a *force* on that object. The combined effect of the many millions of particles in a
gas acting on an area is its pressure:

Pressure = force per unit area

Pressure is expressed in Newtons per square metre (N/m^2).

The pressure of a gas can be *increased* by *increasing its temperature* (heating). The
gas particles will have more kinetic energy and so will be moving faster and striking the
sides of a container harder and more often.

The pressure of a gas can also be *increased* by *reducing the volume* of that gas. The
particles in the gas will be closer together, so they will strike the walls of the container
more often.

Remember: the volume of a gas is equal to the volume of the container.

These ideas help to explain the 'gas laws' or 'gas patterns':

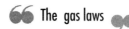

■ Pressure α temperature (provided the volume remains the same),
    or P/T = a constant.

■ Pressure α 1/volume (provided the temperature remains the same),
    or P x V = a constant.

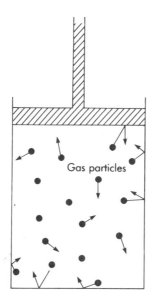

Fig 8.7 Particles striking the sides of a container create pressure.

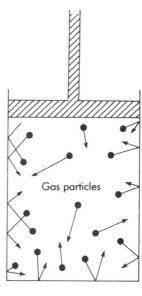

Fig 8.8 Increasing temperature increases pressure.

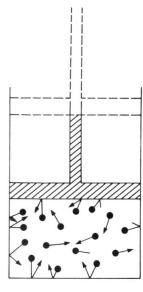

Fig 8.9 Decreasing volume increases pressure.

In order to make calculations using these gas 'laws', temperatures are measured on the *Kelvin* scale of absolute temperature, where OK (Kelvin) is equal to –273° Celsius. OK is known as *absolute zero*, or the temperature at which particles have no kinetic energy.

5 **CHANGING LIQUIDS TO GASES**

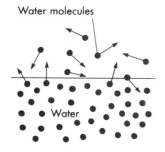
" What's happening when water boils? "

Water molecules

Water

Every second the same number of molecules leave the water as return to the water

Fig. 8.10 Equilibrium between a liquid and its vapour.

EVAPORATION

In a beaker of a liquid (eg water) the particles (water molecules) will have different energies. Some fast-moving molecules will have enough energy to escape the surface of the water. This is called **evaporation.** When the molecules escape the surface, they bump into air molecules and some may even travel back into the liquid. The more molecules escape the surface and become vapour (gas form), the more chance there is that any newly escaped molecules will be knocked back into the water.

The *rate* of evaporation can be *increased* by:

■ blowing across the surface of the water, so that the vapour molecules are removed as they are formed;

■ heating, thereby giving more molecules the energy to escape. If enough energy is transferred to the water, *all* the molecules will be able to escape. We call this *boiling.* Water boils at 100°C at sea level.

■ by reducing the air pressure, thereby allowing the molecules to escape more easily. (This is why water boils at a lower temperature on mountains, where the air pressure is less than at sea level.)

Evaporation in action

1 Pressure cookers will cook food more quickly, because they allow the water to boil at a higher temperature. The increased pressure prevents the high-energy water molecules escaping from the surface of the water.

2 Aerosol cans contain liquids under pressure that are normally gases at atmospheric pressure (these liquids have boiling points just below room temperature). Pressing the nozzle releases the pressure, allowing some of the liquid (called the propellant) to evaporate, carrying the substance to be sprayed with it. Much concern has been shown recently because of some of these propellants, called chlorofluorocarbons (CFCs). These have been shown to damage the ozone layer of the Earth's atmosphere.

3 We cool down more quickly if our skin is wet. This is because our body heat evaporates the water molecules on our skin, taking the heat energy with them.

" Manufacturers are now making 'ozone friendly' chemicals "

" A technical application "

FRACTIONAL DISTILLATION

Let us return to liquids and consider *fractional distillation.* This is a process used in industry to separate liquids of different boiling points. Fractional distillation is used in the chemical industry to separate crude oil into 'fractions', ie mixtures of liquids with

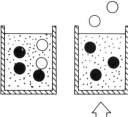

Heat

When the mixture is heated, the lighter molecules (○) move more quickly than the heavier molecules (●)

Fig. 8.11

similar boiling points. The liquids with high boiling points have large, heavy particles, whereas those with low boiling points have small, light particles. The *heavier* particles need *more energy* to help them escape the surface of the liquid. The *forces* which attract the heavier particles to each other are greater than the forces between the lighter particles.

Fractional distillation in action

1 Fractional distillation can also be used to separate other liquids of differing boiling points, such as alcohol from wine.
2 It can also be used to purify zinc. When zinc is extracted from zinc ore it often contains a small amount of lead. These can be separated by fractional distillation, since the boiling point of zinc (908°C) is much lower than that of lead (1651°C).

6 ⟩ SOLUTIONS, EMULSIONS, FOAMS AND GELS

Solutions can be made by *dissolving* substances. The substance that is dissolved is called the **solute.** The substance that does the dissolving is called the **solvent.**

Solvent + solute → solution

A *solvent* is normally a liquid (it could be a gas). Water is a very good solvent. A *solute* can be solid, liquid or gas.

A *concentrated* solution can be made by dissolving a large amount of solute in a small amount of solvent. A *dilute* solution can be made by dissolving a little solute in a large amount of solvent.

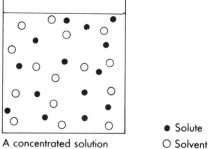
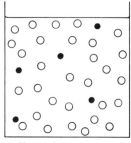

Fig 8.12

A concentrated solution   ● Solute   A dilute solution
                                  ○ Solvent

The *concentration* of solutions can be measured as grams of solute per cubic decimetre of solution (g/dm^3) or as moles of solute per cubic decimetre of solution (mol/dm^3). (The mole is a measure of the amount of substance; it relates to the number of particles present; see Chapter 10.)

A *saturated* solution is one which contains the maximum amount of dissolved solute.

The table shows a summary of information about solutions, emulsions, foams and gels:

❝ Solutions, emulsions, foams and gels ❞

	Description	*Examples*
solution	a clear liquid; a substance is completely mixed with the solvent; a mixture of two or more solutes in a solvent	solids dissolved in liquids, gases in liquids, sea water (sodium chloride in water)
emulsion	droplets of one liquid dispersed in another	oil in water, water in oil, medicines, cosmetics, emulsion paint, light sensitive coating of photographic film
foam	bubbles of gas dispersed in a liquid or solid.	expanded polystyrene, shaving cream, chemical mixture from foam fire extinguisher
gel	a solid arranged in a liquid as a fine network	gelatine, agar, jellies, non-drip paint, hair gel

7 > OSMOSIS

One feature of particles is their size; for example, water particles are much smaller than sugar molecules. This difference in size can have some interesting effects.

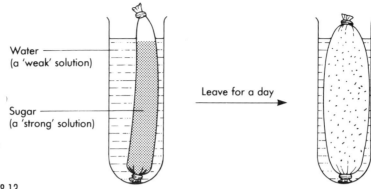

Water
(a 'weak' solution)

Sugar
(a 'strong' solution)

Leave for a day

Fig. 8.13

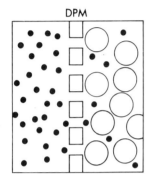

DPM

The small molecules of water pass through the membrane

The large molecules of sugar cannot pass through

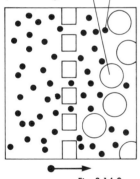

Fig. 8.14 Osmosis.

A concentrated sugar solution is placed in a bag made of visking tubing (a material like cellophane). The bag and its contents are then placed in a beaker of water. After a short time the bag will be seen to be much bigger. Why?

The effect is due to the visking tubing acting as a sort of particle sieve. The tubing material contains tiny holes or pores, just big enough to let the small water particles pass into the bag, but *not* to let the large sugar particles out. As a result, the volume of the bag increases.

The movement of water from a dilute to a concentrated solution is called *osmosis*. Materials such as visking tubing are called *differentially permeable membranes* or DPMs. If the process were allowed to continue, water would pass through the tubing walls until the concentration of the solutions inside and out were the same. Using a differentially permeable membrane to separate the substances is called *dialysis*.

DPMs in action

1 Cell membranes act as DPMs, allowing water to enter cells. Water passes into root hairs (special cells on the tips of roots) by osmosis. The cells contain a solution of sugars, salts and other solutes; water can enter through the cell membrane because the solution inside the cell is more concentrated than outside.

2 Kidney machines, which can take over when some people's kidneys fail because of disease, also use DPMs (flat tubes of cellophane). Harmful substances are removed from the blood by osmosis.

3 Some methods of food preservation work with help from DPMs and osmosis. All the bacteria (which cause food to decay) are single-celled organisms; whole cell membranes act as DPMs. Fruit can be preserved by placing it in a concentrated sugar solution. Since the solution outside the cell is more concentrated than the solution inside, water moves out of the cell and the bacteria are dehydrated and killed. Food preservation by 'salting' can be explained in the same way.

8 > ATOMS, MOLECULES AND IONS

The *particle* is the building block of all matter. There are three types:

THE ATOM

This is the simplest particle; there are just over 100 different atoms. It is from these atoms, and combinations of these atoms, that the other two types of particles can be made. Each atom has its own name and symbol to represent it.

Atom	*Symbol*
Hydrogen	H
Oxygen	O
Carbon	C
Copper	Cu
Chlorine	Cl
Sodium	Na

Each chemical symbol is either a single capital letter (eg H) or else a capital letter followed by a small letter (eg Cl). Atoms are not generally found on their own.

THE MOLECULE

This is a particle that contains two or more atoms chemically joined together. Molecules can contain the same type of atom or different atoms chemically joined (bonded). Each molecule has a name and a chemical formula to represent which atoms are joined together.

Molecule	Name	Formula
 H—H	hydrogen	H_2
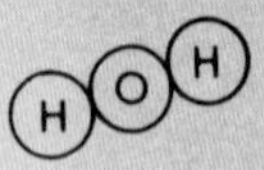 H—O—H	water	H_2O

Fig. 8.15 Each molecule can be represented by a formula.

The numbers show the proportions of atoms present in the molecule. They refer to the atoms immediately before the number, and are always written below the line (subscript).

For example, glucose (a sugar), $C_6H_{12}O_6$ contains 6 atoms of carbon, 12 atoms of hydrogen and 6 atoms of oxygen.

THE ION

❝ Ions have either lost or gained electrons ❞

This is a particle that carries an electrical charge, which may be positive or negative. Each ion has a name and formula. Ions can be derived from single atoms or from combinations. The charge on the ion is shown as a number above the symbols (superscript) . The size of the charge is indicated as a number, for example, 1+, 2+, 3+, or 1-, 2-, 3-.

Ion	Formula
oxide	O^{2-}
chloride	Cl^-
copper	Cu^{2+}
carbonate	CO_3^{2-}

Not all possible combinations of atoms produce molecules and ions. There are rules governing their formation. This makes life a lot easier ; these ideas are explained further in the next section (atomic structure).

9 ⟩ ELEMENTS, COMPOUNDS AND MIXTURES

All substances can be classified according to the types of particles they contain and how these particles are joined (chemically bound or not). Substances can be classified as:

- elements;

- compounds;

- mixtures.

ELEMENTS

❝ Try to understand the difference between element, compound and mixture. ❞

Elements are substances that contain only **one** type of atom. For example *copper* is an element containing copper atoms, hydrogen is also an element. Hydrogen gas contains hydrogen molecules. Elements cannot be broken down into simpler chemical substances.

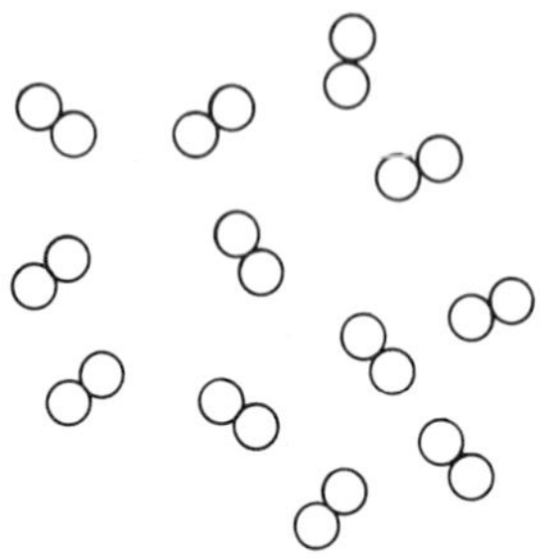

COMPOUNDS

Compounds are substances which contain *more than one* type of atom chemically joined. The particles in a compound may be molecules or ions. A compound can be chemically split into simpler substances.

Water is a compound. It consists of water molecules. Each water molecule contains two atoms of hydrogen and one atom of oxygen. Water can be split by electrolysis into hydrogen and oxygen. *Sodium chloride* is also a compound. It consists of sodium ions and chloride ions. There is one sodium ion for every chloride ion. It can be split by electrolysis into sodium atoms and chlorine molecules.

Fig. 8.16 Hydrogen molecules.

Fig. 8.17 Copper atoms.

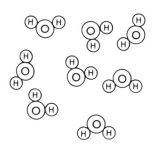

Fig 8.18 Water molecules.

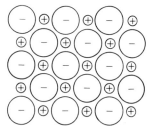

Fig 8.19 Sodium chloride.

MIXTURES

Mixtures are substances which can contain various amounts of elements and/or compounds *mixed together.* They can easily be physically separated. For example, a mixture of iron and sulphur can easily be separated with a magnet.

Other methods of separating mixtures include filtration, distillation and chromatography.

Filtration: the technique for separating solid particles from a liquid (or gas). This is done by passing the liquid (or gas) through a sieve such as filter paper which has very tiny gaps between the fibres to allow the molecules of liquid to pass through but not any solid particles. For example to separate muddy water by filtering, the sand and grit particles stay on the filter paper while the water that passes through is clear.

Other examples of filtration include filters in air conditioning units to remove dust particles from the air, filters in cooker hoods to remove grease and dust from the air; air and oil filters in cars.

Distillation: the process in which a solution is heated to produce a vapour which is then condensed by cooling to become liquid again. The vapour is usually condensed in a Liebig Condenser, a tube around which cold water flows. Distillation is used to separate a single, pure liquid from one or more solids in a solution, e.g. to obtain pure water from sea water; to obtain alcohol from a mixture of alcohol and water.

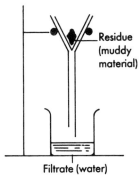

Fig. 8.20

 Methods for separating mixtures

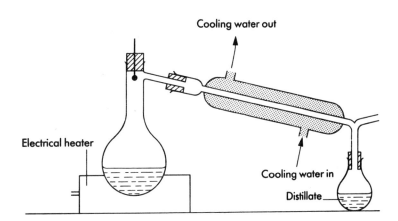

Fig 8.21 Simple distillation

Chromatography: a technique for detecting the parts of a mixture by separating them. Paper chromatography involves placing a drop of the mixture to be separated on a type of blotting paper called chromatography paper which is then dipped into a solvent. As the solvent soaks up through the paper it carries the mixture with it. As different substances dissolve at different rates the solvent carries some parts of the mixture further than others, so separating them. For example you can see the number of different coloured dyes in ink food colouring.

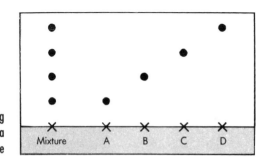

Fig 8.22 Chromatagram showing four different components in a mixture

10 ATOMIC STRUCTURE

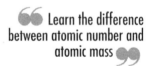

Cloud of electrons

Protons Neutrons

Nucleus

Fig. 8.23 Particles which make up the atom.

66 Learn the difference between atomic number and atomic mass 99

SUB-ATOMIC PARTICLES

Atoms themselves are made up of particles (often referred to as sub-atomic particles). These sub-atomic particles are:

- protons }
- neutrons } found in the nucleus

- electrons   found orbiting the nucleus

The differences in these particles are shown in the table:

Sub-atomic particle	Mass (u) *	Charge
proton	1	+1
neutron	1	0
electron	very small ($^1/_{2000}$)	−1

* (u = atomic mass unit)

PATTERNS FOR ATOMS

- The number of protons in an atom is called the *atomic number.* Atoms have atomic numbers of 1 to 107.

- There are *always* the *same number* of electrons and protons, so every atom is electrically neutral. Charges on the electrons and protons 'cancel out'.

- Electrons are arranged in a series of *shells* around the nucleus. Each shell can only contain a limited number of electrons. For elements with an atomic number up to eighteen the *maximum* numbers in the first 3 shells are shown; thereafter the arrangement becomes more complex.

    1st shell   maximum 2 electrons
    2nd shell   maximum 8 electrons
    3rd shell   maximum 8 electrons

For example, in the sodium atom, which has 11 electrons, the arrangement is: 2 (in 1st shell); 8 (in 2nd shell); 1 (in 3rd shell).

The total number of protons and neutrons in the nucleus is called the **mass number** (each proton and neutron has a mass of 1u). There are usually about the same number of protons as of neutrons in a nucleus. You can work out the structure of an atom from the atomic number and the mass number:

Atomic number = number of *protons* (= number of *electrons*)

Mass number = number of *protons* + number of *neutrons*

These numbers can be added to the chemical symbol for the atom as follows:

Mass number A

Atomic number Z X ← chemical symbol

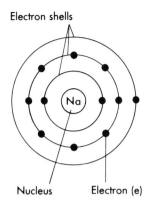

Electron shells

Nucleus   Electron (e)

Fig. 8.24 The sodium atom.

For example, in the sodium atom, $^{23}_{11}$Na:

the atomic number = 11, therefore there are 11 protons and 11 electrons;
the mass number = 23 = number of protons + number of neutrons;
the number of neutrons = mass number − atomic number
$$= 23 - 11 = 12$$

Therefore, sodium has 11 protons, 12 neutrons and 11 electrons. We can show the electron configuration (arrangement of electrons in their shells) for sodium as Na:2,8,1. Figure 8.25 shows the patterns for the atoms of some common elements.

Fig. 8.25

Element	Number of protons in the nucleus (atomic number)	Number of protons and neutrons (mass number)	Number of electrons in each shell			
			Shell 1	Shell 2	Shell 3	Shell 4
Hydrogen	1	1	1			
Helium	2	4	2			
Lithium	3	7	2	1		
Beryllium	4	9	2	2		
Boron	5	11	2	3		
Carbon	6	12	2	4		
Nitrogen	7	14	2	5		
Oxygen	8	16	2	6		
Fluorine	9	19	2	7		
Neon	10	20	2	8		
Sodium	11	23	2	8	1	
Magnesium	12	24	2	8	2	
Aluminium	13	27	2	8	3	
Silicon	14	28	2	8	4	
Phosphorus	15	31	2	8	5	
Sulphur	16	32	2	8	6	
Chlorine	17	35.5	2	8	7	
Argon	18	40	2	8	8	
Potassium	19	39	2	8	8	1
Calcium	20	40	2	8	8	2

❝Isotopes have the same number of protons and different numbers of neutrons❞

ISOTOPES

The type of atom is determined by its atomic number (number of protons). Carbon is carbon because it has 6 protons. Chlorine is chlorine because it has 17 protons. It is possible, however, for atoms such as these to have *different* mass numbers. This means that they contain different numbers of neutrons in their nuclei. Such atoms, which are chemically the same, but differ in their mass numbers, are called **isotopes.**

Chlorine has two isotopes: chlorine 35 (with a mass number of 35), and chlorine 37 (with a mass number of 37). Both these atoms behave in identical ways in chemical reactions (they have the same number of protons and electrons), but they have different numbers of neutrons in their nucleus. This is shown in Figure 8.26. In chlorine gas the proportion of these isotopes is always the same. There are 3 chlorine-35 atoms for every 1 chlorine-37 atom. The average number of protons and neutrons in a chlorine nucleus is therefore

$$\frac{35u + 35u + 35u + 37u}{4} = 35.5u \text{ (where u = 1 atomic mass unit)}$$

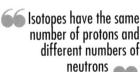

Chlorine—35 atom, $^{35}_{17}$Cl
2e.8e.7e

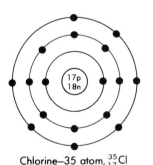

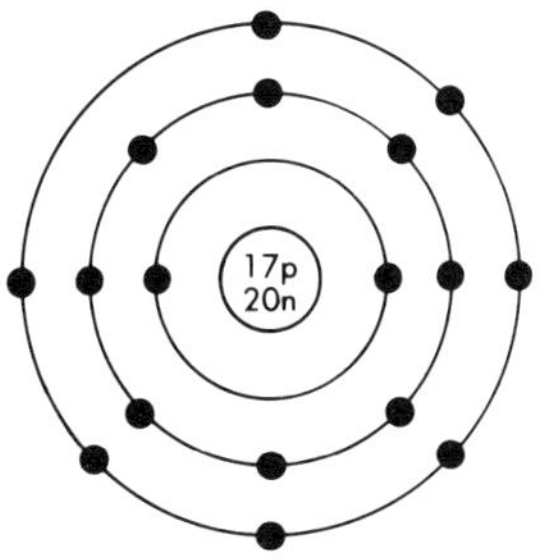

Chlorine—37 atom, $^{37}_{17}$Cl
2e.8e.7e

Fig. 8.26 Isotopes of chlorine.

RELATIVE ATOMIC MASS

Different elements have different proportions of isotopes (some of which may be radioactive; see the following page). The **relative atomic mass** of an element is based on the average mass of all the atoms in the element (taking the isotope carbon 12 as the standard) and will not be a whole number. This is the number that is usually quoted in a list of atomic masses or given in the periodic table.

DETECTING ATOMS - FLAME TESTS

It is not always easy to know which atoms are present in a compound. Some, although not *all*, give distinct colours to flames, a fact used widely in making fireworks. In the laboratory, substances can be tested by placing a small amount on a clean wire in a 'blue' bunsen flame. The colour of the flame indicates the atom present.

Colour of flame	Atom present
apple green	barium
orange (brick red)	calcium
green	copper
blue flashes	lead
lilac	potassium
yellow	sodium
red	strontium

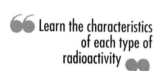

11 ▷ RADIOACTIVITY

Radioactivity is the result of the breakdown of some nuclei in atoms. Some isotopes are unstable and will emit energy in the form of heat and radiation to become more stable, for example, carbon 14 and uranium 235. Some of these isotopes are naturally occurring, like the two examples given, whilst others, such as plutonium 239, can be manufactured. Naturally occurring radioactive isotopes are usually found in the heavier elements, or are the isotopes of lighter elements which have more neutrons present in their nuclei.

RADIOACTIVE DECAY

When the nucleus in radioactive materials breaks down it can emit different types of radioactivity:

- **Alpha** (α) particles: these are fast-moving helium nuclei (groups of 2 protons and 2 neutrons). They are easily stopped by a sheet of paper and will not travel very far through the air. They are weakly deflected by a magnetic field.

Learn the characteristics of each type of radioactivity

- **Beta** (ß) particles: these are very fast-moving electrons which travel further through the air than α particles and are more difficult to stop. They can be stopped by thin sheets of metal, and are deflected by a magnetic field.

- **Gamma** (γ) rays: these are not particles at all, but a form of electromagnetic radiation of very short wavelength. They are very penetrating and are much more difficult to stop. They can be stopped by thick sheets of lead, but are not deflected by a magnetic field.

When radioactive atoms **decay** and emit particles they change into other atoms. For example, when uranium 238 loses an α particle: $^{238}_{92}\text{U} \rightarrow {}^{234}_{90}\text{Th} + {}^{4}_{2}\text{He}$

Similarly, when carbon 14 loses a ß particle: $^{14}_{6}\text{C} \rightarrow {}^{14}_{7}\text{N} + {}^{0}_{-1}\text{e}^{-}$

Radioactive atoms can be created by bombarding non-radioactive atoms with other particles. These could be α particles, ß particles, or more often fast-moving neutrons.

DETECTING RADIOACTIVITY

Radioactivity was first discovered because of its ability to 'fog' photographic plates - in the same way as light affects photographic film. This is the way X-ray photographs are taken today (X-ray was the first name given to radioactivity). Radioactivity, however, also has the ability to ionise gases that it passes through, and it is this property that forms the basis of radiation detection techniques today. The Geiger-Müller tube is an example. The tube is filled with a gas that is mainly argon. When radiation passes into the tube, some of the gas atoms are ionised. This causes a tiny electric current to flow, the size of which can be measured and is proportional to the amount of ionisation produced (ie the radiation present).

HALF-LIFE

Over a period of time, any radioactive material will decay and become stable (non-radioactive). *When* any particular nucleus will decay and release its radiation and energy cannot be predicted. They decay in a *random* way. However, different substances decay at different rates, and the rate of decay of all radioactive material is measured in **half-lives**.

66 The half-life is constant for a particular radioactive material 99

The half-life is the time taken for the radioactivity to reduce by half. For a particular radioactive material the half-life is constant, whatever the conditions. Radioactive decay is unaffected by temperature or pressure. Half-lives can be very long or very short (thousands of years to less than a second). If you plot a graph for the decay of any radioactive material it will always follow the same pattern, as in Figure 8.27.

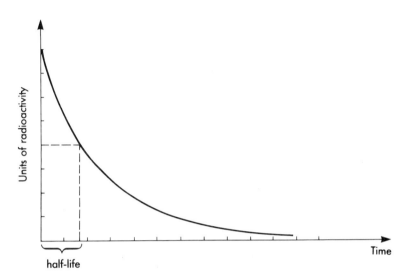

Fig 8.27 The decay curve for radioactive materials.

NATURAL RADIATION

We are constantly exposed to radioactivity from natural sources. This is referred to as *background radiation*. It arises from cosmic rays penetrating the atmosphere, soil, rocks (particularly granite in this country) and building materials, and from the food we eat (mainly owing to a radioactive isotope of potassium). In addition to these we receive small doses of radiation from medical treatment, such as chest and dental X-rays.

BIOLOGICAL EFFECTS OF RADIOACTIVITY

The effect of radiation on living tissue depends on several factors:

1 the strength of the radiation;
2 the length of exposure;
3 how much of the tissue (how many cells) is exposed.

The results of such exposure vary. There may be no serious effect if only a few cells are damaged, but in animals cancer may develop if the radiation dose is high enough. Radiation can also cause genetic mutations, so that future offspring are different in some way. In extreme cases, if enough cells are killed, the plant or animal may die.

USES OF RADIOACTIVITY

Radioactive isotopes can be used in a variety of ways, for example in industry, in medicine, for food production and for radiocarbon dating.

1 Manufacturers can check the thickness of metal containers, or the amounts of materials in packages, by measuring the amount of radiation that passes through. An example is measuring the amount of toothpaste in a tube.

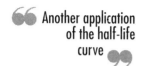

Another application of the half-life curve

2 All living things contain a large amount of carbon. Most of the carbon atoms are of the isotope carbon 12, but a small proportion are of the radioactive isotope carbon 14. This proportion of carbon 12 to carbon 14 is the same for all living things whilst they are alive. When the organism dies, the amount of carbon 14 decreases (half-life 5736 years). By measuring the amount of radioactive carbon *left*, one can date the item by reference to the half-life curve. This technique of carbon 14 dating was recently used to date the Turin Shroud.

3 Small amounts of radioisotopes can be introduced into underground water systems. Geiger counters can then be used to detect the position of leaks.

4 Food irradiation is a method of preserving food by directing radiation (usually gamma rays) on to fresh food. Such irradiation of food can destroy bacteria and prevent the growth of moulds, sterilise the contents of sealed packets, reduce the sprouting of vegetables or prolong the ripening of fruits. This irradiation does NOT make the food radioactive. However, it is not suitable for all food since it can change the taste.

5 Radiation can be used to control pests. Male insects are reared in the laboratory and are sterilised by being exposed to a controlled dose of gamma rays. They are then released into the wild, where they mate, competing with normal males. The females with which the sterilised males mate do not reproduce, so the insect population is quickly reduced.

NUCLEAR FISSION

The atoms of radioactive material have unstable nuclei that break down releasing energy, either as radiation (gamma rays) or as kinetic energy from alpha and beta particles. Nuclear fission is a process in which a radioactive nucleus splits into fragments; this occurs naturally in some elements which have very large unstable nuclei. When this happens often a few neutrons are released as well.

The nucleus of a rare form of uranium (Uranium–235) will break down, at the same time releasing a few neutrons. These fast-moving neutrons can then strike another nucleus. When this happens the second nucleus will also immediately break down, releasing yet more neutrons. Each fission (breakdown) produces more neutrons, which in turn cause other breakdowns. This is called a *chain reaction*, and can happen very quickly. Each time a nucleus breaks down, a large amount of energy is released; this results in a rapid rise in temperature of the uranium and its surroundings. This type of reaction takes place in a nuclear reactor, which is fed with concentrated uranium–235.

Know how a chain reaction occurs

NUCLEAR FUSION

Nuclear fusion is the opposite of nuclear fission. In nuclear fusion energy is released when small nuclei are *joined together* to form larger nuclei. This process is happening all the time in the Sun, and is the source of the Sun's energy. Scientists and technologists have been trying to produce nuclear fusion reactors on Earth for a long time but have still not overcome two major problems:

Nuclear Fusion and Fission are opposites

1 bringing the particles together fast enough;
2 building a 'container' for the reaction that can withstand the high temperatures involved.

The main advantage of nuclear fusion over nuclear fission is that it produces far less radioactive by-products and could use readily available *deuterium* (an isotope of hydrogen).

NUCLEAR POWER

The source of energy for nuclear power comes from the energy stored in the nuclei of a particular type of uranium, uranium-235, which has 92 protons and 143 neutrons in the nucleus. In a nuclear power station, the uranium is in the form of fuel elements in the reactor core.

During nuclear fission, the uranium nuclei are hit by slow-moving neutrons and the uranium nucleus splits into two smaller parts, giving out energy in the process. The neutrons which are released from the uranium nucleus are then used to split more uranium-235 nuclei in a chain reaction. In the nuclear reactor, this reaction is controlled by control rods, made of boron, which absorb neutrons. The heat produced by the reaction is carried away by a coolant liquid to a *heat exchanger* where it is used to generate steam which drives turbines to generate electricity (Fig. 8.28).

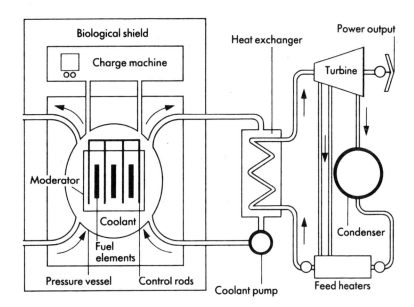

Fig. 8.28 Producing nuclear power

Nuclear power is an important source of energy as an alternative to fossil fuels. One of its main disadvantages is that the waste products are highly radioactive and are therefore very difficult to dispose of safely.

Two advantages of nuclear power are:

1 there are adequate supplies of uranium to last for a very long time;
2 nuclear power stations do not release gases such as sulphur dioxide and carbon dioxide which can harm the environment.

The accident at the nuclear reactor in Chernobyl, USSR, in 1986 was caused by the control rods being removed too far from the reactor core, so that the nuclear fission reaction produced large amounts of heat which could not be removed quickly enough from the reactor. The heat caused an explosion which exposed the top of the reactor core to the atmosphere, and ejected large amounts of radioactive debris. Some of the radioactive substances were carried by strong winds across into Europe, where heavy rainfall caused contamination of areas of Scotland, the Lake District and North Wales.

EXAMINATION QUESTIONS

MULTIPLE CHOICE

QUESTION 1

If fine pollen grains on the surface of water are examined under a microscope, it will be seen that the pollen grains are in random motion, frequently changing direction. The movement is most likely to be due to:
A air draughts blowing on the water
B chemical reaction between the pollen and the water
C attraction and repulsion between charged particles
D collisions between water molecules and pollen grains
E electrolysis of pollen grains

QUESTION 2

When ice is changing from a solid to a liquid at its melting point:
A heat is given out
B its particles become more ordered
C its particles gain energy
D its temperature increases

QUESTION 3

When water changes into steam, the molecules become:

A much larger
B more widely spaced
C less in mass
D separate atoms
E much smaller

QUESTION 4

The separation of a liquid into different substances with similar boiling points is called:

A chromatography
B distillation
C evaporation
D filtration
E heating

QUESTION 5

When copper forms an ion it loses two electrons. This can be shown by:
A Cu; B Cu^-; C Cu^{2-}: D Cu^+; E Cu^{2+}

QUESTION 6

Phosphorous has an atomic number of 15 and a mass number of 31. How many protons does it have?
A 3; B 15; C 16; D 31; E 46

QUESTION 7

Chlorine has two isotopes. What is different about the atomic structure of the isotopes?

A the number of electrons
B the number of protons
C the number of neutrons
D the number of protons plus electrons

QUESTION 8

Which type of radiation would be stopped by a few sheets of paper?

A alpha particles
B beta particles
C gamma radiation
D X-rays
E sound waves

QUESTION 9

A radioactive substance has a half-life of 15 years. What proportion of the substance would be left after 30 years?

A a half
B a third
C a quarter
D a sixth
E an eighth

QUESTION 10

The graph below shows how the activity of a radioactive substance changes with time.

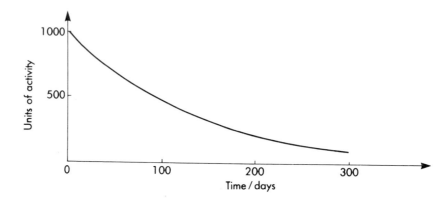

What is the half-life of this substance?
A 50 days; B 100 days; C 200 days; D 500 days; E 1000 days

STRUCTURED QUESTIONS

QUESTION 11

When a teacher discovers an unlabelled radioactive source, she uses the apparatus below to find out the activity of the source and type (or types) of radiation being emitted.

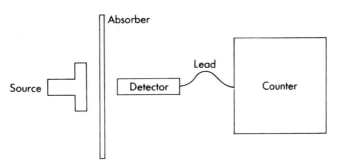

a) What does 'activity of the source' mean?

_____

(1)

The number of counts with **no** absorber is recorded. When a thin piece of tissue paper is used as an absorber the number of counts drops noticeably.

b) What type of radiation has the tissue paper absorbed?

_____

(1)

A sheet of lead 2 cm thick is now used as an absorber, but some radiation is still detected.

c) i) What is this radiation? _____
(1)

ii) Give **one** example of how this radiation can be used in either medicine or industry.

_____

(1)

(MEG)

QUESTION 12

Tubes for toothpaste are filled as shown.
    The empty tube is placed between a radioactive source and a detector.
    Paste is put into the tube and, when the tube is full, it is moved along the production line for sealing.

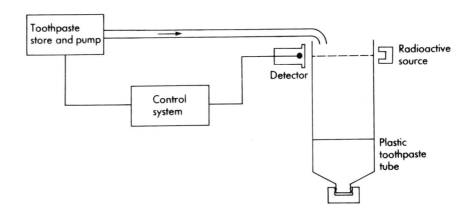

a) When the tube is full what effect will this have upon the beam of radiation reaching the detector?

_____

(1)

b) What instruction will the detector pass to the filling mechanism?

_____

(1)

c) What type of radiation would most likely be used for this purpose?

_____

(1)

d) Name a suitable detecting device.

_____

(1)

e) i) This is an example of a feedback control system. Which of the two kinds of feedback, negative or positive, is being used here?

_____

(1)

   ii) Give one reason for your answer.

_____

(1)

   iii) Some years ago toothpaste tubes were made of lead. Why could this system not have been used then?

_____

(1)

(MEG)

QUESTION 13

The table below refers to the radius of some common atoms and their ions.

Element	Radius of atom	Radius of ion
Lithium	1.3	0.7
Sodium	1.5	1.0
Calcium	1.4	1.0
Tin	1.4	0.9
Oxygen	0.7	1.3
Sulphur	1.0	1.8
Bromine	1.1	2.0
Iodine	1.3	**X**

a) What pattern do you observe about the relative sizes of an atom and its ion when comparing metals and non-metals? *(2)*

b) Predict the size of the radius of the iodine ion, X. *(1)*

c) Name **two** elements from the above list which form negative ions. *(2)*

Look at the periodic table in Chapter 9, and identify the position of sodium and lithium.

d) What is the size of the charge on these ions? *(1)*

e) Sodium chloride has the following properties: high melting point, solid, dissolves in water to become an electrolyte.

   i) State the type of bonding which holds together the sodium and chloride ions. *(1)*
   ii) Describe, with the help of diagrams, how the bonding between sodium and chloride ions differs from the bonding between two chlorine atoms. *(3)*

(MEG)

QUESTION 14
(Levels 4–6)

This question gives you some information in the form of two diagrams. Read the heading to the diagrams and study them carefully before you answer the question.

a) This apparatus is used to make a chromatogram to show the composition of three inks to find out what dyes they contain.

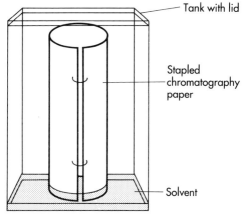
Tank with lid
Stapled chromatography paper
Solvent

Here is the resulting chromatogram.

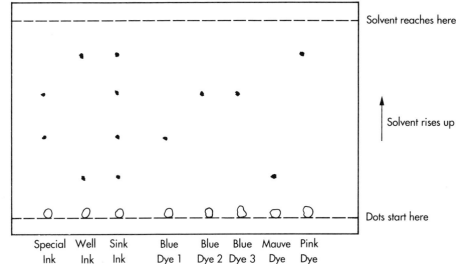
Solvent reaches here
Solvent rises up
Dots start here

Special Ink   Well Ink   Sink Ink   Blue Dye 1   Blue Dye 2   Blue Dye 3   Mauve Dye   Pink Dye

i) Which ink(s) could contain blue dye 1?

_____ (2)

ii) Explain why you cannot say for certain that Special Ink must contain blue dye 2. (3 lines) *(3)*

iii) Mr Smith is accused of forging Mrs Brown's name on a cheque. Mrs Brown always uses Well ink. The ink on the cheque is tested in the same way. Here is the result.

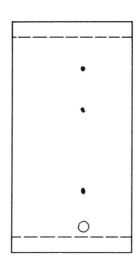

Explain why this is evidence that the document might have been forged. *(2)*

b) You are given a solution of sugar in water.

i) Describe, using a diagram if you wish, how you would obtain a sample of pure water. (5 lines) *(4)*

ii) Why is it not possible to separate the sugar from the water by filtering the solution? (2 lines) *(2)*

[*Total: 13 marks*]
(Integrated Science, NEAB, ULEAC)

QUESTION 15
(Levels 6–8)

This question is about some of the properties and uses of alpha, beta and gamma radiation.

a) i) Radiation is always present in the environment. What is the general name given to this radiation?

_____ *(1)*

ii) Give one natural cause and one man-made cause of this radiation.

1 _____

2 _____ *(2)*

iii) Name the instrument used to measure the radiation level.

_____ *(1)*

b) The diagram shows alpha and beta particles passing between two charged plates.

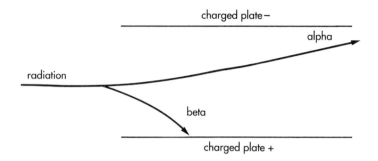

i) Explain why alpha particles are deflected upwards in the electric field, but beta particles are deflected downwards. (4 lines) *(2)*

ii) Some scientists investigating radioactivity bought a pure sample of thorium which gives out beta rays. When they examined the sample several days later they found that it contained protactinium. Why? (4 lines) *(2)*

c) Radioactivity is used in hospitals to investigate the inside of a person's body without having to cut them open. One substance used is Technetium – 99 (^{99}Tc) which gives out gamma (γ) rays.

i) What would be used to detect the gamma radiation? (3 lines) *(1)*

ii) Why is it important to protect hospital workers from gamma rays? (5 lines) *(3)*

iii) 99 is the mass number of Technetium. Explain what is meant by mass number. (4 lines) *(3)*

[Total: 15 marks]
(Integrated Science, NEAB, ULEAC)

QUESTION 16
(Levels 6–8)

A question on particles aimed at level 6.

The diagrams below show the arrangement of molecules of water when it is a solid (ice), a liquid (water) and a gas (steam/vapour).

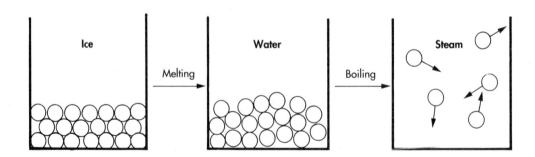

Complete the table below by putting ticks into the appropriate boxes.

State	Molecules have most energy	Molecules change places randomly	Molecules have least energy
ice			
water			
steam			

[Co-ordinated Science NEAB, ULEAC, WJEC]

ANSWERS TO
EXAMINATION QUESTIONS

MULTIPLE CHOICE

ANSWER 1

Key D. It is the water molecules moving about which make the pollen appear to be moving on its own.

ANSWER 2

Key C, the particles gain energy. Option B is incorrect because the particles are gaining energy and moving about more quickly. Option D, temperature rise, does not occur when ice is changing state from a solid into a liquid.

ANSWER 3

Key B, more widely spaced. Options A and E are wrong because the molecules do not change in size, they just have more space.

ANSWER 4

Key B, distillation. Option A is separating different coloured substances using paper.

ANSWER 5

Key E, Cu^{2+}. Electrons are negatively charged, so the ion has a positive charge as it has lost the electrons.

ANSWER 6

Key B, 15 protons: the atomic number.

ANSWER 7

Key C. The number of neutrons varies, the protons and electrons stay the same.

ANSWER 8

Key A, alpha particles, are stopped by paper; Option B, beta particles, are stopped by thin sheets of metal, and option C, gamma radiation, is stopped by thick sheets of lead.

ANSWER 9

Key C, a quarter. In 15 years a half would be left, so in another 15 years, a quarter of the original is left.

ANSWER 10

Key B. It has taken 100 days for the activity to reduce from 1000 units to 500 units (from the graph).

STRUCTURED QUESTIONS

ANSWER 11

a) the number of particles emitted per second by the source
b) alpha radiation
c) i) gamma radiation
    ii) to irradiate foods to kill bacteria

ANSWER 12

a) It will stop the beam.
b) to stop the filling mechanism
c) beta radiation
d) a Geiger-Müller tube
e) i) negative feedback
    ii) it stops the tube from becoming too full
    iii) beta radiation would be stopped by lead

ANSWER 13

a) The diameter of the metal atoms is larger than the diameter of the metal ions. The diameter of the non-metal atoms is smaller than the diameter of the non-metal ions.
b) 2.3
c) any two non-metals, eg oxygen and sulphur
d) 1
e) i) ionic bonding
    ii) In the bonding between sodium and chloride ions, an electron has moved from the outer shell of the sodium atom, so forming a positively charged sodium ion. The electron has joined the outer shell of the chlorine atom, so forming a negatively charged chloride ion. The two ions are attracted to each other.

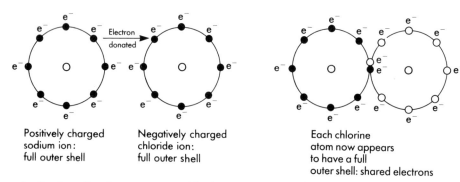

Positively charged sodium ion: full outer shell

Negatively charged chloride ion: full outer shell

Each chlorine atom now appears to have a full outer shell: shared electrons

    In the bonding between two chlorine atoms, one electron from each atom is shared between the two atoms.

ANSWER 14

a) i) look at the dot for blue dye 2. It is on the same level as dots in 2 of the inks.
    Answer: Special ink (1)   Sink ink (1)
    ii) The chromatogram dots for blue dye 2 and 3 and Special ink are on the same level (1)
    so Special ink could contain blue dye 2 (1) or 3 (1)
    iii) the pattern for Well ink only shows 2 dots but this ink pattern shows three dots (1)
    so it must be a different ink (1)
b) i) try to include as much experimental detail here as possible. An accurate, well labelled diagram is also acceptable but may take too much time to draw .
    boil the water in a flask (1)
    use a condenser (1)
    to condense the vapour (1)
    and collect the pure water in a beaker (1)
    ii) the sugar is dissolved in the water and forms a solution (1)
    filtering would only separate solid particles from a mixture (1)

ANSWER 15

a) i) background (1)
    ii) a natural cause of background radiation is from radioactive rocks / minerals (1)
    a man-made cause is from nuclear waste/fall out / medical uses / TV (1)
    iii) a Geiger counter / Geiger Müller / GM tube (1)

b) i) the alpha particles carry a positive charge (1)
        and are attracted to the negative plate (1)
    ii) The nucleus is unstable (1)
        and emits radiation / splits up (1)
c) i) photographic film could be used (1)
    ii) ionisation (1)
        affects living cells / causes cancer (1)
        causes changes in genes / mutations (1)
    iii) the mass number is the number of protons (1)
        plus the number of neutrons (1) in the nucleus (1)

ANSWER 16

The table should look like this:

State	Molecules have most energy	Molecules change places randomly	Molecules have least energy
ice			✓ (1)
water		✓ (1)	
steam	✓ (1)	✓ (1)	

A STUDENT'S ANSWER WITH EXAMINER'S COMMENTS

SUNDAY 22 JUNE 1986

OBSERVER

Radioactive meat on sale for a month

GEOFFREY LEAN ■ Environment Correspondent

(with acknowledgements to 'The Observer')

Following the Chernobyl disaster in April 1986, the government in Britain started measuring the levels of radioactivity in sheep meat.

a) Why was it considered important to measure the radioactivity in sheep meat?

The sheep would have eaten the grass which had radiation on it.

(2)

> ❝ Yes and state also that the radiation levels in meat had to be below a safe level for human consumption. ❞

b) State **two** methods of detecting radiation from the meat.

1 *Using a GM tube*
2 *Using photographic film*

(2)

c) Complete Table 4 below about two radioactive particles.

Name of particle	Description	Charge (+ or –)	How to identify each particle
Alpha	(i) helium nuclei	(ii) +	(iii) stopped by paper
Beta	(iv) electrons	(v) –	(vi) stopped by lead

Table 4

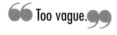
No. Thin metal sheets.

d) The number of counts per minute from a radioactive source is recorded once every half hour. The results are shown in Table 5.

Time/minutes	Corrected counts per minute
0	121
30	86
60	60
90	44
120	29
150	21
180	15

Table 5

i) What is the meaning of the term 'half-life'?

time taken for radioactivity to be half

(2)

Good.

ii) Use the results in the table to calculate the half-life of the source. (Show your working.)

Approx 60 seconds to go from 120 - 60

∴ half life = 60 seconds

(2)

Good.

e) Name **two** sources of background radiation.

1 Rocks

2 TV sets

(2)

TV sets are not usually regarded as a source of background radiation.

f) Discuss the advantages and disadvantages of using radioactive materials in industry and medicine.

They can be dangerous and harm people.
They can kill cancer cells inside people.
X rays are used to see broken bones. They
can sterilise equipment.

(4)
(ULEAC)

Too vague.

Good points here.

State which are advantages/ disadvantages.

REVIEW SHEET

✎ The three states of matter are

1. _____ 2. _____ 3. _____

✎ The _____ theory tells us about the behaviour of matter made up of particles in constant motion.

✎ The particles in a _____ move faster than the particles in a liquid.

✎ The odd 'jiggling' movement of pollen grains in water is called _____ motion.

✎ This odd movement of pollen grains in water can be explained by assuming that water (liquid) is made up of particles and that these particles are _____.

✎ Diffusion means _____ and provides evidence for the _____ theory.

✎ Ammonia molecules move _____ than hydrogen chloride.

✎ Diffusion in liquids is _____ than in gases. This is because the particles have _____ energy.

✎ Gas exchange in the alveoli of the lungs takes place by _____.

✎ When matter is heated it _____. This is because the _____ between the particles increase.

✎ _____ = force per unit area and is measured in _____ per square metre.

✎ _____ the temperature of a gas will increase the _____ of a gas. The gas particles will have more _____ energy and so will be moving faster and striking the sides of a container harder and more often.

✎ _____ the volume of a gas will increase the _____ of a gas. the particles will be _____ and so will strike the walls of the container more often.

✎ To make caclulations for the 'gas laws', temperatures are measured on the _____ scale of absolute temperature. Absolute zero occurs at _____ when particles have no _____ energy.

✎ _____ occurs when fast-moving molecules have enough energy to escape the surface of the water.

✎ List 3 ways by which we can increase the *rate* of evaporation.

1. _____
2. _____
3. _____

✎ In industry, liquids of different boiling points are separated by the process of _____.

✎ Complete this chemical equation

Solvent + solute → [   ]

✎ The substance that is dissolved is called the _____ and the substance that does the dissolving is called the _____.

✎ A _____ solution is one which contains the maximum amount of dissolved solute.

✎ _____ is a word we use to describe the movement of water from a dilute solution to a concentrated solution.

✎ The atom, molecule and ion are all types of _____.

✎ List any four different atoms, giving the symbol as well as the name.

1. _____   3. _____

2. _____   4. _____

✎ A particle which contains two or more atoms chemically joined together is called a _____

✎ We can classify substances as _____, _____ or _____.

✎ A substance containing only one type of atom is an _____. A substance containing more than one type of atom chemically joined is a _____.

✎ The particles of an atom are often called sub-atomic particles. Three types of sub-atomic particle are:

1. _____   2. _____   3. _____

✎ The number of _____ in an atom is called the atomic number.

✎ Every atom has the same number of _____ and _____, so every atom is electrically neutral.

✎ The number of _____ plus the number of _____ gives the mass number of the atom.

✎ In the sodium atom $_{11}^{23}$Na:

the atomic number   = ☐ therefore there are ☐ protons and ☐ electrons;

the mass number   = ☐ = number of protons + number of neutrons;

the number of neutrons = mass number – atomic number

= ☐ – ☐ = ☐

✎ Atoms which are chemically the same, but differ in their mass numbers, are called _____

✎ The _____ of an element is based on the average mass of all the atoms in the element.

✎ List the three types of radioactivity

1. _____   2. _____   3. _____

✎ Radioactivity results from the breakdown of some _____ in atoms.

✎ The _____ is the time taken for radioactivity to reduce by half.

✎ List four possible uses of radioactivity in industry, medicine or other practical ways.

1. _____   3. _____

2. _____   4. _____

GETTING STARTED

The periodic table is a useful way of grouping together *different elements* which have *similar properties*: for example, metals and non-metals. The elements are arranged in order of their *atomic number* (proton number) and approximately in order of *relative atomic mass*.

The periodic table can be used as a basis for predicting the physical and chemical properties of different elements. The position of an element in the table enables you to predict its melting point, density and reactivity, and the formulae of any compounds which the element may form.

Across the periodic table are *periods* or rows, and down the table are the *groups* or columns.

ESSENTIAL PRINCIPLES

1 ▷ PERIODS AND GROUPS

The periodic table is a complete list of all the elements and hence the atoms that exist. It is more than just a list because it is arranged in a definite grid or pattern of rows and columns. Each *row* is called a *period*, and each *column* is called a *group*. The simplest atom (the lightest) appears at the top left, and the most complex (the heaviest) appears at the bottom right. The atoms are arranged in increasing order of mass.

See Chapter 12 for the complete table.

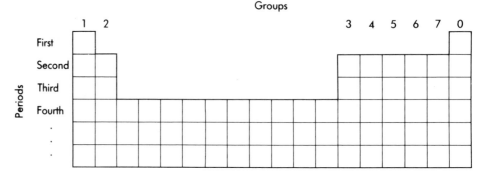

Fig. 9.1

PERIODS

Each period corresponds to an electron shell. As you move across the *first* period you are filling the *first* electron shell:

atom:	H	He
atomic number:	1	2
electron configuration:	1	2

As you move across the *second period* you are filling the *second* electron shell:

atom:	Li	Be	B	C	N	O	F	Ne
atomic number:	3	4	5	6	7	8	9	10
electron configuration:	2,1	2,2	2,3	2,4	2,5	2,6	2,7	2,8

Properties of the periods

In the *third period* you are filling the *third* electron shell:

atom:	Na	Mg	Al	Si	P	S	Cl	Ar
atomic number:	11	12	13	14	15	16	17	18
electron configuration:	2,8,1	2,8,2	2,8,3	2,8,4	2,8,5	2,8,6	2,8,7	2,8,8

This means that as you go *across* the table the atoms are getting *heavier* (more protons and neutrons). As you go *down* the table the atoms are getting *bigger* (more electron shells which take up more space).

GROUPS

The groups can be considered to consist of 'families' of elements that behave in similar ways in chemical reactions. You will notice that as you go *down a group*, the atoms have the *same number of electrons in their outer shell*.

For example, in group 1:

atom	*electron configuration*
H	1
Li	2, 1
Na	2, 8, 1
K	2, 8, 8, 1

Properties of the groups

This is important since it is the *arrangement* of electrons in their shells which determines the way in which atoms behave in chemical reactions.

2 ▷ BONDING AND THE PERIODIC TABLE

There is a stable arrangement for electrons in atoms. This occurs when an atom has a **filled outer shell**. All the atoms in group O have filled outer shells. These atoms do not react with other substances except for a very few special cases.

All other atoms react in order to fill their outer electron shells. They can do this in two ways:

- ionic bonding;

- covalent bonding.

IONIC BONDING

In the reaction between sodium and chlorine atoms, electron transfer has occurred to form ions:

$$Na + Cl \rightarrow Na^+ + Cl^-$$

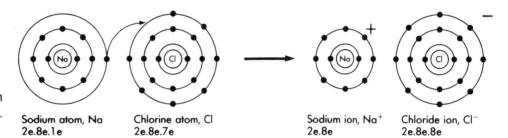

Fig. 9.2 Formation of ions when sodium reacts with chlorine.

Sodium atom, Na   Chlorine atom, Cl   Sodium ion, Na^+ Chloride ion, Cl^-
2e.8e.1e   2e.8e.7e   2e.8e   2e.8e.8e

The sodium atom has *lost* an electron to become a sodium ion: we show this as Na^+. The chlorine atom has *gained* an electron to become a chlorine ion: we show this as Cl^-. Both the ions that are formed have filled outer shells.

Once these two ions have been formed, they will attract each other because of the opposite charges of the ions. (Like charges repel; unlike charges attract.) The reason the electron transfer takes place in this direction is that any transfer of electrons takes energy. It is easier to take 1 electron from sodium than 7 from chlorine. This results in the general rule:

- Metals form **positive ions.**

- Non-metals form **negative ions**.

A positive ion is called a *cation*; a negative ion is called *anion*.

Metal atoms	Group	Electrons lost	Ion formed
lithium	1	1	Li^+
sodium	1	1	Na^+
potassium	1	1	K^+
magnesium	2	2	Mg^{2+}
calcium	2	2	Ca^{2+}
aluminium	3	3	Al^{3+}

Non-metal atoms	Group	Electrons gained	Ion formed
oxygen	6	2	O^{2-}
sulphur	6	2	S^{2-}
chlorine	7	1	Cl^-
bromine	7	1	Br^-
iodine	7	1	I^-

Fig. 9.3 Some atoms and their ions.

Also, as a general rule:

- Group 1 elements form ions with **one positive** charge (they have one electron to lose).

- Group 2 elements form ions with **two positive** charges (they have 2 electrons to lose).

- Group 3 elements form ions with **three positive** charges (they have 3 electrons to lose).

- Group 7 elements form ions with **one negative** charge (they have one space to fill).

- Group 6 elements form ions with **two negative** charges (they have two spaces to fill).

Properties of ionic compounds

The formation of ions in this way (from the reaction between metal and non-metal atoms) results in positively and negatively charged particles which have a strong attraction for each other. These ions form a giant ionic lattice, in which each ion is surrounded by as many ions of the opposite charge as possible, similar to that in Figure 9.4.

These strong forces of attraction mean that ionic substances have high melting points and high boiling points and are solids at room temperature. Ionic substances will also usually dissolve in water. Since ionic compounds contain charged particles they will conduct electricity, but only if the ions are free to move. This can happen if:

- the compound is heated until it is molten;

- the compound is dissolved in water.

Electrolysis

The process of ionic substances conducting electricity is called *electrolysis*. During this process the ions are turned back into atoms. This is illustrated by the electrolysis of molten sodium chloride.

The two rods that extend into the liquid are called the *electrodes*. The positive electrode is called the *anode* and attracts the negative ions (*anions*). The negative electrode is called the *cathode* and attracts the positive ions (*cations*).

At the anode the chloride ion loses electrons and turns back into atoms. The atoms join in pairs to form chlorine molecules. At the cathode the sodium ions gain electrons and turn back into sodium atoms.

This reaction can be summarised as follows:

cathode reaction   anode reaction

$$2Na^+(l) + 2e^- \rightarrow 2Na(l)$$ $$2Cl^-(l) - 2e^- \rightarrow Cl_2(g)$$

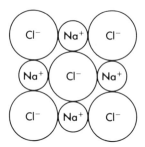

Fig. 9.4 The sodium chloride lattice.

> Try to understand the differences between ionic and covalent bonding

> See also Chapter 12

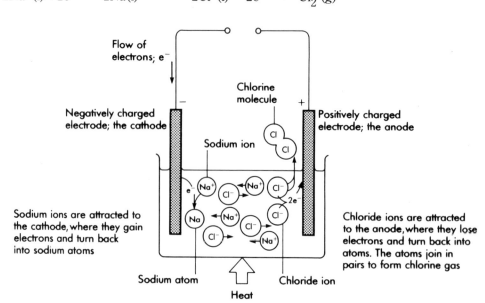

Fig 9.5 Electrolysis of molten sodium chloride.

COVALENT BONDING

Atoms have stable arrangements if their outer electron shells are filled. This can happen by the *sharing* of electrons. Non-metal atoms combine to form molecules by sharing electrons in their outer shells. The exception to this is the atoms in Group 0, which have stable electron arrangements already.

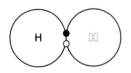

or H – H

Fig. 9.6 The hydrogen molecule.

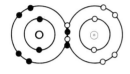

or O = O

Fig. 9.7 The oxygen molecule.

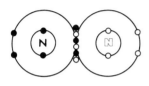

or N ≡ N

Fig. 9.8 The nitrogen molecule.

Two hydrogen atoms will join together to form a hydrogen molecule, by sharing their electrons. Each atom can then be considered to have a filled electron shell (2 electrons). The shared pair of electrons is called a *covalent bond* and can be shown as a line between the two atoms H-H. The molecule is represented as H_2.

An oxygen molecule is formed in a similar way, but because each oxygen molecule has 6 electrons in its outer shell (electron configuration 2,6) it has two 'spaces' to be filled. It does this by each atom sharing **two** of its electrons; this forms a *double covalent bond*. The molecule is represented as O_2.

Similarly, nitrogen atoms will pair up to form nitrogen molecules, but this time by forming a *triple covalent bond*. Each covalent bond is a shared pair of electrons. The nitrogen molecule is represented as N_2.

Non-metal atoms exist in the free state as molecules (see Figure 9.9) because in this way they can have *stable electron arrangements*.

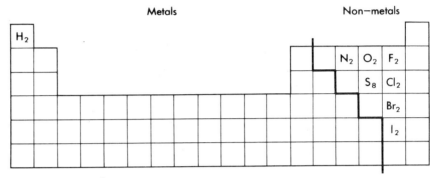

Fig. 9.9 It is only the non metal atoms which form molecules.

SOME COMMON COVALENT COMPOUNDS

Non-metal atoms will combine with other non-metal atoms to form covalent compounds: for example, water (H_2O).

Remember, each line represents a shared pair of electrons, or in other words, a covalent bond.

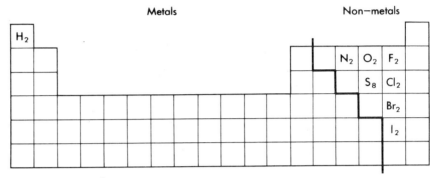

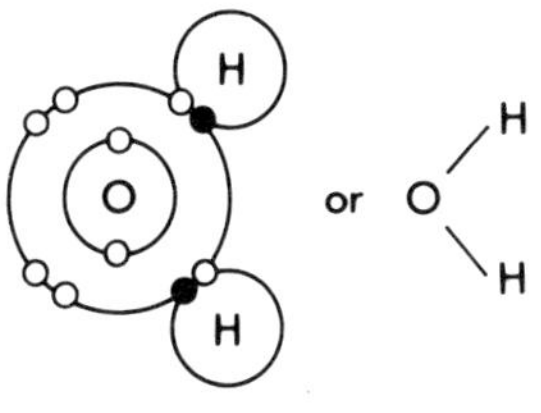

Fig. 9.10 Water molecule.

Name	Formula	Structure
carbon dioxide	CO_2	O = C = O
ammonia	NH_3	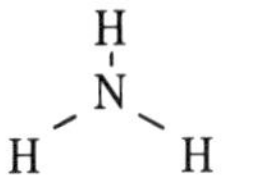 H–N(–H)(–H) with H above
methane	CH_4	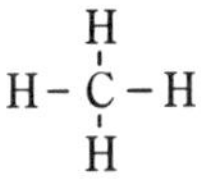 H–C–H with H above and below
ethane	C_2H_6	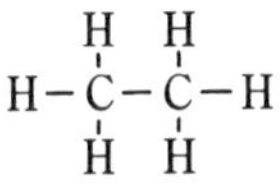 H–C–C–H with H above and below each C
ethene	C_2H_4	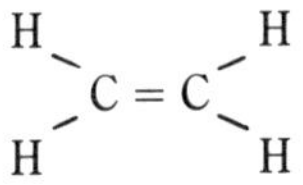 C=C with two H on each
ethyl alcohol	C_2H_5OH	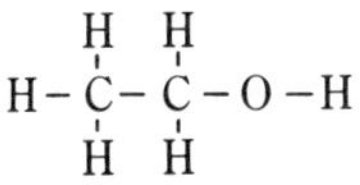 H–C–C–O–H with H above and below the C's

Fig. 9.11 Some common covalent compounds

PROPERTIES OF COVALENT COMPOUNDS

Although the covalent bonds holding together the atoms in a molecule are strong, the forces holding the molecules themselves are weak. This means that covalently bonded substances are often gases or liquids, or solids with relatively low melting points and low boiling points. They do not conduct electricity and do not usually dissolve in water.

COMPARING COVALENT AND IONIC COMPOUNDS

	Ionic compounds	*Covalent compounds*
relation to periodic table	formed between metal atoms and non-metal atoms	formed between non-metal atoms
melting point	high > 250° C	low < 250° C
boiling point	high > 500° C	low < 500° C
electrical conductivity	good conductor when molten or in solution	non-conductors
solubility in water	usually soluble	usually insoluble

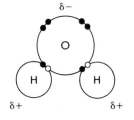

Fig. 9.12 The polar water molecule.

WATER AS A SOLVENT

Water dissolves ionic substances. The reason is that the water molecule is *polar* – it has a slight negative charge (δ–) at one end and a slight positive charge (δ+) at the other. This is a result of the oxygen atoms attracting the electron pairs of the bonds with the hydrogen atoms more strongly. Water can therefore dissolve ionic substances. Water is not the only polar molecule (although it is more polar than most). Water will also dissolve other molecular compounds which are themselves slightly polar, eg ethanol.

3 ▷ GIANT STRUCTURES

METALS AS GIANT STRUCTURES

Metals are giant structures. The metal atoms are 'bonded' together in an unusual way. The metal atoms lose some of their outer electrons and so become, in effect, positive ions. These electrons then move around the atoms freely. The metal atoms/ions are in a sea of electrons. The electrons are free to move and are shared by all the atoms. This idea helps to explain many of the properties of metals.

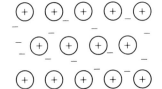

Fig. 9.13 Metals are giant structures.

- *High boiling points and melting points*: the attraction between the 'ions' and electrons is strong, so usually the metals will have high melting points and boiling points and will be strong and hard.

- *Conduction of electricity*: the ease of movement of electrons will mean that metals will easily conduct electricity when a potential difference is applied across the metal.

4 ▷ MACRO-MOLECULES

Some covalently bonded molecules do not have the properties indicated above, because their molecules are *very large*. They have a large number of covalent bonds and form giant molecules, or *macromolecules*.

ELEMENTS

Carbon is an example of an element which forms large numbers of covalent bonds between its atoms. It can do this in two ways, to form *diamond* or *graphite*. These two forms of carbon are called *allotropes*. Some other elements have different allotropic forms, but not necessarily forming giant molecules (eg sulphur).

Diamond is very strong because each carbon atom is linked to four other carbon atoms. A diamond crystal is one giant molecule. Graphite is very strongly bonded, but in layers; each layer is a giant molecule. However, the forces holding the layers together are weak, so they slide over each other. This property is made use of in pencils; the pencil 'lead' is really graphite.

Silicon is in the same group as carbon; it too has similar abilities to form giant structures. The structure of silicon is the same as that of diamond. Silicon dioxide, a compound of silicon, has a giant structure, the atoms being bonded by covalent bonds. We come across this substance quite often; it appears as sand and as quartz in rocks and it can be made into glass. Silicon is in fact the second most common element found in the Earth's crust (28%), the first being oxygen.

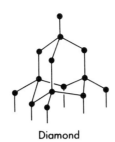
Diamond

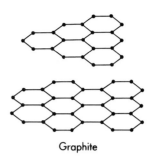
Graphite

Fig. 9.14 Allotropes of carbon

COMPOUNDS OF CARBON

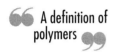

There are many *compounds* of carbon that form very large molecules. They exist because of carbon's ability to form long chains (as well as rings) of covalently bonded carbon atoms. These macromolecules are called *polymers*; some exist naturally, and some are man-made. Examples of these are starch, wool, polythene, and nylon. These compounds contain atoms other than carbon, but it is the carbon atoms that provide the ability to form large molecules.

Although the polymers have large molecules which contain many thousand atoms, the giant molecules of carbon and silicon contain many *billion* atoms.

PROPERTIES OF MACROMOLECULES

The *giant* molecules, such as carbon, have very high melting points and boiling points, will not dissolve in water and generally will not conduct electricity. Graphite, one form of carbon, is an exception. Silicon will also weakly conduct electricity, and is regarded as a 'semi-conductor'; it is this property that makes silicon valuable for use as 'microchips' in computer technology.

The *large* molecules (polymers), such as starch, have higher melting points and boiling points than ordinary molecules, but not as high as giant molecules or ionic compounds (which are also giant structures). They are not very soluble in water (most are insoluble) and will not conduct electricity.

 **VALENCY AND WRITING FORMULAE**

A *formula* for a compound shows the ratio of atoms present in that compound, whether it is ionic or covalent. Each atom has a 'combining power', which is called the *valency*. The valency of an atom depends on the number of electrons in its outer shell and hence its position in the periodic table. For example, atoms in group 1 have a valency of 1; atoms in group 2 have a valency of 2.

In general as one moves *across* the periodic table the valency gradually *increases* to a maximum of 4, then gradually *decreases* to 0. This is not always the case, and there are some important exceptions, but it is a good 'rule of thumb'.

Atom	Na	Mg	Al	Si	P	S	Cl	Ar
Outer shell electrons	1	2	3	4	5	6	7	8
Group no	1	2	3	4	5	6	7	0
Valency	1	2	3	4	3	2	1	0

The reason for this of course is that if we consider atoms reacting to form ions, one atom has to lose electrons, whereas the other atom has to gain electrons. Those atoms (non-metals), like sulphur, which have 6 electrons in their outer shell can be considered to have 2 spaces (to complete the full set of 8). It is easier to fill 2 spaces than it is to remove 6 electrons. When atoms join up to form ions, the number of electrons *leaving* one atom must match the number of electrons being *gained* by the others. How can this happen? It often helps to imagine the atoms to have hooks representing their valencies (electrons to be donated or accepted).

Example 1: *Sodium will react with chlorine to form a compound, sodium chloride*

Na has a valency of 1

Cl has a valency of 1: we can represent it as

When these atoms combine *all* hooks must be attached:

So the formula is NaCl.

Example 2: *Magnesium will react with chlorine to form magnesium chloride*

Magnesium: valency 2:

Chlorine: valency 1: (Cl)

When they join, *all* hooks must be attached, so we need an extra Cl to take care of the otherwise spare hook:

The formula is therefore $MgCl_2$. The 2 as subscript refers to 2 atoms of what is immediately in front, ie Cl atoms.

Example 3: *The formula of aluminium oxide*

Aluminium: valency 3 (Al)

Oxygen: valency 2

When they join, *all* hooks must be attached:

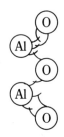

So the formula is Al_2O_3.

Sometimes we can regard a collection of atoms, referred to as a radical, as having a valency. For example:

sulphate SO_4^{2-} : valency 2
nitrate NO_3^- : valency 1
carbonate CO_3^{2-} : valency 2
hydroxide OH^- : valency 1

Example 4: *The formula of copper nitrate*

Copper: valency 2

Nitrate: valency 1 (NO_3^-)

Formula $Cu(NO_3)_2$

Notice the use of brackets with the 2 as subscript outside. This means 2 of whatever is inside the brackets.

You will not be expected to remember all the valencies for these atoms or radicles, but it is worth remembering how they are related to the position in the periodic table .

6 ▸ TRENDS AND THE PERIODIC TABLE

TRENDS DOWN A GROUP: FAMILIES OF ELEMENTS

Each group in the periodic table contains elements which behave in similar ways in chemical reactions. This is because they have the *same number of electrons in their outer shells*. They do, however, differ by degrees in their intensity of reaction as you travel 'down the group'. For example we can look at 3 groups:

■ group 1 - the alkali metals (a group of metals);

■ group 7 - the halogens (a group of non-metals);

■ group 0 - the inert gases (a special group).

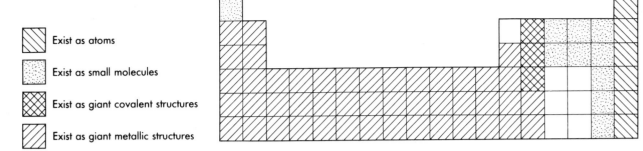

Fig. 9.15 Trends and the periodic table.

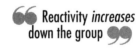	Exist as atoms
	Exist as small molecules
	Exist as giant covalent structures
	Exist as giant metallic structures

Group 1 - the alkali metals

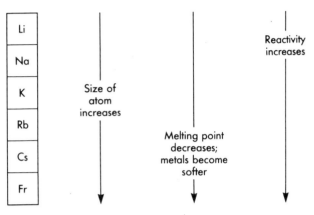

Fig. 9.16 The alkali metals.

■ **Reaction with air:** lithium, sodium and potassium react with air to form oxides. When the metal is cut with a knife its surface quickly tarnishes. The speed of *reaction increases* as you move *down the group*. If any of the alkali metals are represented by M, the general reaction is:

$$4M + O_2 \rightarrow 2M_2O$$

Formulae of oxides formed: Li_2O, Na_2O, K_2O. These oxides dissolve in water to produce alkaline solutions.

■ **Reaction with water:** lithium, sodium and potassium react quickly with water. Lithium when placed on water 'fizzes' and quickly reacts. Sodium will buzz around on the surface of the water giving the odd spark. Potassium reacts more violently, producing a lilac flame. Reactivity increases as you move down the group. Each produces a strong alkaline solution with water. The general reaction is:

> ❝ Reactivity *increases* down the group ❞

$$2M + 2H_2O \rightarrow 2MOH + H_2$$

Formulae of hydroxides produced: LiOH, NaOH, KOH.

■ **Reaction with halogens:** each will react with halogens to form compounds called *halides*. The reactivity will increase as one moves down the group. For example, the down the group reaction with chlorine:

$$2M + Cl_2 \rightarrow 2MCl$$

Formulae of halides formed: LiCl, NaCl, KCI.

■ **Reactivity trends:** the atoms react to form ions which have a charge of 1+. In forming these ions, eg Na^+, an electron has to be removed from the outer shell. Those atoms which have outer shells *further away* from the positive nucleus (the bigger atoms) will require *less energy* to remove that electron, and so will tend to be *more reactive*; hence reactivity *increases* as you move down the group: Cs>Rb>K>Na>Li.

Group7:The halogens

■ **Reaction with metals:** the halogens will react with metals to form metal halides. For example, iron with chlorine:

$$2Fe + 3Cl_2 \rightarrow 2FeCl_3$$

The reactivity of the halogens decreases as you move down the group.

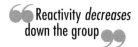

> Reactivity *decreases* down the group

■ **Reaction with water:** the halogens will react with water to form acidic solutions which also act as bleaches. The reactivity *decreases* as you move *down the group*, as does the bleaching power of the solutions. The solutions produced from iodine and bromine are weak acids, whereas chlorine and fluorine will produce strong acids. For example:

$$H_2O + Cl_2 \rightarrow HCl + HOCl \text{ (chloric acid – bleach)}$$

■ **Reactivity trends:** when halogens react with metals they do so to form ions:

F^-, fluoride ion; Cl^-, chloride ion; Br^-, bromide ion; I^-, iodide ion

The ease with which these atoms form ions depends on the number of electron shells the atom has. In order to form an ion, the atom has to gain an electron. The atom with its outer shell closer to the positive nucleus will find this easiest, because of the strong pulling power of the positive nucleus. The *larger* the atom, the *further away* the outer electron shell, so the less influence the nucleus will have. Thus we would expect fluorine to be much more reactive than iodine, which is indeed the case.

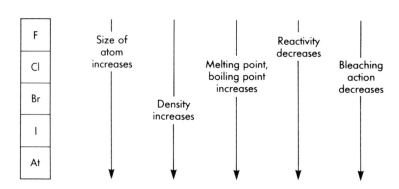

Fig. 9.17 The halogens.

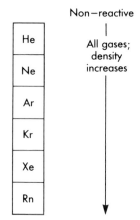

Fig. 9.18 The inert gases.

Group 0 : The inert gases

These gases show no reactivity (with a very few exceptions), because they have stable filled outer orbitals. They do not form molecules but exist as separate atoms (see Figure 9.18).

In summary the trends which are common to all groups are:

■ the diameter of the atom increases so the atom becomes larger
■ the number of electrons in the outer shell is always equal to the group number
■ the atoms lose their outer electrons more easily
■ the density of the element increases

TRENDS ACROSS A PERIOD

Metal/non-metal	Na m	Mg m	Al m	Si n/m	P n/m	S n/m	Cl n/m	Ar n/m
Outer shell electrons	1	2	3	4	5	6	7	8
Valency	1	2	3	4	3	2	1	0
Oxidation no.	+1	+2	+3	+4	−3	−2	−1	0
Melting point/°C	98	650	660	1410	44	113	−100	−189
Boiling point/°C	880	1100	2470	2355	280	444	−35	−186
Oxide nature	basic	basic	amphoteric	acidic	acidic	acidic	acidic	–
Formula of oxide	Na_2O	MgO	Al_2O_3	SiO_2	P_2O_3	SO_2	Cl_2O	–
Formula of chloride	$NaCl$	$MgCl_2$	$AlCl_3$	$SiCl_4$	PCl_3	S_2Cl_2	Cl_2	–

Fig. 9.19 Trends across the 3rd period

As one moves across a period of the periodic table, there is a gradual change in the properties of the elements. Remember, as you move *across* a period you are *adding one more electron* to the outer shell of the atom each time. For example, Figure 9.19 compares the elements of the third period; Figure 9.20 summarises the overall trends.

m = metal: *n/m* = non-metal

Note: Similar trends in properties occur across the second period from lithium to neon. It is a valuable exercise to draw up a table for this period using a data book for the numerical data.

In summary the general trends common to all periods are:

- the elements change from metals to non-metals
- the number of electrons in the outer shell increases from 1 to 8
- the number of outer electrons equals the group number
- the valency of the elements increases from 1 to 4 in groups 1 to 4 then decreases from 4 to 1 in groups 4 to 7
- the melting points and boiling points of the elements increase to a maximum of group 4 and decrease again to group 0

- the oxides of the elements changes from basic to acidic
- the formulae of compounds of the elements shows the change in valency or oxidation number

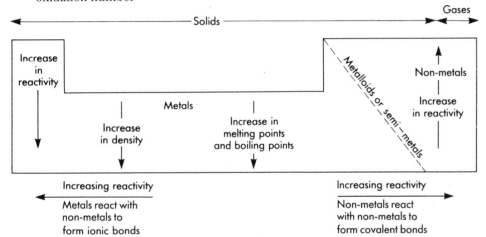

Fig 9.20 Trends in the period table. *Remember*, these are general trends - there are exceptions.

Summary of the properties of metals and non-metals

metals	non-metals
usually have high melting points and are all solids at room temperature (except mercury)	usually have low melting points and boiling points (half are gases) (bromine is liquid at room (temperature)
are shiny when polished	usually dull in appearance
can be easily bent into shape or hammered	brittle and crumbly when solid
good conductors of heat and electricity	poor conductors of heat and electricity when solid or liquid

 Metals and non-metals

E X A M I N A T I O N   Q U E S T I O N S

MULTIPLE CHOICE

Questions 1, 2 and 3 refer to the periodic table shown below.

QUESTION 1

Which letter represents the lightest element?

QUESTION 2

Which letter represents a halogen?

QUESTION 3

Which letter represents a very reactive metal?

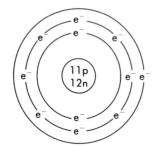

Questions 4 and 5 refer to the diagram opposite showing the atomic structure of sodium.

QUESTION 4

What is the atomic number of sodium?
A 1; B 7; C 11; D 12; E 23

QUESTION 5

What is the valency of sodium?
A 1; B 2; C 3; D 11; E 23

STRUCTURED QUESTIONS

QUESTION 6

1 H	
3 Li	4 Be
11 Na	12 Mg
19 K	20 Ca

					2 He
5 B	6 C	7 N	8 O	9 F	10 Ne
13 Al	14 Si	15 P	16 S	17 Cl	18 Ar

Figure 1

Figure 1 shows the first 20 elements of the periodic table.

a) Explain briefly why the elements in the periodic table are arranged in vertical columns.

_____

_____

(1)

Imagine that a new element has been discovered on the Moon. It has been named 'Lunum'. On the Moon it was a silvery colour but rapidly tarnished when brought back to Earth.
   Lunum can be cut with a knife and bursts into flame on contact with water, releasing hydrogen gas.

b) Using the periodic table given in Figure 1, give the symbol of one element with similar properties.

_____

(1)

c) Explain why Lunum tarnished on Earth yet was silvery on the Moon. (2 lines) *(2)*

d) How would you test Lunum's magnetic properties? What is the likely outcome of the test?

   Test _____

   Outcome _____

(2)

e) i) Lunum is given the symbol Lm; write the chemical formula for:

1 Lunum chloride _____

2 Lunum oxide _____

(3)

ii) Describe three properties you would expect Lunum chloride to have.
(3 lines available)

(3)

f) Lunum is unlikely to be found in its pure state on earth. Suggest a reason for this.
(2 lines available)

(2)
(NICCEA)

QUESTION 7

a) Table 1 compares the number of protons and electrons in sodium and chlorine atoms and gives the arrangement of electrons in each atom.

	Sodium Na	*Chlorine Cl*
Number of protons	–	17
Number of electrons	11	–
Arrangement of electrons	2, 8, 1	2, 8, 7

Table 1

i) Complete the table above. *(2)*

ii) Which particles, apart from protons, are found in the nucleus of a sodium or chlorine atom? *(1)*

iii) In which group of the periodic table are the elements sodium and chlorine placed?

Sodium _____ Chlorine _____

(2)

b) Table 2 compares the number of protons and electrons in sodium and chloride *ions*.

	Sodium Na⁺	*Chlorine Cl⁻*
Number of protons	11	17
Number of electrons	10	18
Arrangement of electrons	2, 8	2, 8, 8

Table 2

i) What change takes place when a sodium ion is formed from a sodium atom? *(1)*

ii) What change takes place when a chloride ion is formed from a chlorine atom?

_____

(1)

c) Figure A below shows the arrangement of sodium and chloride ions in a crystal of sodium chloride.

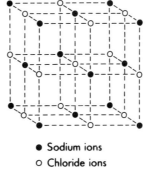

● Sodium ions
○ Chloride ions

Figure A

i) State **two** changes which take place in the crystal when melting occurs.

1 _____

2 _____

(2)

ii) Why does sodium chloride have a high melting point?

_____

(1)

(Total marks 10)

(ULEAC)

QUESTION 8

Three pieces of information are given below.

1 Substances can be elements, compounds or mixtures.
2 Elements can be metals or non-metals.
3 A group in the periodic table contains elements having similar properties.

Using only this information, say which **one** of the substances in **each** of the following lists is different from the other three.

For **each** list give the reason for your choice.

a) Carbon, iron, copper, magnesium.

_____

_____

(1)

b) Neon, hydrogen, argon, helium.

_____

_____

(1)

c) Sulphur dioxide, zinc oxide, copper (II) sulphate, air.

_____

_____

(1)

(WJEC)

QUESTION 9

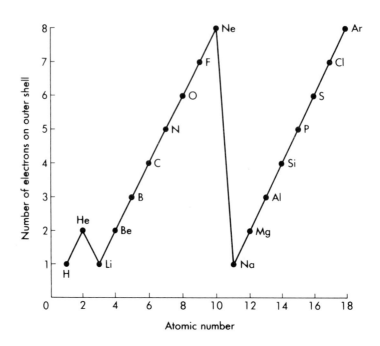

a) The graph shows the relationship between the number of electrons in the outer shell of the first 18 elements in the periodic table and their atomic numbers.
   Use the graph to help you answer the following questions.

   i) Name **two metals** having two electrons on their outer shells.

   _____

   (2)

   ii) Name **two non-metals** having seven electrons on their outer shells.

   _____

   (2)

b) Name the kind of bond formed between elements when

   i) the outer electrons are donated and received

   _____

   ii) the outer electrons are shared

   _____

   (2)

   iii) Considering i) and ii) above, write down the formula of the compounds formed between

   1 aluminium (Al) and chlorine (Cl) _____

   2 boron (B) and fluorine (F) _____

   3 carbon (C) and fluorine (F) _____

   (3)

   iv) What kind of bonds are formed between carbon and fluorine?

   _____

   (1)
   (WJEC)

QUESTION 10

a) The element astatine has an atomic (proton) number of 85 and a mass number of 210.

   i) How many protons are in the nucleus? _____

   (1)

   ii) How many neutrons are in the nucleus? _____

   (2)

   iii) How many electrons are orbiting the nucleus? _____

   (1)

b) Astatine is at the bottom of the same group of the periodic table as chlorine, bromine and iodine. The table below gives some information about these elements.

   i) Use the patterns shown in the table to fill in the spaces for astatine.

	Chlorine	Bromine	Iodine	Astatine
At room temperature	gas	liquid	solid	1
Reaction with iron	very fast	fast	slow	2
Reaction with potassium iodide solution	reacts	reacts	no reaction	3
Effect on indicator paper	bleaches	bleaches	bleaches	4

   (4)

   ii) Which **two** of these elements have their molecules closest together at room temperature?

1 _____

2 _____

(1)

iii) Which **one** of these elements is most likely to have a smell at room temperature?

_____

(1)

(SEG)

QUESTION 11

Fluorine (F) is the most reactive element in group VII of the periodic table of elements. Fluorine reacts with all metals and most non-metals. During the last seventy years or so, it has become an important industrial chemical.

a) Suggest **one** reason why we do not study fluorine in school laboratories.

_____

(1)

b) One compound in which fluorine occurs is fluorspar. Fluorspar is heated with concentrated sulphuric acid to make hydrogen fluoride. Hydrogen fluoride is a gas which does not conduct electricity. It reacts with water to produce highly corrosive hydrofluoric acid.

   i) Complete this flow chart for the manufacture of hydrofluoric acid by writing in the names of the correct substances in the boxes.

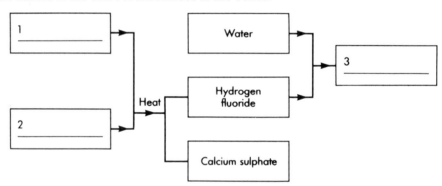

   ii) Briefly explain **two** different pollution problems which might result from manufacture of hydrogen fluoride.

   Problem 1 (3 lines) _____

(2)

   Problem 2 (3 lines) _____

(2)

c) A large chemical company has several chemical plants throughout Europe at which concentrated sulphuric acid is manufactured. However, at only a few of these is hydrogen fluoride also manufactured.

   Suggest **two** different reasons why you think hydrogen fluoride is manufactured only at a few of these plants.

   Reason 1 (2 lines) _____

(2)

   Reason 2 (2 lines) _____

(2)

d) A lot of fluorine is used in the manufacture of fluorocarbons and other compounds.
   Tetrafluoroethene (C_2F_4) is polymerised into PTFE, which is used as the non-stick coating on cooking utensils.
   Difluorodichloromethane (CF_2Cl_2) is used in aerosols and in the cooling coils of refrigerators.

   i) Briefly explain what is meant by the word *polymerised* . (3 lines)   *(1)*

ii) Suggest **two** properties which PTFE should have if it is to be used as a non-stick coating on cooking utensils.

Property 1 (2 lines) _____

(1)

Property 2 (2 lines) _____

(1)

iii) Suggest **one** property of difluorodichloromethane (CF_2Cl_2) which makes it suitable for use in aerosols **and** in the cooling coils of refrigerators.

Property (2 lines) _____

(2)
(SEG)

QUESTION 12
(Levels 8–10)

You are given a lot of information at the beginning of the question so spend some time reading it carefully to help you answer the questions which follow.

Chlorine, bromine and iodine are in group 7 of the Periodic Table. At room temperature chlorine is a gas, bromine is a volatile liquid and iodine is a solid which easily vaporises.

Chlorine is manufactured by the electrolysis of sodium chloride. The sodium chloride must be molten or in the form of a concentrated aqueous solution. Chlorine is given off at the positive electrode.

Chlorine can also be produced from hydrogen chloride. The hydrogen chloride is reacted with oxygen from the air at 400° C in the presence of a catalyst. Chlorine is used in the manufacture of both bromine and iodine.

Bromine is found in sea-water as bromide ions. If chlorine is bubbled through sea-water, bromine is displaced and forms a solution in water.

Iodine can be obtained from certain sea-weeds which absorb the element as iodide ions. The sea-weed is dried and burnt to an ash. The ash is treated with water and the solution formed is evaporated. On cooling, chlorides and carbonates precipitate out. Iodine is then displaced from the remaining solution by adding chlorine.

a) Name the substance formed at the negative electrode during the electrolysis of:

   i) molten sodium chloride. _____ *(1)*

   ii) sodium chloride solution. _____ *(1)*

b) In terms of atomic structure, explain why chlorine can displace both bromine from a solution containing bromide ions, and iodine from a solution containing iodide ions. (9 lines available) *(6)*

c) In terms of their molecular properties, explain the differences in the physical properties of chlorine, bromine and iodine. (3 lines available) *(3)*
[Co-ordinated Science, NEAB, ULEAC, WJEC]

A N S W E R S   T O
E X A M I N A T I O N   Q U E S T I O N S

MULTIPLE CHOICE

ANSWER 1

Key A. It indicates hydrogen.

ANSWER 2

Key D. The halogens are group 7 elements, in the last but one column.

ANSWER 3

Key B. The reactive metals are the group 1 alkali metals.

ANSWER 4

Key C, 11. The atomic number is the number of protons. Option A is the number of electrons in the outer shell. Option D is the number of neutrons.

ANSWER 5

Key A, valency of 1. The number of electrons in the outer shell.

STRUCTURED QUESTIONS

ANSWER 6

a) The column number is the number of electrons in the outer shell.
b) Li
c) The oxygen in the atmosphere of the Earth caused a chemical reaction.
d) Hold it near a suspended magnet and see if the magnet moved. I would not expect it to move, as the other metals in the group are not magnetic.
e) i) 1 $LmCl$; 2 Lm_2O
   ii) It would be a solid.
       It would dissolve in water and conduct electricity.
       It would be an ionic compound.
f) It is a very reactive metal and would be found combined with another element.

ANSWER 7

a) i) Sodium has 11 protons. Chlorine has 17 electrons.
   ii) neutrons
   iii) Sodium is in group 1. Chlorine is in group 7.
b) i) An electron is lost from the sodium atom.
   ii) An electron is gained by the chlorine atom.
c) i) 1 The atoms vibrate more quickly.
       2 The bonds between the sodium ions and chloride ions are broken.
   ii) A lot of energy is needed to break the bonds.

ANSWER 8

a) Carbon is different because it is a non-metal.
b) Hydrogen is different because the others are all non-reactive inert gases.
c) Air is different because it is a mixture of different elements not chemically combined together.

ANSWER 9

a) i) magnesium, beryllium
   ii) fluorine, chlorine
b) i) ionic bonding
   ii) covalent bonding
   iii) 1 $AlCl_3$
        2 BF_3
        3 CF_4
c) covalent

ANSWER 10

a) i) 85
   ii) 125 (210 – 85)
   iii) 85 (same as proton number)
b) i) 1 solid   2 no reaction/very slow reaction   3 no reaction   4 bleaches
   ii) iodine and astatine
   iii) chlorine

ANSWER 11

a) It is very reactive and possibly too dangerous to use.

b) i) 1 fluorspar   2 concentrated sulphuric acid   3 hydrofluoric acid
   ii) Problem 1 – hydrogen fluoride is a very acidic gas. It can dissolve in water vapour in the atmosphere and cause acid rain, which damages buildings and kills trees and fish.
        Problem 2 - hydrogen fluoride gas can dissolve in water vapour in the atmosphere to form a corrosive acid which will cause metals to go rusty very quickly.
c) Reason 1- availability of fluorspar
    Reason 2 - adequate amounts produced for present use
d) i) many small identical monomers joined together to form a long chain polymer
   ii) Property 1- very high melting point
        Property 2 - non-reactive with food
   iii) low boiling point

ANSWER 12

a) i) sodium (1)
   ii) hydrogen (1)
b) from chlorine to iodine the size of the atom increases (1)
    all three atoms have 7 electrons in their outer shell (1)
    all three react by gaining electrons (1)
    the smallest atom, chlorine, does this most easily (1)
    chlorine is more reactive than bromine and iodine (1)
    as the outer shell of electrons is closer to the nucleus (1)
    the positive nucleus exerts a stronger force of attraction (1)
    and attracts electrons readily (1)
    and forms compounds more readily than iodine or bromine (1)
c) down the group from chlorine to iodine (1)
    the size of the diatomic molecules increases (1)
    the melting point and boiling point increases (1)
    the reactivity decreases (1)

A STUDENT'S ANSWER WITH EXAMINER'S COMMENTS

100 g of WONDERWHITE toothpaste is made up as follows:

calcium carbonate	50%
glycerol	23%
distilled water	20%
bonding agent	3%
detergent	2%

Peppermint flavouring and the fluorine compounds NaF and Na_2FPO_3 are also present in small quantities.

a) Name the element found in

   i) group 1 of the periodic table _Sodium_ ✓

   ii) group 7 of the periodic table _Fluorine_ ✓

                                                            (1)

Good. You have used the information given in the question.

b) i) What is the purpose of the fluoride in toothpaste?
       to stop decay ✓

Yes.

   ii) What gas is produced when an acid is added to calcium carbonate?
       carbon dioxide ✓

Good.

   iii) How does calcium benefit the human body?
       strong bones ✓

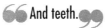
And teeth.

                                                            (1½)

c) i) How many different atoms are there in the compound having the formula Na_2FPO_3?

4 different

Good. Na, F, P, O.

ii) What is the total number of atoms in one molecule of this compound?

7 ✓

iii) Calculate the number of grams of distilled water needed to make 250 g of toothpaste.

50 grams

Well done. 20% of water is needed in 100g.

(1½)

d) A summary of the properties of some of the elements in group 7 is given below.

Name	Symbol	Colour	State at room temperature (20°C)	M. pt °C	B. pt °C
Chlorine	Cl	greenish/yellow	gas	–101	–34
Bromine	Br	dark red	liquid	–7	58
Iodine	I	dark grey		114	183

Study the table and then answer the following questions.

i) What is the state of iodine at room temperature?

solid ✓

(1)

Yes. It doesn't melt until 114°C.

ii) Astatine (At) is another member of group 7 and comes below iodine in the group.

Considering the patterns shown in the table, **predict**

1 the colour of astatine  **very dark grey or black**

2 its state at room temperature **solid** ✓

Good prediction

(2)

(WJEC)

R E V I E W   S H E E T

 In the periodic table, each *row* is called a _____ and each *column* is called a

_____ . Atoms are arranged in _____ order of mass.

 As you move across the *first period* you are filling the _____ electron shell, and so on.

As you go *across* the table the atoms are getting _____ .

 As you go *down a group*, the atoms have the same number of electrons in their _____

 Complete the following table for the *second period*

atom:	Li	Be	B	C	N	O	F	Ne
atomic number:	3	4	5	6	7	8	9	10
electron configuration:								

 Complete the following table for the *first group*

atom	electron configuration
H	
Li	
Na	
K	

 A stable arrangement for electrons in atoms occurs when an atom has a _____ .

 Metals form _____ ions; non-metals form _____ ions. A positive ion is

called a _____ ; a negative ion is called an _____

 Group 1 elements form ions with _____ positive charge (they have _____

electron to lose).

 If the ions are free to move, then ionic compounds will _____ electricity.

 The ions can be made free to move in an ionic compound by:

1. _____

2. _____

 The process of ionic substances conducting electricity is called _____ . During this

process the ions are turned back into _____ .

 The shared pair of electrons in a hydrogen molecule is called a _____

 Water dissolves ionic substances because the water molecule is _____

 Metals have _____ boiling points and _____ melting points.

 Metals are _____ conductors of electricity.

 Each atom has a 'combining power' which is called the _____ . This depends on the

number of _____ in its _____ shell and hence its position in the periodic table.

 Complete the following table.

Atom	Na	Mg	Al	Si	P	S	Cl	Ar
Outer shell electrons	1	2	3	4	5	6	7	8
Group no	1	2	3	4	5	6	7	0
Valency								

✎ Complete the following table of common covalent compounds by writing in the structure of each compound.

Name	Formula	Structure
carbon dioxide	CO_2	
ammonia	NH_3	
methane	CH_4	
ethane	C_2H_6	
ethene	C_2H_4	
ethyl alcohol	C_2H_5OH	

✎ Complete the following diagram, using the correct word (either 'increases' or 'decreases') in each box.

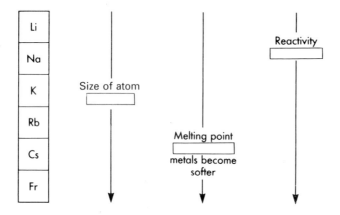

✎ List four trends common to all *groups*.

1. _____
2. _____
3. _____
4. _____

✎ List four trends common to all *periods*.

1. _____
2. _____
3. _____
4. _____

CHEMICAL REACTIONS

GETTING STARTED

Chemical reactions are described as interactions between particles (atom, molecules or ions) which involve the 'breaking' and 'making' of chemical bonds. They follow a general pattern:

Reactants ⟶ **Products**
(starting materials)   (new materials)

In any chemical reaction **new substances** are always formed. These have different sets of either physical or chemical properties to those of the reactants. However, in any chemical reaction the **mass** always stays the same. That is, the *total mass of the products* is always the same as the *total mass of the reactants*. The reason for this is that chemical reactions only involve the *rearrangement* of the particles involved.

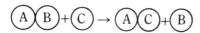

This idea is similar to dismantling a model of a house, and using the same bricks to build a small factory. This allows us to write equations and to make calculations for particle interactions, such as the mass of reactants needed to produce 1 kg of a certain product, an invaluable ability in the chemical industry.

Not all substances will react with each other, but many do. Some combinations of reactants need a push to get them going - usually in the form of heat. This is referred to as the *activation energy*. Reactions with high activation energies are slow. In the chemical industry *catalysts* are often used to *speed up reactions*, because time is money.

Chemical reactions always involve energy. In some reactions, energy is transferred to the surroundings in the form of heat (*heat given out*); these are called *exothermic reactions*. Here the products are warmer than the reactants. In other reactions, energy in the form of heat is transferred from the surroundings to the substances (*heat taken in*); these are called *endothermic reactions*. Here the products are *cooler* than the reactants. In the chemical industry ways are often looked for to save energy, because energy costs money.

WRITING CHEMICAL EQUATIONS

IONIC EQUATIONS

PATTERNS OF PARTICLE INTERACTIONS

ENERGY AND REACTIONS

RATE OF REACTION

CATALYSTS

CALCULATIONS IN CHEMICAL REACTIONS

1 ▷ **WRITING CHEMICAL EQUATIONS**

ESSENTIAL PRINCIPLES

66 Try and work through this section slowly and logically **99**

A chemical reaction always follows the general pattern:

Reactant(s) → Product(s)

There may be one or more reactants and one or more products, but the mass of the reactants at the beginning will be the *same* as the mass of the products at the end. In an equation representing the reaction, you will have the same number of atoms (represented by their symbols) on the left hand side as you will have on the right hand side. Bear in mind that all that is happening is a *rearrangement* of these atoms.

EXAMPLE 1

Sodium reacts with chlorine to form sodium chloride

Step 1   Write the equation in words.

sodium + chlorine → sodium chloride

Step 2   Write each substance as a formula (see page 171).

$Na + Cl_2 \rightarrow NaCl$

Remember, sodium is an element, Na; reactive gaseous elements are diatomic, Cl_2; the formula for sodium chloride is NaCl (Na^+Cl^-).

Step 3   Imagine the reaction as particles.

$Na + Cl_2 \rightarrow NaCl$

66 Balancing the equation **99**

Step 4   Balance the equation.

There are 2 Cl on the left, so there must be 2 Cl on the right. The only way to obtain this is to have 2 NaCl on the right, as follows:

2 NaCl   (Na)(Cl)
         (Na)(Cl)

$Na + Cl_2 \rightarrow 2NaCl$

(Na) + (Cl)(Cl) → (Na)(Cl)
                  (Na)(Cl)

Now, to *balance* the equation, we must have 2 Na on the left.

$2Na + Cl_2 \rightarrow 2NaCl$

(Na)
     + (Cl)(Cl) → (Na)(Cl)
(Na)   (Na)(Cl)

4 atoms   4 atoms

Remember, when balancing an equation: **never** change the actual formulae.

EXAMPLE 2

Magnesium reacts with hydrochloric acid to produce magnesium chloride and hydrogen.

Step 1   Write the equation in words.

magnesium + hydrochloric acid → magnesium chloride + hydrogen

Step 2   Write each substance as a formula.

$Mg + HCl \rightarrow MgCl_2 + H_2$

Step 3   Imagine the reaction as particles.

$$\text{(Mg)} + \text{(H)(Cl)} \rightarrow \text{(Mg)}\overset{\text{(Cl)}}{\underset{\text{(Cl)}}{}} + \text{(H)(H)}$$

Step 4   Balance the equation.

$$Mg + 2HCl \rightarrow MgCl_2 + H_2$$

$$\text{(Mg)} + \text{(H)(Cl)} \rightarrow \text{(Mg)}\overset{\text{(Cl)}}{\underset{\text{(Cl)}}{}} + \text{(H)(H)}$$
$$\text{(H)(Cl)}$$

5 atoms   5 atoms

EXAMPLE 3

Sulphuric acid neutralises sodium hydroxide.

Step 1   Write the equation in words.

sodium hydroxide + sulphuric acid → sodium sulphate + water

Step 2   Write each substance as a formula.

$$NaOH + H_2SO_4 \rightarrow Na_2SO_4 + H_2O$$

Step 3   Imagine the reaction as particles.

$$\text{(Na)(OH)} + \overset{\text{(H)}}{\underset{\text{(H)}}{\text{(SO}_4\text{)}}} \rightarrow \overset{\text{(Na)}}{\underset{\text{(Na)}}{\text{(SO}_4\text{)}}} + \overset{\text{(H)}}{\underset{\text{(H)}}{\text{(O)}}}$$

Step 4   Balance the equation.

$$2NaOH + H_2SO_4 \rightarrow Na_2SO_4 + 2H_2O$$

This example also shows that we can regard some groups of particles as one unit which is not usually changed in a chemical reaction, for example the sulphate ion: SO_4^{2-}. Other such examples are the hydroxide ion (OH^-), the nitrate ion (NO_3^-) and sometimes the carbonate ion (CO_3^{2-}) in displacement reactions.
More unusual examples are the hydrogen carbonate ion (HCO_3^-), the sulphite ion (SO_3^{2-}) and the nitrite ion (NO_2^-).

STATE SYMBOLS

The equations written above tell us which substances react, but they do not tell us the *state* of the reactants or products. This is important, since some reactants will only react if they are in a particular state. For example, they may need to be in a gaseous form, or to be dissolved in water. We can show the state of reactants and products by adding symbols of state:

 **Symbols of state**

- (g) represents a state of *gas*;

- (l) represents a state of *liquid*;

- (s) represents a state of *solid*;

- (aq) represents the aqueous state (*dissolved in water*)

For example, in the equation

$$Mg(s) + 2HCl(aq) \rightarrow MgCl_2(aq) + H_2(g)$$

HCl(aq) indicates that *dilute* hydrochloric acid is being used.

IONIC EQUATIONS

There is another way of showing reactions involving ions. These are called *ionic equations*. In these equations, ions that are unaffected in a reaction are ignored and only those that are affected in some way are written down. To illustrate this, in Example 3 of the previous section, the sulphate ion (SO_4^{2-}) and the sodium ion (Na^+) are unaffected, so we can ignore them. We can rewrite the equation in ionic terms as:

$$OH^-(aq) \quad + \quad H^+(aq) \quad \rightarrow \quad H_2O\,(l)$$

This ionic equation is also the general pattern for all neutralisation reactions.

PATTERNS OF PARTICLE INTERACTIONS

The number of possible particle interactions may seem bewildering at first, but fortunately there are patterns that will help us predict what will happen for different types of particle interactions.

PATTERNS OF MOLECULE INTERACTIONS

Combustion of fuels

Look for patterns

Fuels are substances that give out a lot of energy when they burn; their reactions are strongly *exothermic*. The fuels react with the oxygen in the air. The *fossil fuels* we use (coal, gas and oil) contain carbon and hydrogen and are referred to as *hydrocarbons*. The products of complete combustion are carbon dioxide and water.

Coal is mainly carbon:

$$\text{carbon} \quad + \quad \text{oxygen} \quad \rightarrow \quad \text{carbon dioxide}$$
$$\text{C} \quad + \quad O_2 \quad \rightarrow \quad CO_2$$

Natural gas is methane:

$$\text{methane} \quad + \quad \text{oxygen} \quad \rightarrow \quad \text{carbon dioxide} \quad + \quad \text{water}$$
$$CH_4 \quad + \quad 2O_2 \quad \rightarrow \quad CO_2 \quad + \quad 2H_2O$$

Combustion in action

Natural gas is often considered to be a very suitable fuel for greenhouses since it produces not only heat, but also carbon dioxide, which the plants can use as well as water to keep the atmosphere humid. However, if natural gas is burned in a limited amount of air, then combustion is *incomplete* and carbon monoxide (CO) will also be produced. The gas is poisonous because it combines strongly with haemoglobin in the blood, forming *carboxy-haemoglobin,* preventing it from carrying oxygen around the body. For this reason it is important to keep a room well ventilated when coal or gas is being burned.

Respiration and photosynthesis

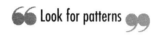

See Chapter 4, Plants

Respiration, which takes place in the cells of the body, is very similar to the combustion reactions. The fuel this time is food (carbohydrates and sugars). This process can be written as:

$$\text{food} \quad + \quad \text{oxygen} \quad \rightarrow \quad \text{carbon dioxide} \quad + \quad \text{water} \quad + \quad \text{energy}$$

If we choose glucose ($C_6H_{12}O_6$), as an example of food, then this can be represented as

$$C_6H_{12}O_6 \quad + \quad 6O_2 \quad \rightarrow \quad 6CO_2 \quad + \quad 6H_2O \quad + \quad \text{energy}$$

Photosynthesis is in effect the opposite of respiration; the plant combines carbon dioxide from the air, and water taken in through the roots. The energy for this reaction is provided by sunlight:

$$\text{energy} \quad + \quad \text{carbon dioxide} \quad + \quad \text{water} \quad \rightarrow \quad \text{sugar} \quad + \quad \text{oxygen}$$
$$\text{energy} \quad + \quad 6CO_2 \quad + \quad 6H_2O \quad \rightarrow \quad C_6H_{12}O_6 \quad + \quad 6O_2$$

Photosynthesis and respiration in action

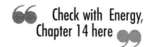

Check with Energy, Chapter 14 here

Respiration in animals (and in green plants at night) releases carbon dioxide into the air. Most of this carbon dioxide is converted back into sugars and carbohydrates by green plants, which in turn release oxygen into the atmosphere. As a result, the balance of 20% oxygen to <0.05% carbon dioxide is maintained. This balance is being upset by man. For example, by burning fossil fuels (increasing carbon dioxide levels) and by cutting down large areas of rain forest (reducing oxygen levels), man has created a slight increase in the levels of carbon dioxide in the atmosphere recently. This in turn has given rise to concern that the Earth will warm up slightly, owing to the greenhouse effect.

Reactions with Oxygen

Some reactions with oxygen

- Most elements react with oxygen to form oxides
- Metals react to form basic oxides. These oxides are ionic and have high melting points.
- Non-metals react to form acidic oxides. These usually have very low melting points. Many non-metallic oxides are gases that are soluble in water to form acids.
- Some oxides react with both acids and bases. These are called *amphoteric oxides.* These oxides have both basic and acidic properties. Some examples of amphoteric oxides are aluminium oxide, lead (II) oxide and zinc oxide.
- There are also neutral non-metallic oxides, e.g. water (H_2O), carbon monoxide (CO) and nitrogen (II) oxide (NO).
- All reactions involving oxygen are exothermic.

PATTERNS OF ION INTERACTIONS

Redox reactions

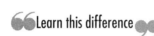
Learn this difference

A *redox reaction* is one in which oxidation and reduction take place. *Oxidation* is the addition of oxygen or the removal of hydrogen. It is also the removal of electrons. *Reduction* is the removal of oxygen or the addition of hydrogen. It is also the addition of electrons.

Substances that are good at oxidising substances are called *oxidising agents,* eg oxygen and chlorine. Substances that are good at reducing other substances are called *reducing agents,* eg carbon and hydrogen.

As an example, in the reaction between lead oxide and carbon, lead oxide is the oxidising agent and carbon is the reducing agent:

lead oxide	+	carbon	$\rightarrow$	lead	+	carbon dioxide
2PbO	+	C	$\rightarrow$	2Pb	+	CO_2

The lead oxide has been reduced by carbon to lead (the oxygen has been removed), while the carbon has been oxidised to carbon dioxide (oxygen has been added).

Another example is the reaction between iron and chlorine gas:

iron	+	chlorine	$\rightarrow$	iron (III) chloride
2Fe	+	$3Cl_2$	$\rightarrow$	$2FeCl_3$

The iron has been oxidised to iron chloride. Three electrons have been removed from the iron atom. Chlorine has been reduced to the chloride ion, one electron has been added to each of the three chlorine atoms.

Redox reactions in action

Oxidation cannot take place without reduction, so the reactions are called *redox reactions.* Reducing agents are used in the extraction of metals from their ores. Carbon (in the form of coke) can be used to extract lead, iron and zinc. In all these cases the metal ore is being reduced to the metal by the removal of oxygen.

Why metals go rusty

An understanding of oxidation is useful when dealing with the corrosion of metals. *Corrosion* is a process which involves the production of metal ions from their atoms (oxidation - the removal of electrons). For example, iron rusts to form iron oxide in the presence of oxygen and water. The reaction could be represented by:

See metals and corrosion, Chapter 12

$$Fe - 3e^- \rightarrow Fe^{3+}$$

Displacement reactions

Displacement reactions are examples of redox reactions which involve an element and a salt solution.

■ *Metal/salt solutions*: some metals will displace other metal ions from solutions of their salts. The metal's ability to do this is related to its position in the reactivity series (see Chapter 12). If a metal is *above* the metal ion in solution, then one will *displace* the other. For example:

zinc	+	copper sulphate	$\rightarrow$	zinc sulphate	+	copper
Zn	+	$CuSO_4$	$\rightarrow$	$ZnSO_4$	+	Cu
Zn(s)	+	Cu^{2+}(aq)	$\rightarrow$	Zn^{2+}(aq)	+	Cu(s)

■ *Halogen/halide solutions*: a halogen can also displace a halide from a solution of its salt. Its ability to do this depends on its reactivity, ie its position in the periodic table. *Remember* the order of reactivity F>Cl>Br>I of the halogens:

chlorine	+	potassium iodide	$\rightarrow$	potassium chloride	+	iodine
Cl_2	+	2KI	$\rightarrow$	2KCl	+	I_2
Cl_2(g)	+	$2I^-$ (aq)	$\rightarrow$	$2Cl^-$ (aq)	+	I_2

Chlorine is *more reactive* than iodine, so it has a *greater attraction* for electrons, and so it displaces the iodine.

Precipitation reactions

Some reactions between solutions of metal salts will take place because there is a possibility of a *solid* being formed. This solid is called a *precipitate*.

potassium iodide	+	lead nitrate	$\rightarrow$	potassium nitrate	+	lead iodide
2KI(aq)	+	$Pb(NO_3)_2$ (aq)	$\rightarrow$	$2KNO_3$(aq)	+	PbI_2(s)

Notice that all that has happened is that the ions have swapped partners. This chemical change occurs because one possible combination, PbI_2, is insoluble in water.

Precipitation in action

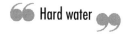
Hard water

Precipitation reactions can be used to remove the hardness from water. Hardness in water is caused by the presence of calcium or magnesium ions. These ions can be precipitated out of solution (so removing the hardness) by adding sodium carbonate (washing soda). Calcium carbonate and magnesium carbonate, which are both insoluble, are formed.

Neutralisation reactions

In these reactions an acid is *neutralised* by a base. A salt and water are formed. The general pattern of the reaction is as follows:

acid + base $\rightarrow$ salt + water

Check with Chapter 11

In ionic terms, this reaction is expressed as

H^+(aq) + OH^-(aq) $\rightarrow$ H_2O(l)

An example is the reaction between hydrochloric acid and sodium hydroxide:

HCl + NaOH $\rightarrow$ NaCl + H_2O

PATTERNS FOR REVERSIBLE REACTIONS

Some reactions involving particles are *reversible,* ie they can proceed in both directions even at the same time. An example occurs in the Haber process, where nitrogen and hydrogen are combined to produce ammonia, but ammonia simultaneously decomposes to produce nitrogen and hydrogen.

The Haber process

nitrogen	+	hydrogen	$\rightleftharpoons$	ammonia
N_2	+	$3H_2$	$\rightleftharpoons$	$2NH_3$

The sign $\rightleftharpoons$ indicates that the reaction can go in *both* directions. By changing the conditions, we can determine in which direction the reaction proceeds, and what proportion of ammonia is formed.

- High *pressure* favours the production of ammonia.

- High *temperature* increases the rate of reaction between nitrogen and hydrogen (production of ammonia).

- However, high *temperature* also favours the decomposition of ammonia (production of nitrogen and hydrogen).

A balance has to be made. Optimum conditions are usually about 400°C.

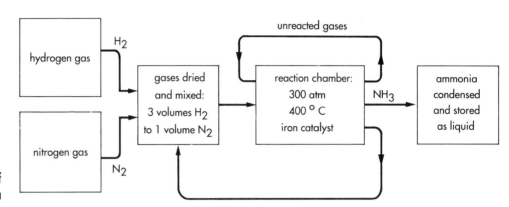

Fig 10.1 Stages in the production of ammonia

Another example is the hydration (water content) of copper sulphate crystals. (This can be used as a test for water.)

Copper sulphate crystals (*blue*) $\overset{\text{heat}}{\rightleftharpoons}$ anhydrous copper sulphate (*white*) + water

---

ENERGY AND CHEMICAL BONDS

In any chemical change, energy is either given out or absorbed. In any reaction between particles, bonds holding the particles in the reactants together will need to be broken, and new bonds will need to be formed when the particles rearrange themselves to form the products.

- Energy is needed to *break* bonds.

- Energy is released when bonds are *formed*.

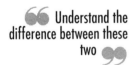 Understand the difference between these two

If the energy that is released when new bonds are formed in the products is *greater than* the energy required to break the bonds in the reactants, then the reaction is *exothermic* (energy is released to the surroundings). If the reverse is true, then the reaction is *endothermic*. The amount of energy that is absorbed or released in a reaction is referred to as the *heat of reaction* and is measured in kJ/mol. Note that a kJ, or a kilojoule, is a unit of energy; a mol, or mole, is a measure of a quantity of particles.

The heat of reaction is given the symbol ΔH. If a reaction is exothermic, then ΔH is negative, and energy is given out. If a reaction is endothermic, then ΔH is positive, and energy is absorbed.

The following is an example of an exothermic reaction:

 An exothermic reaction

$$HCl(aq) \ + \ NaOH(aq) \ \rightarrow \ NaCl(aq) \ + \ H_2O(l)$$
$$\Delta H = -55.9 \text{kJ/mol}$$

The amount of energy that is absorbed or released in a reaction can be calculated from *bond energies*. The amount of energy that is required to break different bonds have been calculated. Consider the reaction between hydrogen and chlorine, to produce hydrogen chloride:

$$H_2(g) \ + \ Cl_2(g) \ \rightarrow \ 2HCl$$

Bonds present $\quad H - H \quad Cl - Cl \quad \rightarrow \quad H - Cl$
$$H - Cl$$

In the case of the *reactants*
- the energy needed to break one H — H bond is +437 kJ/mol;
- the energy needed to break one Cl — Cl bond is +244 kJ/mol.

The total energy required to break all bonds = +437 +244 = +681 kJ/mol.

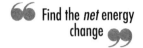
Find the *net* energy change

In the case of the *products*
- the energy released when one H — Cl bond is formed is –433 kJ/mol;
- the total energy released on forming 2 H — Cl bonds = 2 x (–433) = –866 kJ/mol.

As a result, the energy change for the reaction is

$$\Delta H = +681 - 866 = -185 \text{kJ/mol: The reaction is } exothermic.$$

These overall energy changes for a reaction can be represented on an energy level diagram (Figure 10.2).

Fig 10.2 Energy level diagrams   Exothermic reaction   Endothermic reaction

Activation energy

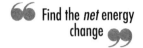
Important point

Almost all chemical changes need an amount of energy to get them going. This initial amount of energy can be quite small or sometimes quite large. This initial energy requirement is called the *activation energy* and is often the energy required initially to break bonds to allow a reaction to proceed. Fuels need to be supplied with a source of heat to *start* the combustion reaction, eg from a match. Activation energy must not be confused with the energy change in exothermic or endothermic reactions, both of which may require an initial input of energy.

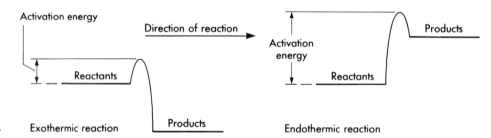

Fig. 10.3 Activation energy.   Exothermic reaction   Endothermic reaction

5   **RATE OF REACTION**

The speed at which the reaction takes place can vary and depends on a number of factors:

- the surface area of solid reactants;

- the concentration of reactants (including pressure in the case of gases);

- the temperature;

- the presence of a catalyst.

In order for a chemical reaction to take place, the particles of the reactants must *collide* (bump into each other). The *more often* the particles collide, the more likely they are to react, and so the *faster* the reaction.

INCREASING THE SPEED OF A REACTION

Increasing the surface area of solid reactants

A greater surface area will provide more opportunities for particles to collide. For example, calcium carbonate will react with hydrochloric acid to produce calcium chloride, water and carbon dioxide:

$$CaCO_3 \quad + \quad 2HCl \quad \rightarrow \quad CaCl_2 \quad + \quad H_2O \quad + \quad CO_2$$

Powdered calcium carbonate will react much faster than lumps of calcium carbonate (marble chips), because the surface area of the powder is much greater. There will be more calcium carbonate in contact with the acid. Stirring the powder in the acid will further increase the speed of reaction for the same reason.

Transporting or storing fine powders which can burn is a problem, since it might only take a spark to cause a very rapid reaction (explosion); eg flour, especially in flour mills when powder is in the atmosphere.

Increasing the concentration of the reactants

This will increase the number of particles present and so increase the chance of any collision. For example, in the reaction above, if the concentration of the hydrochloric acid is increased, then there is more chance of the particles interacting, and so the reaction will proceed at a faster rate.

Increasing the temperature of the reactants

Increasing the temperature of reactants provides the particles with *more kinetic energy*, so they will move faster. This increases the number of collisions per second, and hence increases the rate of the reaction. In the reaction above, increasing the temperature of the acid will increase the speed of the hydrochloric acid particles and so the number of collisions per second.

6 ▷ CATALYSTS

A *catalyst* is a substance that changes the rate of a chemical reaction, but remains unchanged at the end of a reaction and can be re-used. Catalysts are used to speed up reactions. Substances used to slow down reactions are called *inhibitors*.

GAS REACTIONS AND CATALYSTS

One way in which catalysts are thought to work in reactions involving gases is that the surface of the catalyst provides sites where the reacting molecules can meet. The transition metals are often used as catalysts in this way.

Manufacture of ammonia

$$N_2 + 3H_2 \rightleftharpoons 2NH_3$$

Iron is used as a catalyst. Nitrogen and hydrogen do not combine in the gas state; when they collide they bounce off each other without reacting. However, they are *adsorbed* on to the catalyst surface, where they come into contact and react.

Manufacture of sulphuric acid

One stage involves the production of sulphur trioxide from sulphur dioxide:

$$2SO_2 + O_2 \rightleftharpoons 2SO_3$$

Vanadium (V) oxide is the catalyst and works in a similar way to the iron in the previous example.

Pollution control on cars

Technological application

Petrol engines in cars burn petrol (a hydrocarbon fuel) and produce carbon dioxide and water as waste products. In addition, however, carbon monoxide and some oxides of nitrogen are produced which pollute the atmosphere. The car exhaust systems in California (where the problem of pollution from cars is a serious one) are fitted with a metal catalyst. As the hot exhaust gases pass over the catalyst, the pollutants are converted into carbon dioxide and nitrogen.

Antioxidants

Certain chemicals can be added to foods which slow up the natural oxidation of foods. These chemicals (antioxidants) are acting as catalysts; they are reducing the rate of a chemical reaction which would otherwise result in loss of flavour and decay.

ENZYMES

Check Chapter 3 the Human Body

Many chemical reactions take place in living things (often in the cells). These reactions are controlled by biological catalysts called *enzymes*. Enzymes are protein molecules, which consist of long chains that can be folded and coiled into different shapes. Each enzyme has its own special shape; it is this shape which causes the enzyme to act as a catalyst. Figure 10.4 shows how the molecule(s) on which the enzyme acts fits the protein molecule like a key in a lock.

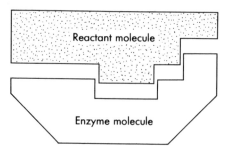

Fig. 10.4 Enzyme action: the lock and key principle.

Enzymes have unique properties:

Properties of enzymes

- They are *specific:* because the way an enzyme works depends on its shape, it will only work for one molecule or reaction.

- They will only work within a small temperature range, eg enzymes in the human body will only work around normal body temperature (37°C).

- They are very sensitive to pH changes and most only work within small pH ranges, eg pH6 → pH7.

- They can help large molecules break into smaller ones, help small molecules join to form larger ones, or help atoms rearrange within a molecule.

Enzymes in action

Digestion again

Enzymes take part in every stage of the digestive process, helping to break large molecules into smaller ones. The enzyme in saliva, called *salivary amylase*, breaks down starch into smaller sugar molecules.

Yeasts contain enzymes which help convert sugar into alcohol in the process of brewing.

Enzymes are becoming increasingly important in industry, eg for the manufacture of biodegradable dressings for wounds, biological washing powders, new food sources – mycoprotein.

7 CALCULATIONS IN CHEMICAL REACTIONS

As we saw previously, in any chemical change:

- the total mass of the products = the total mass of the reactants

- the total number of atoms in the products = the total number of atoms in the reactants

Check your syllabus requires this topic

This number is known as the Avogadro Constant

These two facts allow us to make *calculations* involving chemical reactions. In order to do this in a satisfactory way, we need some means of counting the number of particles present; for this purpose a unit called the MOLE was invented. It is a measure of the amount of substance; it is equivalent to

6×10^{23} particles (a very large number)

When large amounts of coins are handed into the bank they do not count them individually but rather they weigh them. In order to convert the weight of the coins to a number, the bank needs to know certain facts – 'How much do 100 lp coins weigh?' or 'How much do 100 2p coins weigh?'

We can apply the same principle to particles, since each atom has its own distinct mass: the *relative atomic mass*. The number we use has to be very much larger than 100, since the mass of each atom is very small. That number is the MOLE. The conversion of numbers to mass is very simple:

MOLES OF ATOMS

The relative atomic mass of an atom in grammes contains one mole (1 mol) of **atoms**.

Atom	Atomic mass	Mass of 1 mol of atoms
hydrogen	1	1g
carbon	12	12g
oxygen	16	16g
chlorine	35.5	35.5g
sodium	23	23g

In other words, in 32g of oxygen we have 2 mol of atoms; in 8g of oxygen we have 0.5 mol of atoms.

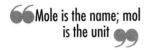

MOLES OF MOLECULES

The *molecular* mass in grammes contains 1 mol of **molecules.**

Molecule	Molecular Formula	Mass of molecule	Mass of 1 mol of molecules
oxygen	O_2	32	32g
water	H_2O	18	18g
carbon dioxide	CO_2	44	44g
hydrogen	H_2	2	2g

In other words, in 36g of water there are 2 moles; in 9g of water there are 0.5 moles.

MOLES OF IONIC COMPOUNDS AND IONS

The same rules apply for formulae representing *ionic compounds* and for *individual ions*.

Compound or ion	Formula/ion	Formula mass/ mass of ion	Mass of 1 mol
hydrochloric acid	HCl	36.5	36.5g
sodium hydroxide	NaOH	40	40g
sulphuric acid	H_2SO_4	98	98g
sulphate ion	SO_4^{2-}	96	96g
chloride ion	Cl^-	35.5	35.5g

USING THE MOLE IDEA

What mass of magnesium chloride is produced when 12 g of magnesium reacts with excess hydrochloric acid? (Excess means that you have more acid than you need, so the mass of this compound is not a restriction and can be ignored.)

Write down the equation for the reaction:

$$Mg + 2HCl \rightarrow MgCl_2 + H_2$$

This tells us that *one* particle of magnesium produces *one* particle of magnesium chloride. Therefore, *one* mole of magnesium produces *one* mole of magnesium chloride. To answer the question:

Step 1: Convert masses to moles.

The atomic mass of magnesium is 24, so the mass of 1 mol of magnesium is 24g. The number of moles present in 12 g of Mg = 0.5.

Step 2: Use the equation.

1 mol of Mg produces 1 mol of $MgCl_2$, so 0.5 mol of Mg produces 0.5 mol of $MgCl_2$.

Step 3: Convert moles to mass.

1 mol of $MgCl_2$ has a mass of 95 g, so 0.5 mol of $MgCl_2$ has a mass of
$0.5 \times 95g = 47.5g$

Answer. 47.5 g of $MgCl_2$ is produced.

MOLAR SOLUTIONS

Often reactions take place in solution, so we need to know concentrations of the reactants in solutions. Concentrations are given in mol/dm^3.

$$66 \; 1 \; cm^3 = \frac{1}{1000} \; dm^3 \; 99$$

A solution which contains $1 \; mol/dm^3$ contains 1 mol per dm^3 (litre) or, in words, one mole per cubic decimetre, and this is often expressed as a 1 M solution (1 molar). Thus a 2 M solution contains $2 \; mol/dm^3$.

A 1 M solution of sulphuric acid contains 1 mol of H_2SO_4/dm^3, or in other words, 98 g of H_2SO_4/dm^3. We can use this information to work out the number of moles present in a solution. For example, how many moles are present in $25 \; cm^3$ of a $2 \; mol/dm^3$ solution of NaOH?

$$\text{No. of moles} = \text{concentration} \times \text{volume (in } dm^3) = 2 \times \frac{25}{1000} = 0.05 \text{ mol.}$$

These principles can be used to calculate the concentration of solutions. For example, if $25 \; cm^3$ of a $2 \; mol/dm^3$ solution of sodium hydroxide exactly reacts with $10 \; cm^3$ of sulphuric acid, what is the concentration of the sulphuric acid?

Use the equation for the reaction:

$$2NaOH \; + \; H_2SO_4 \; \rightarrow \; Na_2SO_4 \; + \; 2H_2O$$

Step 1: From the question, the number of moles of NaOH used

$$= \text{concentration} \times \text{volume}$$
$$2 \qquad \times \; 25/1000$$
$$= 0.05 \text{ mol}$$

Step 2: From the equation, 2 mol of NaOH reacts with 1 mol of H_2SO_4. Therefore, 0.05 mol of NaOH reacts with 0.025 mol of H_2SO_4.

Step 3: Since no. of moles $=$ concentration $\times$ volume
$$0.025 \qquad\qquad = \text{concentration} \times 10/1000$$
$$2.5 \qquad\qquad\; = \text{concentration}$$

Therefore, the concentration of $H_2SO_4 = 2.5 \; mol/dm^3$.

EXAMINATION QUESTIONS

MULTIPLE CHOICE

QUESTION 1

Which of the following formulae correctly shows the reaction between sodium and chlorine?

A   Na   + Cl_2 $\rightarrow$ $NaCl_2$
B Na_2 + Cl_2 $\rightarrow$ Na_2Cl_2
C   Na   +   Cl $\rightarrow$ NaCl
D   2Na   + Cl_2 $\rightarrow$ 2 NaCl
E   2 Na   + Cl_2 $\rightarrow$ $2 NaCl_2$

QUESTION 2

Which pair of substances are pollutants produced by a petrol-burning engine?
A   carbon and sulphur dioxide
B   carbon monoxide and lead compounds
C   carbon monoxide and steam
D   carbon dioxide and steam
E   nitrogen dioxide and steam

QUESTION 3

Which one of the following is the main reason for using catalysts in industrial processes?
A   to increase the temperature of the reaction mixtures
B   to increase the yield of the reaction mixtures
C   to increase the rate of formation of the products
D   to remove impurities from the reaction mixtures.   (SEG)

QUESTION 4

Which of the following reactions is a redox reaction?
A   changing lead oxide to lead, using carbon
B   neutralising sodium hydroxide
C   making carbohydrates during photosynthesis
D   releasing energy during respiration

QUESTION 5

A chemical reaction occurs when
A   an electric current is passed through a copper wire
B   salt solution is heated
C   crude oil is distilled
D   dilute hydrochloric acid is added to magnesium ribbon
E   ice melts to form water

QUESTION 6

What is the mass of oxygen contained in 36g of pure water?
A   16g; B   32g; C   48g; D   64g; E   70g

QUESTION 7

A metal, M, forms a hydroxide, $M(OH)_3$. The mass of one mole of the hydroxide is
78 g. What is the relative atomic mass of M? (H = 1, O = 16)
A   27; B   30; C   59; D   61; E   78

                                                                        (ULEAC)

QUESTION 8

What is the concentration in mol/dm^3 (mol/litre) of 250 cm^3 of a solution containing
1.0 g of sodium hydroxide? (M_r = 40)
A   0.025; B   0.1; C   0.25; D   1.0; E   2.0

STRUCTURED QUESTIONS

QUESTION 9

In an experiment to find a suitable catalyst for a certain reaction, the following results
were obtained.

Temperature of each experiment (°C)	Substance under test as a catalyst	Time for the reaction to be completed (seconds)
20	cobalt chloride	18
20	sodium nitrate	30
20	cobalt nitrate	12
20	sodium chloride	41

a) Use the table to answer the following questions.
   i) Which substance gives the greatest increase in the rate of reaction?

   _____

   ii) Which substance is the least effective as a catalyst?

   _____

   iii) Which metal ion is most likely to be the best catalyst?

   _____

   iv) Which ion is the least effective as a catalyst?

   _____
                                                                        (4)

b) Give two reasons why catalysts are very important to the efficiency of several industrial processes. Give two processes in which catalysts are used. (3 lines)
                                                                        (4)
                                                                      (WJEC)

QUESTION 10

Time (s)	Volume of hydrogen (cm^3)
0	0
30	25
60	50
90	75
100	100

A student added magnesium ribbon to dilute hydrochloric acid and recorded the volume of hydrogen released every 30 seconds; the results are shown below.

a) What is the relationship between the volume of gas released and the time taken? (2 lines)
                                                                        (2)

b) How would you present the results so that the relationship might be more easily seen? (2 lines)
                                                                        (1)

c) If you were doing this experiment, describe two safety precautions you would take.

   i) _____

   ii) _____
                                                                     (NICCEA)

QUESTION 11

a) When hydrogen peroxide is left to stand in a clear glass container, it slowly decomposes to produce oxygen and water.
   i) Write a balanced symbolic equation to show how 2 mol of hydrogen peroxide decomposes.
                                                                        (2)

   ii) From your equation calculate how many moles of oxygen would be produced if 10 mol of hydrogen peroxide completely decomposed.
                                                                        (1)

   iii) Hydrogen peroxide can be used by hairdressers. Suggest a reason why it is usually stored in brown bottles.
                                                                        (1)

b) Adding manganese (IV) oxide to hydrogen peroxide affects the rate at which oxygen is produced, as shown in the graph below.

   i) What volume of oxygen will be produced after 125 s by adding 1 g of MnO_2 powder?
                                                                        (1)

   ii) From the information on the graphs, state **two** factors which affect the rate of oxygen production and the evidence for your answer.
                                                                        (4)

   iii) Give **one** other factor, not indicated on the graphs, which might affect the rate of reaction.
                                                                        (1)

c) Devise a simple experiment that would enable you to check whether any of the manganese (IV) dioxide had been used up in the reaction. State clearly which procedures you would take and what measurements you would make. You need not include a diagram
                                                                        (5)
                                                                      (MEG)

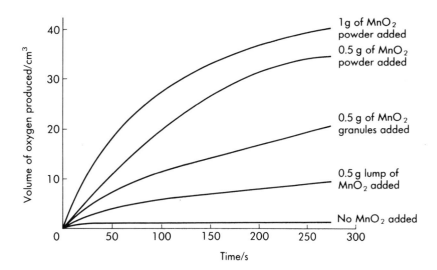

QUESTION 12
(Levels 8–10)

A structured question consisting of four sub questions (a) to (d) which can be answered independently of each other so if you cannot do one part go onto the next. Most of the question is aimed at level 10 except for part (a) aimed at level 8, and (d) (ii) aimed at level 9.

Methane burns in the presence of oxygen to form water and carbon dioxide.

$$CH_4 \ + \ 2O_2 \ \rightarrow \ CO_2 \ + \ 2H_2O \quad \Delta H \ = \ -890 \, kJ/mol$$

a) Describe the bonding of each of the following compounds. Include the names of the types of bond involved. *(4)*

   i) Methane (3 lines available) _____

   ii) Carbon dioxide (3 lines available) _____

b) i) Explain why a source of ignition (heat) is needed before methane will start burning in oxygen. (5 lines available) *(3)*

   ii) Explain why this reaction gives out energy. (4 lines available) *(3)*

c) Hydrogen reacts with chlorine.

$$H_2 \ + \ Cl_2 \ \rightarrow \ 2HCl$$

Approximate bond energies:

H – H   436 kJ/mol
Cl – Cl   242 kJ/mol
H – Cl   431 kJ/mol

Calculate how much energy is released or absorbed by this reaction. (2 lines) *(3)*

d) Some copper (II) sulphate solution is poured into a beaker and its temperature is recorded every 15 seconds. After a short time some zinc is added to this solution. The temperature is recorded for a total time of two minutes as shown on the graph overleaf.

   i) Explain why the graph line is as shown. (6 lines available) *(4)*

   ii) The equation for the reaction between copper (II) sulphate and zinc is shown below.

$$CuSO_4 \ + \ Zn \ \rightarrow \ ZnSO_4 \ + \ Cu$$

   If 16.25 g of zinc are added to excess copper (II) sulphate solution, what mass of copper will be formed? (4 lines) [The relative atomic mass of copper is 64 and of zinc is 65.] *(3)*

[Science Double Award SEG]

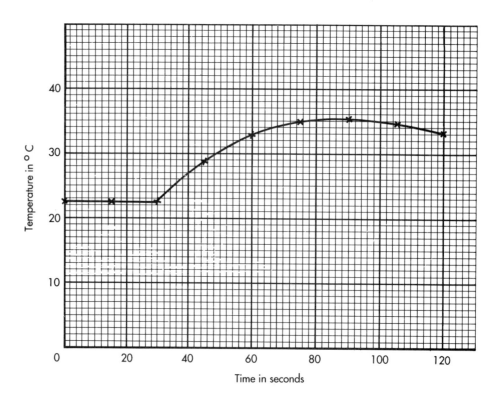

ANSWERS TO EXAMINATION QUESTIONS

MULTIPLE CHOICE

ANSWER 1

Key D; There must be four atoms on each side to balance.

ANSWER 2

Key B; steam is not considered to be a pollutant, so the correct answer is carbon monoxide and lead compounds.

ANSWER 3

Key C; remember catalysts increase the rate of reactions but are not used up by the reactions.

ANSWER 4

Key A; the redox reaction here involves the removal of oxygen from lead oxide and the addition of oxygen to carbon to form carbon dioxide.

ANSWER 5

Key D; the other choices are physical changes.

ANSWER 6

Key B; The mass of one mole of water is 18 g [(2 x 1) + 16 = 18]. There are 2 moles of water which contain 2 mol of oxygen = 2 x 16 = 32 g.

ANSWER 7

Key A; The relative formula mass of the hydroxide OH is 17. There are three hydroxides, so the mass is 3 x 17 = 51. Then, 78—51 = 27, the mass of one mole of M.

ANSWER 8

Key B; There is 1 g in 250 cm^3, so there are 4 g in 1 litre. The mass of one mole of NaOH is 40, so $4 \div 40$ is 0.1.

STRUCTURED
QUESTIONS

ANSWER 9

a) i)   cobalt nitrate
    ii) sodium chloride
    iii) cobalt
    iv) sodium

b) they increase the rate of reaction;
    they lower the amount of energy required to start a reaction;
    manufacture of sulphuric acid;
    manufacture of ammonia.

ANSWER 10

a) The volume of gas increases as the time increases, every 30 seconds; 25 cm^3 of gas is released until the final 10 seconds.

b) on a graph

c) i)   wear safety goggles
    ii) make sure no acid is spilt

ANSWER 11

a) i) $2H_2O_2 \rightarrow 2H_2O + O_2$
    ii) 5 mol
    iii) to stop light affecting the substance

b) i) $30cm^3$
    ii) Mass of Mn O_2; 1 g of powder works faster than 0.5 g
         powder is faster than granules as there is more surface area
    iii) temperature

c) Weigh the dry manganese dioxide, then add to hydrogen peroxide. When reaction stops, dry and weigh again. If the two weights are the same, then no manganese dioxide has been used.

ANSWER 12

You are given information in the form of an equation. Use this information to help you remember the structure of methane and carbon dioxide.

a) i)   covalent bonding (1)
         single bonds between carbon and each hydrogen atom (1)

    ii) covalent bonding (1)
         double bond between carbon and each oxygen atom (1)

b) i)   heat is required to break the bonds (1)
         radicals are then formed (1)
         which then react (1)

    ii) energy is required to break bonds (1)
         energy is released when bonds are made (1)
         in this reaction more energy is released than used (1)

c) breaking bonds H – H   = 436
                   Cl – Cl   = 242
                                = 678 kJ (1)

    making bonds H – Cl   = 431 x 2
                                = 862 kJ (1)

    energy released   = 862 – 678
                                = 184 kJ (1)

d) i) temperature of copper sulphate solution
is room temperature approx. 22°C (1)
as zinc reacts with copper (II) ions the temperature rises (1)
after about 80 seconds the reaction is complete (1)
solution starts to cool towards room temperature (1)

ii) Note you are given the equation and the relative atomic masses of copper and zinc in the question.

1 mole of zinc produces 1 mole of copper (1)
65 g of zinc produces 64 g of copper (1)

16.25 g of zinc produces $\dfrac{64 \times 16.25}{65}$ = 16 g of copper (1)

A STUDENT'S ANSWER WITH EXAMINER'S COMMENTS

Our atmosphere is a mixture of gases.

a) Which gas makes up most of this mixture?

nitrogen ✓

66 Good. **99**

(1)

b) Energy is released within most organisms by a chemical reaction called *respiration*.

i) Which gas is used up during respiration?

oxygen ✓

(1)

ii) Which natural process replaces the gas used up in respiration?

photosynthesis ✓

(1)

c) Explain how each of the following could change the amount of *carbon dioxide* in our atmosphere.

i) people cutting down large areas of forest.

trees remove carbon dioxide so less trees means
not so much ✓ CO_2 removed

66 Good – the level would increase (state the change). Include equation as well. **99**

(3)

ii) people burning more fossil fuels.

fossil fuels produce CO_2 so more ✓ would be produced

Fuel + oxygen → $CO_2 + H_2O$

66 Yes. Again state that the level would increase. Good idea to use equation. **99**

(3)

d) What effect will cutting down trees **and** burning fossil fuels have on the amount of *oxygen* in our atmosphere?

It will decrease ✓ the oxygen as fuel uses up oxygen to burn.

(1)
(SEG)

R E V I E W   S H E E T

✎ In any chemical reaction the _____ always stays the same.

✎ Catalysts are often used to _____ reactions.

✎ In any chemical reaction the total mass of the products (new materials) is always the same as the total mass of the _____ (starting materials).

✎ Reactions in which heat is *given out* are called _____ reactions; reactions where heat is *taken in* are called _____ reactions

✎ Insert the correct word

(g) represents a state of _____

(l) represents a state of _____

(s) represents a state of _____

(aq) represents the _____ state (*dissolved in water*).

✎ Hydrocarbons is a word used for the _____ fuels.

✎ Complete the following equations

Coal is mainly carbon:

$$\text{carbon} \quad + \quad \text{oxygen} \quad \rightarrow$$
$$\text{C} \quad + \quad \text{O}_2 \quad \rightarrow$$

Natural gas is methane:

$$\text{methane} \quad + \quad \text{oxygen} \quad \rightarrow$$
$$\text{CH}_4 \quad + \quad \text{2O}_2 \quad \rightarrow$$

✎ Complete the following equations for respiration.

$$\text{food} \quad + \quad \text{oxygen} \quad \rightarrow$$

If we choose glucose ($C_6H_{12}O_6$), as an example of food, then this can be represented as

$$\text{C}_6\text{H}_{12}\text{O}_6 \quad + \quad 6\text{O}_2 \quad \rightarrow$$

✎ Complete the following equations for photosynthesis

$$\text{energy} \quad + \quad \text{carbon dioxide} \quad + \quad \text{water} \quad \rightarrow$$
$$\text{energy} \quad + \quad 6\text{CO}_2 \quad + \quad 6\text{H}_2\text{O} \quad \rightarrow$$

✎ _____ is the opposite of respiration.

✎ _____ is the addition of oxygen or the removal of hydrogen.

✎ _____ is the removal of oxygen or the addition of hydrogen.

✎ Oxidation cannot take place without reduction so the reactions are called _____ reactions. When these reactions involve an element and a salt solution they are called _____ reactions.

✎ Some reactions between solutions of metal salts will take place because there is a possibility of a *solid* being formed. This solid is called a _____

✎ The general pattern of a neutralisation reaction is:

$$\text{acid} \quad + \quad \text{base} \quad \rightarrow$$

An example is the reaction between hydrochloric acid and sodium hydroxide:

$$\text{HCl} \quad + \quad \text{NaOH} \quad \rightarrow$$

✎ A reaction which can go in *both* directions is called a _____ reaction. This is indicated by the sign $\boxed{}$.

✎ Energy is needed to _____ bonds. Energy is released when bonds are

_____

✎ Almost all chemical equations need an amount of energy to get them going. We call this initial

energy requirement _____ energy.

✎ In this energy level diagram, the heat of the reaction is given the symbol ΔH. Which reaction is endothermic and which is exothermic?

```
     Reactants                                          Products
 _ _  _____ _ _ _ _ _ _                        _____
                 |                                   ↑
                 | ΔH negative                       | ΔH positive
                 | value                             | value
                 ↓     Products                       |  
                    _____          Reactants   |
                                   _ _  _____ _ _ 
```

$\boxed{\text{_____ reaction}}$ $\boxed{\text{_____ reaction}}$

✎ List four factors which affect the *rate* at which a reaction takes place.

1. _____

2. _____

3. _____

4. _____

✎ The _____ particles collide the more likely they are to react, and so the

_____ the reaction.

✎ Catalysts speed up reactions; _____ slow down reactions.

✎ A *biological* catalyst is sometimes called an _____ . These are _____ molecules.

✎ Name four properties of an enzyme.

1. _____

2. _____

3. _____

4. _____

✎ The _____ is equivalent to 6×10^{23} particles.

The relative atomic mass of an atom in grammes contains one mole (1 mol) of atoms.

Atom	Atomic mass	Mass of 1 mol of atoms
hydrogen	1	1 g
carbon	12	12 g
oxygen	16	16 g
chlorine	35.5	35.5 g
sodium	23	23 g

In other words, in 32 g of oxygen we have ☐ mol of atoms; in 8 g of oxygen we have ☐ mol of atoms.

GETTING STARTED

Almost all compounds which contain ions can be classified as either acid, base or salt.

Acids are substances which have a sharp or sour taste. We can recognise this taste in fruits or in vinegar. Acids can also be corrosive; they can dissolve many substances such as metals and some rocks. This can be very useful but can also be a nuisance, as with the corrosion of iron and buildings by acids in the atmosphere, eg acid rain.

Bases are substances which can neutralise acids; they react with acids to produce salts. Bases include the oxides, hydroxides and carbonates of metals. Most bases are insoluble in water; those which do dissolve are called *alkalis*.

Salts are substances which are formed when acids are neutralised by bases. These salts are giant ionic structures and often form crystals. The neutralisation of acids by bases can be explained in terms of the interaction between hydrogen ions (H^+) and hydroxide ions (OH^-).

$$H^+ + OH^- \rightarrow H_2O$$

ACIDITY

ACIDS AND WATER

ALKALIS

DETECTING ACIDS AND ALKALIS

FOLLOWING ACID/ALKALI REACTIONS

MAKING ACIDS AND ALKALIS

PATTERNS OF ACID REACTIONS

ACIDS IN ACTION

SALTS

SALTS IN ACTION

ESSENTIAL PRINCIPLES

An *acid* is a substance which:

- has a sour taste;
- will change the colour of plant dyes (indicators);
- will neutralise bases;
- will react with many metals to form salts;
- produces hydrogen ions when dissolved in water.

| 1 | ACIDS AND WATER |

ACIDS IN WATER CONTAIN HYDROGEN IONS

Acids only behave as acids when they are dissolved in water. So we only really meet them as solutions in water. The reason for this is that water is a *polar* solvent. In water the acid produces hydrogen ions (H^+). All acids contain hydrogen ions in water. The importance of water can be demonstrated by dissolving some citric acid crystals (the acid from fruits such as oranges and lemons) in water and some citric acid crystals in another solvent, such as ethoxyethane (ether).

When the citric acid crystals are dissolved in *ether* the solution will *not* affect the colour of indicators, nor will it react with bases or metals. However, in *water* the citric acid behaves as an acid, changing the colour of the indicator.

In fact, the acid reacts with the water to produce a hydrated hydrogen ion called a hydroxonium ion (H_3O^+):

$$H^+ \quad + \quad H_2O \quad \rightarrow \quad H_3O^+$$

 **Acids provide Hydrogen ions**

It is really this ion that is responsible for acidity; however, in order to keep things simple we can think of acids as just providing hydrogen ions in water. These symbols can be regarded as representing the same ions:

$$H^+ \qquad H^+(aq) \qquad H_3O^+(aq)$$

STRONG AND WEAK ACIDS

Those acids which give up all their hydrogen ions in water are called *strong* acids whereas those which only provide some of their hydrogen ions are called *weak* acids.

Strong acids	*Weak acids*
sulphuric acid	citric acid (citrus fruits)
nitric acid	ethanoic (acetic) acid (vinegar)
hydrochloric acid	malic acid (apples)

SOME COMMON ACIDS

Acid	*Formula*	*Ions present*		
hydrochloric acid	HCl	H^+	Cl^-	(chloride)
sulphuric acid	H_2SO_4	$2H^+$	SO_4^{2-}	(sulphate)
nitric acid	HNO_3	H^+	NO_3^-	(nitrate)
ethanoic acid	CH_3COOH	H^+	CH_3COO^-	(ethanoate)

Notice the names of acids are taken from the ion present. This ion is referred to as the *acid radical.* Ethanoic acid (acetic acid) is a *weak* acid, because not all of the ethanoic acid molecules in solution split up to provide hydrogen ions, but only a proportion of them.

CONCENTRATION OF ACID SOLUTIONS

Acid solutions can be *concentrated* or *dilute*, depending upon how much water is present. The concentration of a solution can be measured in mol/dm³, as we've already seen. For example, a 1 M (1 molar) solution of sulphuric acid contains 98g H_2SO_4 per dm³. This is calculated from the formula mass of H_2SO_4 = $(2 \times 1) + 32 + (4 \times 16)$ = 98.

Strong acids must not be confused with *concentrated* acids. Wex can have concentrated solutions of strong *and* weak acids as well as dilute solutions of strong *and* weak acids. The acids that are used in a laboratory are dilute acids of concentrations 2 M, 1 M, 0.1 M etc.

2 **ALKALIS** An *alkali* is a substance which:

- is a soluble base;
- will change the colour of indicators;
- will neutralise acids;
- contains hydroxide ions.

SOME COMMON ALKALIS

Name	Formula	Ions presents		
sodium hydroxide	NaOH	Na^+	(sodium)	OH^-
ammonium hydroxide	NH_4OH	NH_4^+	(ammonium)	OH^-
calcium hydroxide	$Ca(OH)_2$	Ca^{2+}	(calcium)	$2OH^-$

In the same way as there are strong and weak acids, so there are strong and weak alkalis. Aqueous sodium hydroxide is a strong alkali, whereas aqueous ammonia is a weak alkali.

3 **DETECTING ACIDS AND ALKALIS** There are two main ways of *detecting* acids and alkalis:
1. using *indicators*: substances whose colours are changed by acids and alkalis;
2. using *pH meters*: instruments whose meter reading is affected by the H^+ and OH^- ions in the solution.

INDICATORS

 Learn the pH scale

The most commonly used indicator is *universal indicator*, since it not only tells us if something is acid or alkaline but also if the acid (or alkali) is strong or weak. It can be used as a liquid (usually green) or soaked on to a type of blotting paper and used as a paper. The paper, of course, has to be wet in order to work, since acids only behave as acids in solution. The *colour* of the indicator matches a number which indicates the acidity of the solution.

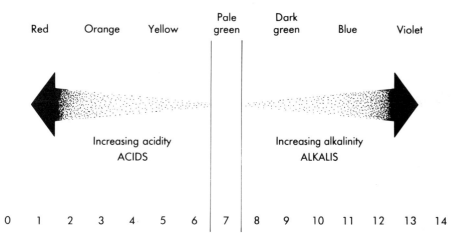

Fig. 11.1 The pH scale.

The strength of an acid or alkali is measured on the *pH* scale. The pH scale has a range of 1 to 14 and is a measure of the hydrogen ion concentration (acidity). Notice that low numbers indicate *high* acidity (and high H^+ ion concentration).

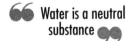

Water is a neutral substance

- If a solution turns the indicator *light green*, then it is *neutral* and has a pH of 7.
- If a solution turns the indicator *yellow* then it is a *weak* acid and has a pH of 6.

Other indicators

The reactions of other, less common, indicators are as follows:

Indicator	in acid	in alkali	in water (neutral)
litmus	red	blue	purple
phenolphthalein	colourless	pink	colourless

4 FOLLOWING ACID/ALKALI REACTIONS

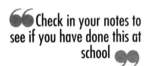

Check in your notes to see if you have done this at school

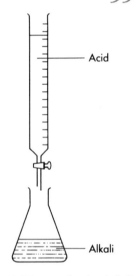

--- Acid

--- Alkali

Fig. 11.2 Titration of acid and alkali.

Indicators can also be used to follow the course of a *neutralisation* reaction between an acid and an alkali. If universal indicator is added to a strong alkaline solution, the indicator will turn *violet*. If a *solution of acid* is added, a small amount at a time, then the indicator will change colour *through blue to green*, at which point the solution is *neutral* (the acid has reacted with all the alkali present). If acid *continues* to be added, the indicator will eventually turn *red*, indicating the solution is now *strongly acidic*. You may have performed an experiment such as this and will have noticed how difficult it is to add just the right amount of acid to produce a neutral solution (green colour with the indicator). If you need to produce a neutral solution, an accurate measuring device (a *burette*) is required and it would also be helpful to use an indicator (like phenolphthalein) which has a more distinct colour change. The process, shown in Figure 11.2, is called *titration*. The acid is titrated into the alkali, using an indicator to show when the exact amount of acid has been added.

An example is the reaction between hydrochloric acid and sodium hydroxide, when a salt (sodium chloride) and water are produced. We can use the titration method to find the exact quantity of hydrochloric acid to neutralise the sodium hydroxide solution exactly.

hydrochloric acid + sodium hydroxide → sodium chloride + water
$HCl(aq)$ + $NaOH(aq)$ → $NaCl(aq)$ + $H_2O(l)$

A measured volume of sodium hydroxide is placed in the flask, together with a few drops of indicator. The hydrochloric acid is then added from the burette, a little at a time, and the liquid is swirled in the flask to make sure the solutions are mixed. When the indicator *just changes colour* then the exact amount of acid has been added to neutralise the alkali. The volume of the acid required can be read off the burette. If the same experiment is repeated with the same volumes of acid and alkali but without the indicator, then a neutral solution can be produced which contains only sodium chloride and water. This can be shown by evaporating the water in the flask, when crystals of sodium chloride will be left.

5 MAKING ACIDS AND ALKALIS

The oxides of non-metals when dissolved in water give acidic solutions. The oxides of metals are bases and those which dissolve in water produce alkaline solutions. Thus acids and alkalis relate to the elements' position in the periodic table (see Figure 11.3).

LiOH						H_2CO_3	HNO_3		
NaOH	Mg(OH)₂					H_3PO_4	H_2SO_4	HClO₄	
KOH	Ca(OH)₂								

Fig. 11.3 The change from alkalis on the left to acids on the right when oxides of elements react with water.

6 **PATTERNS OF ACID REACTIONS**

Acids are very useful substances, because they react with a large number of other substances in fairly *predictable* ways. They are used extensively in industry in the manufacture of a large variety of materials.

REACTIONS WITH METAlS

The reaction follows a general pattern:

"Hydrogen given off"

"Spot the pattern"

"Check Chapter 9 here"

metal	+	**acid**	→	**salt**	+	**hydrogen**
zinc	+	hydrochloric acid	→	zinc chloride	+	hydrogen
Zn	+	2HCl	→	$ZnCl_2$	+	H_2
magnesium	+	sulphuric acid	→	magnesium sulphate	+	hydrogen
Mg	+	H_2SO_4	→	$MgSO_4$	+	H_2

The solution that is produced is neutral, and the salt produced depends on the acid. Some metals react with acids faster than others. The metal's reactivity depends on its position in the *reactivity series* (see Chapter12).

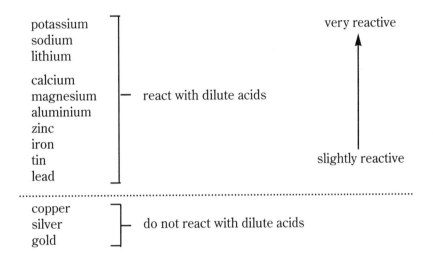

potassium
sodium
lithium

calcium
magnesium
aluminium
zinc
iron
tin
lead

— react with dilute acids

very reactive

slightly reactive

copper
silver
gold

— do not react with dilute acids

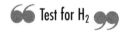

"Test for H_2"

When hydrogen gas is produced it can be tested for by igniting a test tube of hydrogen with a lighted splint; the result is a 'pop'.

REACTIONS WITH METAL OXIDES

Metal oxides are bases and react with acids to produce salt and water. All metal oxides will react with dilute acids. The reaction follows a general pattern:

metal oxide	+	**acid**	→	**salt**	+	**water**
copper (II) oxide	+	nitric acid	→	copper nitrate	+	water
CuO	+	$2HNO_3$	→	$Cu(NO_3)_2$	+	H_2O
magnesium oxide	+	sulphuric acid	→	magnesium sulphate	+	water
MgO	+	H_2SO_4	→	$MgSO_4$	+	H_2O

REACTIONS WITH METAL HYDROXIDES

Metal hydroxides are bases which will react with acids to produce salt and water. Metal hydroxides which are soluble are called *alkalis*. All metal hydroxides react with acids. The reaction follows a general pattern:

metal hydroxide	+	**acid**	→	**salt**	+	**water**
calcium hydroxide	+	hydrochloric acid	→	calcium chloride	+	water
$Ca(OH)_2$	+	2HCl	→	$CaCl_2$	+	$2H_2O$
potassium hydroxide	+	sulphuric acid	→	potassium sulphate	+	water
2KOH	+	H_2SO_4	→	K_2SO_4	+	$2H_2O$

REACTION WITH CARBONATES

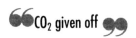

Metal carbonates can be thought of as bases; they too will react with acids to produce salt and water, but they also produce carbon dioxide. The reaction follows a general pattern:

acid	+	**carbonate**	→	**salt**	+	**water**	+	**carbon dioxide**
sodium carbonate	+	nitric acid	→	sodium nitrate	+	water	+	carbon dioxide
Na_2CO_3	+	$2HNO_3$	→	$2NaNO_3$	+	H_2O	+	CO_2
calcium carbonate	+	hydrochloric acid	→	calcium chloride	+	water	+	carbon dioxide
$CaCO_3$	+	$2HCl$	→	$CaCl_2$	+	H_2O	+	CO_2

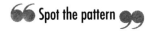

This is a general pattern for all carbonates, and as some rocks are carbonates it can be used as a test to help identify rocks. For example, limestone, marble and chalk are all mainly calcium carbonate and will therefore react with hydrochloric acid. When a small amount of acid is placed on the surface the rocks fizz and give off carbon dioxide.

There is an exception to this 'rule'; sulphuric acid will not react well with calcium carbonate rock, since during the reaction a layer of calcium sulphate builds up on the surface, preventing any further reaction.

The carbon dioxide produced can be tested for by bubbling the gas through limewater, when the limewater turns cloudy.

7 ACIDS IN ACTION

ACID RAIN

The rain which normally falls is very slightly acidic (pH 5). This is due to a small amount of carbon dioxide from the atmosphere which dissolves in the rain water to produce a weakly acidic solution:

$$H_2O \quad + \quad CO_2 \quad \rightarrow \quad H_2CO_3$$

Acid rain, however, has a pH of between 5 and about 2.2. The strongest acid rain has an acidity comparable to that of lemon juice. The causes of acid rain are not fully understood, but enough is known to realise that the burning of fossil fuels (hydrocarbons) and the exhaust emission from cars contribute greatly to acid rain.

Fossil fuels like coal and oil contain impurities of sulphur, so that when they burn they produce sulphur dioxide in addition to the normal products of combustion (carbon dioxide and water). Sulphur dioxide is an acidic gas. The exhausts of cars also emit gases other than the normal products of combustion. In the car engine where the petrol (hydrocarbon fuel) is burned, the temperature is so high that nitrogen from the air reacts with oxygen to form oxides of nitrogen which escape through the exhaust, together with unburned hydrocarbons and carbon monoxide.

This mixture of gases (particularly sulphur dioxide and the oxides of nitrogen) react in the atmosphere with water to produce rain which contains sulphuric and nitric acids. It is this that gives the rain its reactivity. Acid rain will obviously be a problem in parts of the world which are industrialised (burn fossil fuels in power stations and factories) and have large numbers of cars, eg Europe, USA, Canada and Japan.

Effects of acid rain

Acid rain will corrode metals and will react with some building materials (limestone and marble), gradually eating them away. Perhaps the largest worry, however, is the effect it has, either directly or indirectly, on living things.

When acid rain falls on to the soil it progressively dissolves away many of the minerals (salts) in the soil. Metal ions are leached (dissolved) out of the soil and washed into rivers and lakes, which become increasingly acidic and increasingly concentrated in metal ions. The first metal ions to be removed from the soil are magnesium (Mg^{2+}) and calcium (Ca^{2+}), because they dissolve most easily. These are needed by plants to ensure healthy growth, so are no longer available.

The next metal ions to be leached out of the soil are aluminium (Al^{3+}) and the heavier metal ions of lead (Pb^{2+}), and copper (Cu^{2+}). These ions are particularly troublesome, since they are poisonous. Dissolved aluminium in the water prevents the gills of fish working, as well as being poisonous to other organisms, including ourselves. (*Note*: it is not the acid water that kills the fish, but the dissolved metal ions.)

The areas that are affected more than others are those with thin soil covering and granite rock, such as Scotland, Dartmoor, the Black Forest in Germany, and Scandinavia. Areas which are lucky enough to have deep soil covering limestone rock are not so badly affected, since the limestone rock and its soil can neutralise the effects of the acid rain. The degree to which an area is affected also depends on its position, since the acidic gases are carried on prevailing winds.

Combating acid rain

A very relevant aspect of science

1   Some lakes which are very acidic have large amounts of lime (calcium hydroxide) added to them to neutralise the acidity. This is only a temporary measure, however, since it has to be frequently repeated and costs a large amount of money.
2   Power stations which burn coal and oil can be fitted with equipment which will remove the sulphur dioxide from the gases before they are released into the atmosphere.
3   Car exhausts can be fitted with catalytic converters which can convert the harmful gases into harmless ones. These cannot be fitted to the majority of cars in this country, however, since most cars run on leaded petrol. The lead in the petrol will prevent the catalyst from working.

ACIDS AND FOOD PRESERVATION

Using acids in the kitchen

The pickling of foods such as onions and eggs and the making of chutneys helps preserve the food. The acid that is used is found in vinegar. This acid is called *ethanoic acid* (*acetic acid* is its more common name). The reason it works is that any bacteria which enter the food are killed by dehydration due to *osmosis* (see Chapter 8). It also means that the pH is too low for enzymes (biological catalysts) to work, and this prevents the natural deterioration of food.

ACIDS AND DIGESTION

Using acids in your body

The human digestive system contains many different enzymes whose job it is to help the large food molecules of carbohydrates and proteins to be broken down into smaller molecules. The carbohydrates end up as simple sugars and the proteins as amino acids. These much smaller molecules are able to pass through the wall of the gut and so to be passed around the body. The enzymes which are responsible for this breakdown only work within limited pH ranges, so the acidity at various parts of the digestive system is important.

Saliva in the mouth contains the enzyme *salivary amylase*, which converts starch into sugar. It works best at body temperature and at a pH of between 6 and 7 (about neutral).

Check Chapter 3 on the Human Body

The stomach lining produces gastric juice. This contains hydrochloric acid (about pH 2), which kills most of the micro-organisms in the food. Gastric juice also contains the enzyme *pepsin*, which starts to break down large protein molecules. Pepsin obviously works best at a much lower pH than salivary amylase. In the small intestine more enzymes act on the food. Also bile, an alkaline liquid produced by the liver, is released into the small intestine. Bile helps to emulsify fats; this means it helps break large fat droplets into much smaller ones (this is a property of all alkalis). The bile also helps neutralise the hydrochloric acid from the stomach, enabling other enzymes which require higher pH values to work on the food molecules.

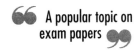
A popular topic on exam papers

Indigestion is often caused by too much acid in the stomach and can be relieved by taking 'antacid' tablets. These contain bases which neutralise the excess acid in the stomach. Examples are Settlers and Rennies, which both contain calcium carbonate and magnesium hydroxide.

ACIDITY AND THE SOIL

Most plants prefer to grow in a soil which is slightly acidic, about pH 6-7. There are even some plants which prefer more acidic soils (pH 4.5-6) such as azaleas, rhododendrons and heathers. No plants will grow in strongly alkaline soils, however, although some plants will grow in weakly alkaline soils (up to pH 8). When there is a change from growing one type of plant to another, the acidity of the soil has sometimes to be changed to get the best results. In addition the soil acidity itself may well change over a period of time because of the plants themselves. Needing to reduce the acidity of the soil is a common problem to farmers; they do this by adding lime to the soil. Lime is calcium oxide, but calcium hydroxide (slaked lime) or calcium carbonate (limestone or chalk) is often used:

$$CaO + 2H^+ \rightarrow Ca^{2+} + H_2O$$
(lime or quicklime)
$$Ca(OH)_2 + 2H^+ \rightarrow Ca^{2+} + 2H_2O$$
(slaked lime)
$$CaCO_3 + 2H^+ \rightarrow Ca^{2+} + H_2O + CO_2$$
(limestone)

ACIDS IN INDUSTRY

Sulphuric acid is one of the most important acids in industry and is produced in very large quantities each year. It has a wide variety of uses in the manufacture of other substances. Sulphuric acid is manufactured by the contact process. Sulphur is the starting point:

$$S \rightarrow SO_2 \rightarrow SO_3 \rightarrow H_2SO_4$$
heated in   reacts with   reacts with
air   more oxygen   water
                  over catalyst

Sulphuric acid is needed for the manufacture of agricultural chemicals (fertilisers), plastics, paints and pigments, detergents and soaps, fibres, dyestuffs, oil and petrol, as well as other chemicals (including other acids).

    Nitric acid is another important industrial chemical, and is manufactured in quantity for use mainly in the manufacture of fertilisers and explosives.

8 ⟩ SALTS

These are ionic substances which are formed in reactions between acids and bases or between acids and metals. If solutions of these salts are allowed to evaporate, then crystals (giant ionic structures) are formed. Solutions of these salts will conduct electricity, showing that they contain ions.

NAMING SALTS

The name of the salt depends on the ions present. Each salt contains a positive ion, or *cation*, that is derived from the metal, eg Na^+, Mg^{2+}. In addition, each salt contains a negative ion, or *anion* that is derived, from the acid, eg SO_4^{2-} (sulphate), or CO_3^{2-} (carbonate).

    The name of the salt comes from a combination of both ions, eg magnesium sulphate ($Mg^{2+} SO_4^{2-}$). The charge on the metal ion depends on its group in the periodic table (see Chapter 9 and Figure 11.4). Some metals (those from the transition metal block in the periodic table) can have ions with different charges. An example is iron, where the charge on the ion is indicated by roman numerals in the name:

iron (II) sulphate $FeSO_4$ Fe^{2+} ion present
iron (III) sulphate $Fe_2(SO_4)_3$ Fe^{3+} ion present

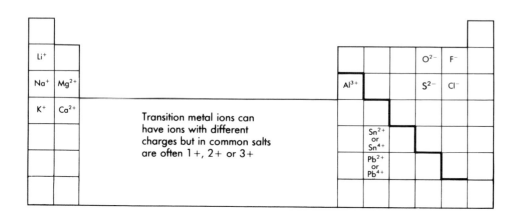

Fig. 11.4 The charge on the ion depends on its group in the periodic table.

PATTERNS FOR SALTS

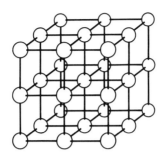

Fig. 11.5 Ionic lattice of a salt.

Solubility

In the case of cations, all salts containing sodium, potassium or ammonium ions are soluble. Although the ammonium ion (NH_4^+) is not a metal ion, it may be regarded as such in salts.

In the case of anions, all *nitrates* (NO_3^-) are soluble; all chlorides (Cl^-) are soluble (except silver and lead); all sulphates (SO_4^{2-}) are soluble (except barium, calcium and lead); but all carbonates (CO_3^{2-}) are insoluble (except Na^+, K^+, NH_4^+).

The solubility of a salt often increases with temperature, although there are a few exceptions. The reason for this is that in order for the water to dissolve the salt it has to break down the ionic lattice (Figure 11.5). The higher the temperature, the greater the kinetic energy of the particles (water molecules and ions). *Remember*: water is able to dissolve ionic substances because it is a polar molecule (see Chapter 9).

COLOUR OF SALTS

The colour of salts is often due to the metal ion present.

Ion	Colour	Ion	Colour
Na^+	colourless	Fe^{2+}	green
K^+	colourless	Fe^{3+}	red
Cu^{2+}	blue/green		

SALTS IN ACTION

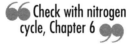

Check with nitrogen cycle, Chapter 6

Salts are present in the sea and in the soil and provide plants with the elements they need. For example, nitrogen as *nitrates* (NO_3^-) in the soil provides the plant with vital materials to manufacture amino acids. Phosphorus, as *phosphates* (PO_4^{3-}) is essential for energy transfer within the plant cell. In addition, potassium (K^+) makes many enzymes active, while calcium (Ca^{2+}) provides a raw material for cell walls. Magnesium (Mg^{2+}) is a vital component of chlorophyll, and sulphur, as sulphates (SO_4^{2-}), is a component of some amino acids. Because each of these elements is needed by plants, their salts are manufactured as fertilisers. Examples are ammonium nitrate, ammonium phosphate and potassium chloride. Fertilisers containing these three salts are called N, P, K fertilisers because they provide nitrogen (N), phosphorus (P) and potassium (K).

As well as in agriculture, salts are used in other, industrial or medical, applications. Calcium sulphate (gypsum) is used as wall plaster and plaster of Paris. Silver chloride is used as photographic film emulsion. Iron (II) sulphate is used in iron tablets to treat anaemia.

EXAMINATION QUESTIONS

MULTIPLE CHOICE

Questions 1–3 below refer to the following pH numbers.
A pH 1; B pH 4; C pH 7; D pH 10; E pH 14

QUESTION 1

What is the pH of a strongly alkaline solution?

QUESTION 2

What is the pH of a neutral solution?

QUESTION 3

What is the pH of a weakly acidic solution?

QUESTION 4

How many grams of sulphuric acid H_2SO_4, are present in a 2 M solution of sulphuric acid? (H= 1, S=32, O= 16)

A 49g; B 50g; C 98g; D 194g; E 196g

QUESTION 5

What gas is released when zinc reacts with hydrochloric acid?
A   carbon dioxide   D   nitrogen
B   chlorine   E   oxygen
C   hydrogen

QUESTION 6

What new substance, apart from magnesium sulphate, is formed when magnesium oxide reacts with sulphuric acid?
A carbon dioxide   D a salt
B hydrogen   E water
C oxygen

QUESTION 7

How would you correctly identify the gas produced when an acid reacts with a carbonate?
A   use a glowing splint   D   use limewater
B   use a lighted splint   E   pass the gas through an acid
C   carefully smell the gas

STRUCTURED QUESTIONS

QUESTION 8

a) A list of pH values is given below:
    pH 1   pH 4   pH 7   pH 9   pH 14

    Select from this list the pH value of each of the following substances. Each value may be used once, more than once or not at all.

    i) distilled water _____
    (1)

    ii) toothpaste _____
    (1)

    iii) vinegar_____
    (1)

ATAKA

Contains Formic Acid
Keep out of reach
of children
Do not breathe in vapour
Wash off skin immediately
CORROSIVE POISON
CAUSES BURNS
NOT TO BE TAKEN

Contents 250cm³

b) A householder bought a bottle of the stain remover called ATAKA shown alongside.

    i) Which piece of laboratory apparatus would you use to confirm that the bottle contains 250 cm^3?

    _____
    (1)

    ii) A little of the liquid is accidentally dropped on the carpet. Suggest a household substance which could be used to prevent damage, and explain your choice.

    name _____

    explanation _____

    _____
    (3)
    (NICCEA)

QUESTION 9

In a chemist's shop, two brands of indigestion tablets are on sale, Burney and Rumbley. Sarah did an experiment to try to find out which one would be better.

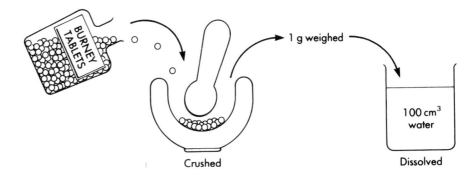

Crushed   Dissolved

She crushed the tablets and dissolved 1 g of each kind of tablet in 100 cm^3 of distilled water. Then she did an experiment to find out what volume of the same acid solution was needed to neutralise each tablet solution.

a) What is the chemical in the stomach that can cause indigestion?

_____

(1)

b) i) What is meant by a *neutral* solution? (2 LINES)   (1)

   ii) Give two reasons why Sarah crushed the tablets rather than using whole tablets.

   1 _____

   2 _____

(2)

The apparatus she used is shown below.

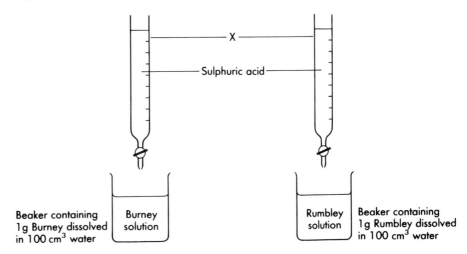

c) i) What is the name of the apparatus **X** that she used?

   _____

(1)

   ii) What indicator might Sarah use to show when neutralisation has taken place?

   _____

(1)

   iii) What colour change would have taken place at neutralisation?

Colour in tablet solution	Colour at neutralisation

(2)

iv) Name **one** chemical which you might find in an indigestion tablet.

_____

(1)

v) Write a word equation for the reaction of sulphuric acid with this chemical.

_____

(2)

d) The results of the experiment were as follows:

Volume of sulphuric acid needed to neutralise Burney tablet solution = 25 cm^3
Volume of sulphuric acid needed to neutralise Rumbley tablet solution = 20 cm^3

i) Which of the tablets would be better to cure indigestion?

_____

ii) Give a reason for your answer. (2 lines) *(2)*

e) State and explain **two** safety measures (precautions) that Sarah should take whilst doing this experiment.

Safety measure	Reason
1 _____ _____ _____	_____ _____ _____
2 _____ _____ _____	_____ _____ _____

(2)
(Total marks 15)
(ULEAC)

QUESTION 10

a) The components of washing powders Soapso and Sudso are listed below.

Washing powder	Soapso	Sudso
Sodium sulphate %	29	35
Sodium carbonate %	20	0
Sodium silicate %	20	26
Sodium soap %	0	6
Detergent %	15	13

Dilute nitric acid was added to each powder in turn. Only one of the powders fizzed. The gas turned limewater milky.

i) Which powder fizzed? _____

(1)

ii) Which sodium compound was reacting with the acid? _____

(1)

iii) Name the gas given off. _____

(1)

iv) Draw and label apparatus which you would use to add the acid to the soap powder. Your diagram should show how you would pass the gas through limewater.

(4)

v) Why is it sensible to wear gloves when using nitric acid? (3 lines) *(1)*

b)

i) From the items above select **one** which is *not* acidic. _____

(1)

ii) Name **one** which would have a pH value below 7. _____

(1)

Soothers

NEW IMPROVED SOOTHERS BRING
30% MORE ACID NEUTRALISING POWER

EACH TABLET CONTAINS: Calcium Carbonate B.P. 534mg.
Magnesium Hydroxide B.P. 160mg.
KEEP OUT OF REACH OF CHILDREN.

'MILK OF MAGNESIA'
LIQUID

Shake bottle well before using. Please use
'Milk of Magnesia' within six months
of opening. Each 5ml contains 415mg
MAGNESIUM HYDROXIDE B.P.

BENNIES

Each tablet contains: Calcium Carbonate 680mg.
Light Magnesium Carbonate Ph. Fur. 80mg.
If symptoms persist, consult your doctor.

iii) Soothers, Bennies and Milk of Magnesia all claim to neutralise acid indigestion.

What is meant by 'neutralise'? _____

_____

(1)

iv) Name the **two** substances produced when Milk of Magnesia reacts with hydrochloric acid.

A _____ B _____

(2)

v) Where in the body might this reaction occur? _____

(1)

vi) If each packet of Soothers contains 12 tablets, what is the total mass of magnesium hydroxide in the packet?

_____

(1)

vii) Imagine some powdered Bennies were accidentally mixed with washing soda. Using your knowledge of the chemical properties of the contents of each, describe how you would separate them. (4 lines) *(4)*

c) Study the graph below, which shows the variation of pH in the mouth of a child who only eats at meal times.

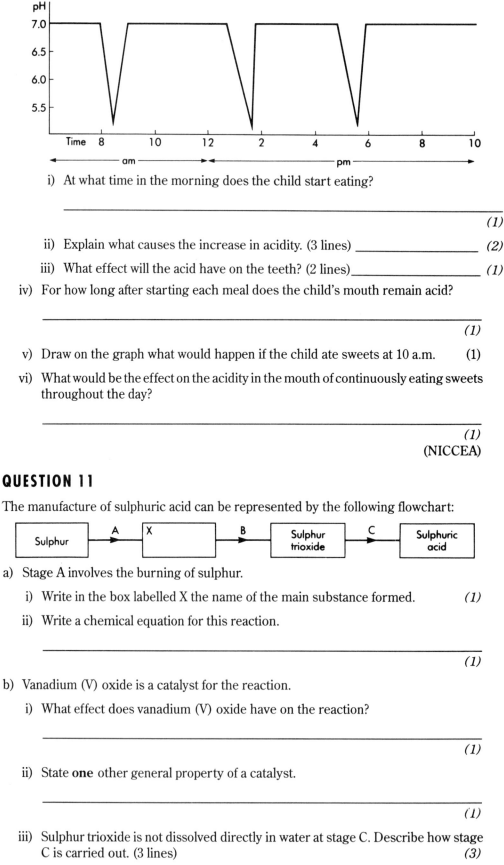

i) At what time in the morning does the child start eating?

_____

(1)

ii) Explain what causes the increase in acidity. (3 lines) _____ *(2)*

iii) What effect will the acid have on the teeth? (2 lines)_____ *(1)*

iv) For how long after starting each meal does the child's mouth remain acid?

_____

(1)

v) Draw on the graph what would happen if the child ate sweets at 10 a.m. (1)

vi) What would be the effect on the acidity in the mouth of continuously eating sweets throughout the day?

_____

(1)
(NICCEA)

QUESTION 11

The manufacture of sulphuric acid can be represented by the following flowchart:

| Sulphur | →A X | →B Sulphur trioxide | →C Sulphuric acid |

a) Stage A involves the burning of sulphur.

   i) Write in the box labelled X the name of the main substance formed. *(1)*

   ii) Write a chemical equation for this reaction.

_____

(1)

b) Vanadium (V) oxide is a catalyst for the reaction.

   i) What effect does vanadium (V) oxide have on the reaction?

_____

(1)

   ii) State **one** other general property of a catalyst.

_____

(1)

   iii) Sulphur trioxide is not dissolved directly in water at stage C. Describe how stage C is carried out. (3 lines) *(3)*

c) i) Sulphur dioxide is produced in most power stations in Britain as part of the waste gases. Explain what effect this gas may have on

    1 living organisms (3 lines) _____

    2 buildings (4 lines) _____

(5)

   ii) Suggest a method of removing sulphur dioxide from the waste gases. (3 lines) *(2)*
(ULEAC)

QUESTION 12

(Levels 4–6)

An example of a short, structured question typical of this level. Notice the use of straightforward words of instruction such as 'name' 'what is' 'complete'.

The following news item appeared in the *Daily Mirror* on 16 February 1987.

TV newsreader Jan Leeming was sprayed with acid when she challenged a gang of muggers in the BBC studios last night.

The three men sprayed the ammonia-like substance into her face and grabbed her handbag minutes before the 9.10 news bulletin.

There is a mistake in the article because ammonia is not an acid.

a) Name a suitable indicator which could be used to test if the substance was acid or alkaline.

_____

(1)

b) What colour would an acid turn this indicator?

_____

(1)

c) Ammonia is an alkali.
   What colour would ammonia turn this indicator?

_____

(1)

d) What is the reaction between an acid and an alkali called?

_____

(1)

e) Complete the following equation.

Acid   +   Alkali   =   _____   +   _____

(2)

[Co-ordinated Science, NEAB, WJEC, ULEAC]

ANSWERS TO EXAMINATION QUESTIONS

MULTIPLE CHOICE

ANSWER 1

Key E, pH 14.

ANSWER 2

Key C, pH 7.

ANSWER 3

Key B, pH 4.

ANSWER 4

Key E, 196 g. The solution is 2 M, so it's $2 \times [2+32+(16 \times 4)] = 196$.

ANSWER 5

Key C, hydrogen. Option A, carbon dioxide, is released when acids react with carbonates.

ANSWER 6

Key E, water. Option B, hydrogen, is released when acids react with metals, not metal oxides.

ANSWER 7

Key D, limewater. The gas released by acids and carbonates is carbon dioxide, which turns limewater milky. Option A is the test for oxygen, and option B is the test for hydrogen.

ANSWER 8

a) i) pH 7; ii) pH 9; iii) pH 4
b) i) a measuring cylinder or graduated beaker
   ii) Most household cleaners are alkaline and would neutralise the acidic Ataka.

ANSWER 9

a) hydrochloric acid
b) i) a solution that is neither acidic nor alkaline
   ii) 1 to increase the surface area
      2 to increase the rate of reaction
c) i) a burette
   ii) universal indicator
   iii) purple or blue in solution, green at neutralisation
   iv) calcium carbonate
   v) calcium carbonate + sulphuric acid = calcium sulphate + carbon dioxide + water
d) i) Burney tablets
   ii) They are a stronger tablet, as more acid is needed to neutralise them.
e) 1 to wear safety goggles – to stop any acid entering the eyes
   2 to wear plastic gloves – to stop acid getting on the skin.

ANSWER 10

a) i) Soapso
   ii) Sodium carbonate
   iii) carbon dioxide
   iv)

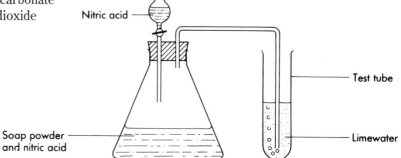

Nitric acid

Soap powder and nitric acid

Test tube

Limewater

   v) Nitric acid is corrosive and can burn your skin.

b) i) bicarbonate of soda (or Milk of Magnesia)
   ii) lemonade (or vinegar)
   iii) to remove the acidity
   iv) A, magnesium chloride; B, water
   v) in the stomach
   vi) 1,920 mg
   vii) Calcium carbonate and magnesium carbonate are insoluble, so you could mix with water. The washing soda dissolves but the Bennies contains insoluble substances, so filter and evaporate to dryness.

c) i) 8am
   ii) drinking an acidic drink, eg orange juice
   iii) attacks the enamel
   iv) about 1 hour
   v) The line should dip to pH 5.5 after 10 a.m., and then rise to pH 7.0 by 11 a.m.
   vi) The pH would be about 5.5, slightly acidic all day.

ANSWER 11

a) i) **X** is sulphur dioxide
   ii) $S + O_2 \rightarrow SO_2$

b) i) increases the rate of reaction
    ii) Is not used up in the reaction
    iii) Sulphur trioxide is dissolved in 98% sulphuric acid, and water is then added.

c) i) 1 can kill leaves on trees, so trees die; can cause breathing problems for humans
        2 causes damages to limestone buildings, as it corrodes the limestone and causes the buildings to crumble.
    ii) to pass the waste gases through an alkali to neutralise the sulphur dioxide.

ANSWER 12

a) write the name of any indicator you are familiar with, for example, universal indicator, litmus (1)

b) these indicators change to red with acid (1)

c) a blue colour (1)

d) neutralisation (1)

e) the rest of the equation should read: salt (1), water (1)

A STUDENT'S ANSWER WITH EXAMINER'S COMMENTS

Judith Harris is an Environmental Health Officer. She took samples of water from the local river. Waste water from the Turbo-Chemical Company flows into the river.

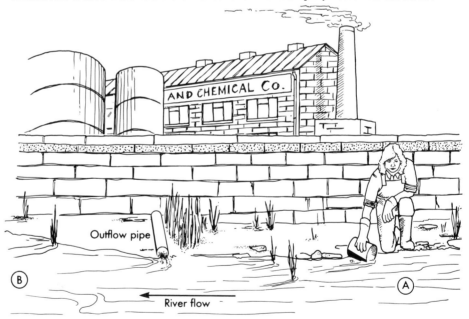

Judith then measured the pH of the water. She found that water from point A had a pH of 7.0 while that at point B had a pH of 2.0.

a) i) What can you state about the river water at A and at B?

> The water at B is acidic.

(2)

ii) What is likely to have changed the pH value of the water in travelling from A to B?

> The outflow pipe.

(1)

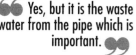 State water at A is neutral.

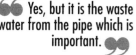 Yes, but it is the waste water from the pipe which is important.

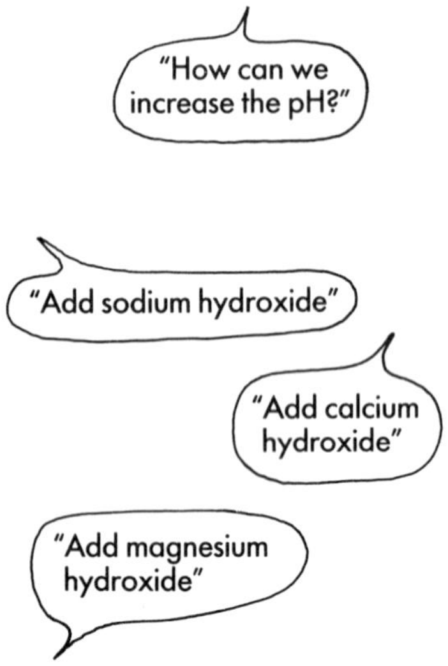

b) The local Environmental Health Regulations state that waste water from factories must have a pH between 7.5 and 9.5. The pH can be increased by adding alkaline substances. Mr Harminder Singh, the works chemist, talked to three of his laboratory technicians about possible substances to be added to the waste water (Figure 1). Some facts about these substances are shown in Table 1.

Alkaline substance	Solubility at 10°C (g/100 g of water)	pH of saturated solution
Calcium hydroxide	0.125	12.0
Magnesium hydroxide	0.070	9.3
Sodium hydroxide	102	14.0

Table 1

i) Which is the most soluble of these alkaline substances, and what is the pH of its saturated solution?

sodium hydroxide

(2)

ii) What would be the effect of adding too much calcium hydroxide?

The waste water would be too alkaline.

(1)

iii) Which saturated solution has the lowest pH?

Magnesium hydroxide

(1)

iv) Which substance should Mr Singh choose? Why should he choose it?

Sodium hydroxide
It is very soluble

(3)

v) You are provided with several litres of the waste water and the following apparatus and chemicals:
  beakers with a 1 litre mark
  balance
  universal indicator paper
  glass stirring rods
  suitable containers for weighing the chosen substance
  spatula
  chosen substance

Describe how you would find out how much of the chosen substance has to be added to the waste water to increase its pH to about 8.0.

Add some of the substance to the waste water, stir and take the pH. Add some more until the pH is neutral.

(8)

(Total marks 18)
(ULEAC)

Figure 1

"How can we increase the pH?"

"Add sodium hydroxide"

"Add calcium hydroxide"

"Add magnesium hydroxide"

Yes, and state pH 14.0 for the second mark

Good.

Yes and it has the highest pH.

State: take pH of waste water; use measured volume of waste water eg 1 litre; add *measured* amount of sodium hydroxide; stir to dissolve; record result each time; continue until pH 7.

R E V I E W   S H E E T

✎ Name four properties of an acid

1. _____

2. _____

3. _____

4. _____

✎ Acids only behave as acids when they are _____ in water. This is because water is a _____ solvent.

✎ Acids which give up all their hydrogen ions in water are called _____ acids; those

which only give up some of their hydrogen ions are called _____ acids.

✎ List the following acids under the correct heading in the table.

sulphuric acid   citric acid (citrus fruits)
ethanoic (acetic) acid (vinegar)   nitric acid
hydrochloric acid   malic acid (apples)

   Strong acids   *Weak acids*

✎ Name four properties of an alkali

1. _____

2. _____

3. _____

4. _____

✎ List two ways of detecting acids or alkalis

1. _____

2. _____

✎ _____ indicator is the most commonly used indicator.

✎ Low numbers on the pH scale indicate _____ acidity. The pH number 7 indicates a

_____ solution, the colour of the indicator turning _____ . A high number

on the pH scale indicates increasing _____ .

✎ Complete the following table with the colours you would expect to find.

Indicator	*in acid*	*in alkali*	*in water (neutral)*
litmus			

✎ If universal indicator is added to a strong alkaline solution, the indicator will turn a _____ colour.

✎ Complete the following equations:
   metal   +   acid   →
   zinc   +   hydrochloric acid   →

✎ Complete the following chart

potassium
sodium
lithium

calcium
magnesium   — react with dilute [＿＿＿]
aluminium
zinc
iron
tin
lead

[＿＿＿] reactive

[＿＿＿] reactive

....

copper
silver   ⊢ do not react with dilute [＿＿＿]
gold

✎ How can we test for hydrogen gas?

_____

✎ Bases are substances which can neutralise acids. Metal oxides are bases and react with acids to

produce _____

✎ How can we test for carbon dioxide in a reaction with carbonates?

_____

✎ A small amount of _____ from the atmosphere dissolves in rain water to give 'acid rain'.

✎ List three ways of combating acid rain

1. _____

2. _____

3. _____

✎ _____ are ionic substances which are formed in reactions between acids and bases

or between acids and metals.

✎ Each salt contains a _____ ion and a _____ ion.

✎ The solubility of a salt often increases with _____

✎ The colour of salts is often due to the metal ion present. Complete the following table.

Ion	Colour	Ion	Colour
Na^+		Fe^{2+}	
K^+		Fe^{3+}	
Cu^{2+}			

✎ List four practical uses of salts

1. _____

2. _____

3. _____

4. _____

12

METALS AND POLYMERS

GETTING STARTED

We make use of materials according to their properties, which in turn are determined by the way in which their atoms are bonded together. Two very useful groups of materials are *metals* and *polymers* (a type of macromolecule). Understanding the structure of these helps the scientist to manufacture materials for specific purposes, as well as to have a better understanding of their properties.

All *metals* are elements (an individual metal contains only one type of atom). Metals exist as compounds in rocks; those rocks which contain large enough quantities of metals to be mined are called ores. Metals can be extracted from ores by techniques such as smelting (reduction using carbon) or electrolysis. Metals have a number of useful properties:

- conductors of heat and electricity;

- solids (except mercury);

- strong, malleable and ductile;

- high melting points and densities;

- shiny.

There are exceptions to these general properties, and different metals do exhibit these properties to varying degrees, eg copper is used for electrical wiring because it is a better conductor than many. It is important to realise, however, that the choice of a metal for a particular job not only depends on its properties but also on its cost. (Gold is a better conductor than copper but is not used in electrical wiring though it is used for electrical contacts in microchips in computers!)

Many *macromolecules* (large molecules) are based on carbon and its ability to form long chains. Macromolecules have a number of useful properties; they are found in living things, eg as wool (a protein), or as starch (a carbohydrate). They can also be man-made from carbon-based compounds, eg detergents and polymers. Scientists can *synthesise* (make) macromolecules such as polymers to have specific properties, eg polythene is a long carbon chain which has attached to it hydrogen atoms. By replacing the hydrogen atoms with fluorine atoms, a different polymer can be made (PTFE) which is used on non-stick frying pans. The properties of these compounds are determined by the way the carbon atoms are *joined* in the chain (single bonds or double bonds, etc.) and the type of atoms *attached* to the chain.

ESSENTIAL PRINCIPLES

1 ▶ METALS AS ELEMENTS

❝ Check with Chapter 9 ❞

All metals are *elements* and are grouped on the left-hand side of the periodic table. The common everyday metals are found in the block referred to as the *transition metals*. Metals are giant structures in which the metal atoms exist as positive ions in a sea of electrons. This gives rise to their characteristic physical properties of strength, hardness and the ability to conduct electricity.

						1 **H** Hydrogen 1												4 **He** Helium 2
7 **Li** Lithium 3	9 **Be** Beryllium 4											11 **B** Boron 5	12 **C** Carbon 6	14 **N** Nitrogen 7	16 **O** Oxygen 8	19 **F** Fluorine 9	20 **Ne** Neon 10
23 **Na** Sodium 11	24 **Mg** Magnesium 12											27 **Al** Aluminium 13	28 **Si** Silicon 14	31 **P** Phosphorus 15	32 **S** Sulphur 16	35.5 **Cl** Chlorine 17	40 **Ar** Argon 18
39 **K** Potassium 19	40 **Ca** Calcium 20	45 **Sc** Scandium 21	48 **Ti** Titanium 22	51 **V** Vanadium 23	52 **Cr** Chromium 24	55 **Mn** Manganese 25	56 **Fe** Iron 26	59 **Co** Cobalt 27	59 **Ni** Nickel 28	64 **Cu** Copper 29	65 **Zn** Zinc 30	70 **Ga** Gallium 31	73 **Ge** Germanium 32	75 **As** Arsenic 33	79 **Se** Selenium 34	80 **Br** Bromine 35	84 **Kr** Krypton 36
85 **Rb** Rubidium 37	88 **Sr** Strontium 38	89 **Y** Yttrium 39	91 **Zr** Zirconium 40	93 **Nb** Niobium 41	96 **Mo** Molybdenum 42	**Tc** Technetium 43	101 **Ru** Ruthenium 44	103 **Rh** Rhodium 45	106 **Pd** Palladium 46	108 **Ag** Silver 47	112 **Cd** Cadmium 48	115 **In** Indium 49	119 **Sn** Tin 50	122 **Sb** Antimony 51	128 **Te** Tellurium 52	127 **I** Iodine 53	131 **Xe** Xenon 54
133 **Cs** Caesium 55	137 **Ba** Barium 56	139 **La** Lanthanum 57 ·	178 **Hf** Hafnium 72	181 **Ta** Tantalum 73	184 **W** Tungsten 74	186 **Re** Rhenium 75	190 **Os** Osmium 76	192 **Ir** Iridium 77	195 **Pt** Platinum 78	197 **Au** Gold 79	201 **Hg** Mercury 80	204 **Tl** Thallium 81	207 **Pb** Lead 82	209 **Bi** Bismuth 83	**Po** Polonium 84	**At** Astatine 85	**Rn** Radon 86
Fr Francium 87	226 **Ra** Radium 88	227 **Ac** Actinium 89 †															

◀——————— Metals ———————▶◀ Non-Metals ▶

Fig 12.1 The position of metals in the periodic table.

In the majority of their reactions, metal atoms react to form *positive ions*. The charge on the ion depends on the *position* in the periodic table.

Group	Charge on ion	Example
1	1+	Na
2	2+	Ca
3	3+	Al

The transition metals can form ions with *different* charges; they are said to have *variable valency*. In compounds, the charge on the metal ion is indicated by roman numerals. Transition metal compounds are often coloured.

Compound	Colour	Formula	Metal ion
Copper (II) sulphate	blue	$CuSO_4$	Cu^{2+}
Iron (II) sulphate	green	$FeSO_4$	Fe^{2+}
Iron (III) oxide	red	Fe_2O_3	Fe^{3+}
Copper (I) oxide	red	Cu_2O	Cu^+
Copper (II) oxide	black	CuO	Cu^{2+}

2 ▶ PROPERTIES AND USES OF METALS

❝ Some uses of metals ❞

The general physical properties of metals, which provide them with a variety of uses, are shown in Figure12.2

Some metals have individual properties which give them particular uses. *Iron*, for example, can be easily magnetised, so is used to make magnets and electromagnets; *mercury* is a liquid which expands well on heating, so is used in the manufacture of thermometers. *Gold* is a metal which is rare and never corrodes, so can be used as a money standard and for making jewellery.

Metal	Property	Use
Iron	toughness	equipment and machinery that will be knocked about in use – steel
Aluminium, silver	metallic sheen	mirrors, reflectors
Aluminium, gold	reflecting heat and light	coating of firemen's protective clothing; space 'shuttle' heat shield of gold foil
Zinc, copper	malleability	easy shaping of metal structures by presses, also 'hand beating' of metals into shape – brass
Copper, aluminium, gold	ductility	wide variety of wires - electrical and ornamental
Iron, aluminium, tungsten	high melting point	wires for electric fires, metals for boilers, cookers, pans, electric light filaments (tungsten m.p. about 3500°C)
Aluminium, iron, copper	good heat conductor	radiators in central heating systems, copper for cooking pans
Copper, aluminium	electrical conductivity	electrical wiring
Lead, aluminium, iron, zinc	corrosion resistance	roofing, flashings, foil and food containers – soft drink and beer cans, zinc coating – 'galvanised' steel
Aluminium, magnesium	low density	aircraft construction, lightweight vehicles and wheels

Fig. 12.2 Some typical metals and their uses

---

3 ▷ CHANGING PHYSICAL PROPERTIES

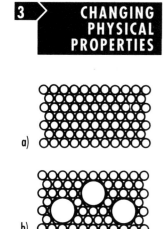

Fig. 12.3 Atoms in a) pure metal and b) an alloy

MAKING ALLOYS

Alloys are solid mixtures of metals and are formed by melting together two or more different metals. The properties of the alloy that is formed are *not* simply an average of the properties of the original metals. The properties also depend on the proportion of each metal present, eg solder is an alloy of lead (67%) and tin (33%) and has a lower melting point. This is not to say, however, that the properties of new alloys are simply a hit or miss affair. The properties of alloys are determined partly by the *metal atoms present*, but more importantly by how these atoms can *pack together* in the structure (see Figure 12.3) . With information such as this, scientists can produce alloys with specific properties.

One very important group of alloys is *steels*. Mild steel is an alloy of the metal iron mixed with a small quantity of carbon (a non-metal). The introduction of a small quantity of carbon increases the strength of the iron enormously, because the carbon atoms fit into the giant structure of iron atoms, preventing the iron atoms moving so freely when the material is hammered, twisted or stretched.

Different steels can be produced with different properties, depending on the amount of carbon present. In addition, other metals can be added, such as chromium and tungsten, to change the properties still further.

HEAT TREATMENT AND WORK HARDENING

Heating a metal such as steel and then allowing it to cool down quickly or slowly can change its properties, eg hot metal that is cooled quickly by quenching (plunging into cold water) will often make the metal more brittle.

Metal that is continually being worked (hammered or bent into shape) will gradually become harder; this is called *work hardening*. This can be removed by heating and by allowing the metal to cool down slowly; this is called *annealing*.

Examples of common alloys;

Some properties of common alloys

Alloy	Use	Constituents	Important Properties
spring steel	suspension springs	iron; 0.3% - 0.6% carbon	Contains sufficient carbon that will produce a spring metal
stainless steel	surgical instruments; cutlery	iron; <1% carbon; 18% chromium	resistant to corrosion
chromium–vanadium steel	axles and wrenches	iron; chromium; vanadium; carbon	very strong, great resistance to strain
high speed tungsten steels	cutting metals; drills, etc.	iron with up to 20% tungsten	maintains sharp edge at high temperatures
brass	screws; taps; ornaments	copper/zinc. The more zinc there is the stronger the alloy (up to 34% zinc)	strong; does not easily corrode
bronze	castings of intricate shapes, statues, etc.	copper; up to 12% tin	easily cast; resists corrosion
an aluminium alloy	aircraft framework	aluminium; copper; magnesium	very strong for its weight; aluminium is a light metal but is not very strong so is alloyed with other metals to increase strength

These are just some examples of some useful alloys. Exam questions involving alloys often require you to match the properties of an alloy which may be given to a particular use.

4 ▷ THE CHEMICAL PROPERTIES OF METALS

Check with Chapter 9, Periodic Table

THE REACTIVITY SERIES

When metals react they do so to form positive ions. Some metals are more reactive than others; this means the atoms form ions more easily. The metals can be placed in order of their reactivity, which depends on the ease with which they can form positive ions. This is referred to as the *reactivity series* for metals. This order of reactivity tends to be about the same no matter with what the metals are reacting.

Reactivity series

potassium	greatest tendency to form ions
sodium	
lithium	
calcium	
magnesium	
aluminium	
carbon	
zinc	increasing tendency to form ions
iron	
tin	
lead	
hydrogen	
copper	
silver	
gold	least tendency to form ions

The reactivity series can help us understand:

- why some metals corrode and not others;

- how we can prevent corrosion;

- why some metals react with dilute acids and not others;

- why some metals are extracted from their ores by reduction with carbon and why some can only be extracted by electrolysis;

- why metals were discovered in the order they were.

REACTIONS OF METALS

Metal and oxygen

When heated in air, metals are *oxidised* to form metal oxides which are bases. The more reactive metals will burn in air. Gold and silver are metals which are not oxidised by heating in air. For example,

$$2Mg(s) + O_2(g) \rightarrow 2MgO(s)$$

Metals and water

The more reactive metals react with water to produce hydrogen. Potassium, sodium, lithium and calcium will react with cold water, to produce hydroxides:

$$2Na(s) + 2H_2O(l) \rightarrow 2NaOH(aq) + H_2(g)$$

On the other hand, magnesium, zinc and iron will only react with steam, to form oxides:

$$Zn(s) + H_2O(g) \rightarrow ZnO(s) + H_2(g)$$

Metals and acids

All the metals in the reactivity series above copper will form hydrogen by reacting with hydrochloric acid. For example,

$$Mg(s) + 2HCl(aq) \rightarrow MgCl_2(aq) + H_2(g)$$

Dilute nitric acid, however, does not give hydrogen. The lower in the reactivity series the metal, the slower the reaction.

Metals and metal salt solutions

If a metal is placed in a solution of the salt of another metal, a reaction may or may not take place. We can predict whether a reaction will occur if we know the position of the metals in the reactivity series. A metal high in the reactivity series, which has the greater tendency to form ions, will displace a metal low in the reactivity series from solution. For example,

$$Mg(s) + CuSO_4(aq) \rightarrow MgSO_4(aq) + Cu(s)$$

Spot the pattern

There's a pattern here

And a pattern here

Metals plus acids produce hydrogen

Identify the pattern

Mg is above Cu in the reactivity series, so electrons are transferred from the magnesium atom to the copper ion. This can be shown as an *ionic* equation, since it does not matter what negative ion is present:

$$Mg(s) + Cu^{2+}(aq) \rightarrow Mg^{2+}(aq) + Cu(s)$$

METALS AND CELLS

The difference in tendency of metals to form ions can be very useful. If two different metals are placed in a solution containing ions and are linked by a wire, then electrons will flow through the wire. This means that a current is flowing through the wire, and there is a voltage between the two metals. This arrangement is called a *simple cell* (see Figure 12.4).

All cells contain three things:

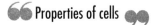 Properties of cells

- a + terminal (the positive electrode or **anode**);

- a – terminal (the negative electrode or **cathode**);

- a solution containing ions through which electricity can pass - the **electrolyte**.

The voltage that is produced between the two metals generally depends on their relative positions in the reactivity series. If the metals are far apart in the reactivity series then a large voltage is produced, whereas if the two metals in the pair are close together then a small voltage is produced. Let's refer back to the reactivity series:

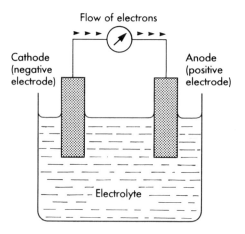

Fig 12.4 A simple cell.

Metal pair	Voltage produced
magnesium/copper	large voltage
iron/zinc	small voltage

Dry cells (batteries) that you can buy essentially consist of metal pairs in an electrolyte, except that one of the metals is replaced by carbon (in the form of graphite). In normal dry cells the electrolyte is a weak acid; alkaline batteries have electrolytes which are alkalis.

METALS AND CORROSION

Corrosion is a chemical reaction. Corrosion of a metal will only take place if the metal is in contact with a solution containing ions. When the metal corrodes it loses electrons to form positive ions:

 Corrosion can be costly

Metal atom − electron(s) $\rightarrow$ **metal ion**
M(s)   − e⁻ $\rightarrow$ M⁺

Metals corrode at different rates, depending on their position in the reactivity series. Magnesium will corrode more quickly than copper, because it is higher in the reactivity series and has a greater tendency to form ions. As an example, iron will corrode (rust) when it is in contact with water and air. The water acts as a weak electrolyte (a solution containing ions) because it contains dissolved substances. Iron will corrode much more quickly when in contact with sea water, because this is a much stronger electrolyte (it contains a larger amount of dissolved salts). This is a real problem for ships; also cars that are kept near the sea (in seaside towns) tend to corrode more quickly than their counterparts inland. The reaction occurring in the corrosion of iron is as follows:

$$Fe(s) \quad - \quad 3e^- \quad \rightarrow \quad Fe^{3+}(aq)$$

Corrosion can be a greater problem with structures built of more than one metal, eg if the steel plates of a ship's hull are riveted together with brass rivets, then the steel will corrode much more quickly than if the rivets were also made of steel. The sea water is acting as the electrolyte, so that a simple cell is set up between the iron (steel) and the copper (in the brass). The iron has a greater tendency to form ions than the copper, so will corrode much more rapidly.

The *rate of corrosion* of a metal therefore depends on:

- the position of the metal in the reactivity series;

- the concentration of the electrolyte with which the metal is in contact;

Factors affecting the rate of corrosion

- the nature of any other metal with which it is in contact;

- the temperature of the metal - a higher temperature speeds up chemical reactions (this is why car exhausts corrode quickly).

Preventing corrosion

A popular exam topic

1 **Surface coating:** the simplest method of preventing metals from corroding is either to paint the metal or to cover it with a polymer layer which is bonded to the surface. Some oil rigs in the North Sea are protected in this way.

Technological application

2 **Sacrificial protection:** in this process one metal is 'sacrificed' to protect another. In *galvanising*, iron is coated with a thin layer of zinc. Since the zinc is higher in the reactivity series, it will corrode, leaving the iron metal intact. A similar method is used to protect ships and oil rig platforms in the North Sea. This time, large blocks of zinc are welded to the ship's hull or the legs of the oil rig. These corrode away, protecting the legs, and can be easily replaced with new ones.

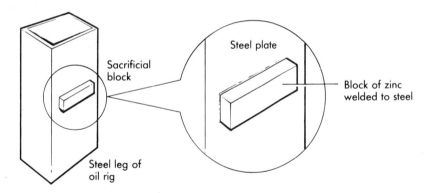

Fig. 12.5 Sacrificial corrosion.

3 **Electroplating:** another method of preventing corrosion is to cover the surface of the metal with a thin layer of another metal which does not corrode. This is done by placing the metal to be protected in an electrolysis cell connected as the cathode (see Chapter 9). Examples of electroplating are tin cans (steel coated with a thin layer of tin), and chromium-plated bumpers on cars.

5 ▷ **THE HISTORY OF METALS**

The most abundant metal in the Earth's crust is aluminium, yet it was one of the last to be discovered. Why should this be so? Yet again, reference to the reactivity series can help us answer this question.

Metal	Approximate date of first use
Gold, silver, copper	5000 BC
Tin	2500 BC
Iron	1200 BC
Zinc	BC/AD
Aluminium	AD 1825

If we compare this list with the reactivity series, we can see that it shows the *reverse* pattern. In other words, the metals that were *discovered first* were those that showed the *least* tendency to form ions. In fact the metals gold and silver and small amounts of copper can be found on the ground in their *native state*, ie as the metals themselves. The other metals however only exist in the Earth's crust as compounds, ie the metals are present as metal ions chemically locked with other substances. The *more reactive* a metal (the higher in the reactivity series), the *more stable* it becomes as a *compound*. This means that it will be difficult to extract it from its ore (to change the ion into an atom).

Many metals exist in the Earth's crust as metal ores. Some of the most common are shown in the table below.

Metal ore	Compound	Formula	Metal
Limestone	calcium carbonate	$CaCO_3$	calcium
Bauxite	aluminium oxide	Al_2O_3	aluminium
Haematite	iron oxide	Fe_2O_3	iron
Pyrites	iron sulphide	FeS_2	iron
Galena	lead sulphide	PbS	lead
Chalcopyrite	copper iron sulphide	$CuFeS_2$	copper

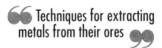
Techniques for extracting metals from their ores

There are two basic techniques for extracting the metal from the ore; either **reduction**, using heat energy and carbon as the reducing agent, or **electrolysis**, using electrical energy. In either case the problem is the same - to reduce the metal *ion* to a metal *atom*. The technique that is chosen depends on cost and the reactivity of the metal.

REDUCTION BY CARBON

Carbon is a suitable reducing agent for obtaining many metals from their oxides. For example,

lead oxide + carbon → lead + carbon dioxide
$2PbO$ + C → $2Pb$ + CO_2

Coke is a relatively cheap and abundant source of carbon which is capable of reducing oxides of all the metals below aluminium in the reactivity series. Coke is therefore suitable for large-scale metal extraction.

Iron extraction

Iron is extracted from its ore *haematite* (which contains iron oxide) by smelting in a *blast furnace*. Once the furnace is started it operates as a continuous process, the raw materials being added at the top and the molten iron and molten waste being run off at the bottom.

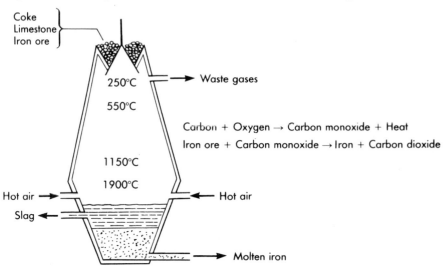

Fig. 12.6 The blast furnace used to extract iron from iron ore.

The raw materials include *iron oxide ore*, which will be reduced to iron; *coke*, which provides the reducing agent; and *limestone*, which is added to remove the waste material from the iron ore.

During the process, at the *bottom* of the furnace a *blast* of hot air is forced up into the hot, raw materials. The air provides oxygen, which reacts with the carbon to produce carbon monoxide:

$$2C(s) \; + \; O_2(g) \; \rightarrow \; 2CO(g)$$

Carbon monoxide is a powerful reducing agent, and reduces the iron oxide to iron, which is molten at the temperature of the furnace:

carbon monoxide + iron oxide → iron + carbon dioxide
$$3CO(g) \qquad + \; Fe_2O_3(s) \; \rightarrow 2Fe(l) \; + \; 3CO_2(g)$$

Iron ore contains a lot of rocky material as impurity (mainly silica). This would soon clog the furnace and have to be removed, requiring the furnace to be shut down and allowed to cool - a very costly process. The limestone (calcium carbonate) reacts with the silica at high temperature to produce a molten glassy material (calcium silicate). This is less dense than the molten iron and floats to the top of the molten iron; where it is tapped off as *slag*.

 **Producing *slag* and pig iron**

The molten iron is very dense and travels down through the furnace. It is tapped off at the bottom hole into large moulds called pigs. The iron that is produced is called *pig iron*.

The hot waste gases (including carbon monoxide and carbon dioxide) are removed through the top of the furnace.

Other metals, such as lead, zinc and copper, can also be extracted in this way. Sulphide ores (eg galena, PbS) first have to be roasted in air to convert the compound to a metal oxide:

lead sulphide + **oxygen** → **lead oxide** + **sulphur dioxide**
$$2PbS(s) \qquad + \; 3O_2(g) \; \rightarrow \; 2PbO(s) \qquad + \; SO_2(g)$$

ELECTROLYSIS

Another method of reducing a metal ore to the metal is by the process of **electrolysis**. Metals are present in metal ores as *positive ions*. If electricity is passed into a solution of the ore, or into the molten ore (both states where the ions are free to move), then the positive metal ions will be attracted to the negative electrodes. All the metals can be extracted from their ores by electrolysis.

An electrolysis cell always contains a positive electrode (*anode*), a negative electrode (*cathode*) and an electrolyte – a liquid containing ions (an aqueous solution of an ionic substance or a molten ionic substance).

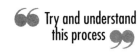 **Try and understand this process**

The anode and cathode are connected to an electrical power source. The electricity is conducted through the liquid electrolyte by the ions themselves moving.

The *positive* metal ions are attracted to the cathode.
The *negative* ions are attracted to the anode.

Let's examine the reactions occurring.
At the cathode: the positive metal ions gain an electron and become **atoms:**

$$M^+ \; + \; e^- \; \rightarrow \; M$$

The metal is deposited as a layer on the cathode.

At the anode: the negative ions lose electrons and become **atoms:**

$$X^- \; - \; e^- \; \rightarrow \; X$$

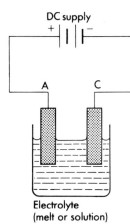

DC supply

A   C

Electrolyte
(melt or solution)

Fig 12.7 An electrolysis cell.

An example of electrolysis is the extraction of aluminium from its ore. The ore bauxite (mainly aluminium oxide) is first concentrated by removing the impurities. The concentrate (alumina) is then dissolved in molten cryolite at about 1000°C to give a solution which provides free-moving aluminium ions. Aluminium oxide has a melting point above 2000°C, so melting the oxide to provide free moving aluminium ions is not practical. The anodes and cathodes are made of carbon. Aluminium, when it is formed, is molten, so it is tapped off from the bottom of the cell (see Figure 12.8).

Let's examine the reactions occurring.

At the cathode: $\qquad Al^{3+} \; + \; 3e^- \; \rightarrow \; Al$
At the anode: $\qquad 2O^{2-} \; - \; 4e^- \; \rightarrow \; O_2$

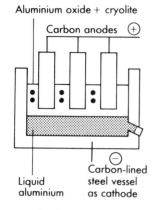

Fig 12.8 The electrolysis of alumina to extract aluminium.

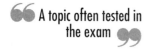

A topic often tested in the exam

All metals above aluminium in the reactivity series are normally extracted by electrolysis, because they are too reactive to be reduced by carbon. Sometimes metals lower down, such as zinc, are extracted by electrolysis.

THE CHOICE OF EXTRACTION METHOD

Metals exist in ores in an oxidised state. In order to extract the metal, the ores all have to be reduced; this requires adding electrons to the metal ion and so requires energy:

$$\text{metal ion} \quad + \quad \text{electrons} \quad \xrightarrow{\text{reduction}} \quad \text{metal atom}$$

The choice of the extraction method for a metal depends largely on two things:

1   the activity of the metal;
2   the cost of energy to perform the reduction.

Carbon can act as a reducing agent for all the less reactive metals (those below aluminium in the series). Carbon in the form of coke is plentiful and its combustion provides a relatively cheap form of energy (in the form of heat). Electrolysis is normally much more expensive, so is used if there is no alternative. However, an electrolysis metal extraction plant is often sited to take advantage of cheap electrical power, eg hydro-electric power. There is also an advantage in a metal extraction plant being sited near the mine, since the transport of crude ore would cost more than the transport of the metal.

Organic compounds are found in petroleum (crude oil), coal, natural gas and living organisms.

Petroleum (crude oil) is a mixture of a hydrocarbon : compounds consisting of molecules made up of atoms of carbon and hydrogen only. It is separated by fractional distillation into various *fractions* each of which contains molecules with similar chain lengths. The table shows the different fractions produced by the fractional distillation of petroleum.

Boiling range (°C)	Fraction	Use
<30	liquified gases	Calor gas, butane
20–200	petrol	petrol for cars, solvents
175–250	paraffin (kerosene)	oil stoves, aircraft fuel
200–350	diesel oil	diesel engine fuel in trains, lorries, tractors, etc.
300–400	lubricating oil	lubricant
350–450	fuel oil	fuel for power stations and ships
350–500	wax, grease	candles, wax paper, lubricant
>500 (solid)	bitumen	road making, roofing material

Fig. 12.9

When the carbon atoms which form the spine of these molecules are joined by single carbon–carbon bonds, they are described as *saturated hydrocarbons*, for example ethane C_2H_6.

The hydrocarbon molecules in petroleum vary in size. As the molecules in a hydrocarbon get larger:

- the boiling point increases

- it flows less easily (becomes more viscous)

- it ignites less easily (less flammable)

- it is less volatile

Fig. 12.10

Large hydrocarbon molecules can be broken down by a process known as *cracking* to produce shorter more useful molecules.

When the carbon atoms are linked by a double bond they are described as *unsaturated hydrocarbons,* for example, ethene C_2H_4.

These compounds are reactive and useful for making other substances.

Macromolecules are large molecules which can have very useful properties. Some macromolecules are very large, consisting of long chains of smaller molecules linked together, forming a repeating pattern. These are called *polymers*; the smaller molecules which form the pattern are called *monomers*.

DETERGENTS

 Check if your syllabus requires this topic

The job of a detergent is to help water clean materials by washing away grease and dirt. Water is a good solvent, particularly for ionic substances, but it is not good at dissolving greasy substances. The detergent molecules help by breaking up the grease into smaller globules which can be carried away by the water.

How detergents work

Detergent molecules consist of long carbon chains which have two different parts. One part of the molecule is water-loving (*hydrophilic*) because it carries an electric charge (ionic). The other part of the molecule is water-hating (*hydrophobic*) because of the long covalently bonded chain. To help explain the process we can represent these molecules as pin shapes (see Figure 12.11).

The water-hating (or grease-loving) part of the molecule buries itself in the grease while the water-loving part stays in the water. During agitation the water can get between the grease and the surface to be cleaned. The grease forms globules that are kept apart by the charges on the detergent ('like' charges repel). The detergent and grease form an emulsion in the water.

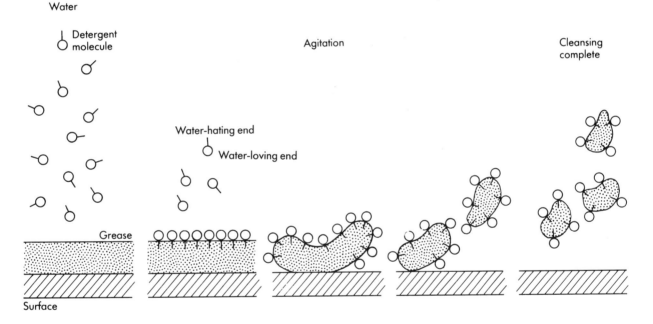

Fig. 12.11 How detergents work

Detergents in action

There are two types of detergents. *Soap detergents* are made from animal or vegetable fats and alkalis. Sodium stearate (see Figure 12.12) is a typical soap. In water, the sodium ion floats free, leaving one end of the molecule negatively charged.

Soapless detergents are made using chemicals from oil and acids. A typical soapless detergent is shown in Figure 12.13. Again in water, the sodium ion is separated from the molecule, leaving one end negatively charged.

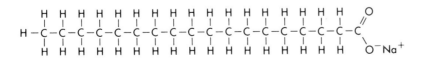

A soap molecule

Fig. 12.12 A typical soap (sodium stearate).

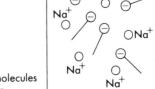

Soap molecules in water

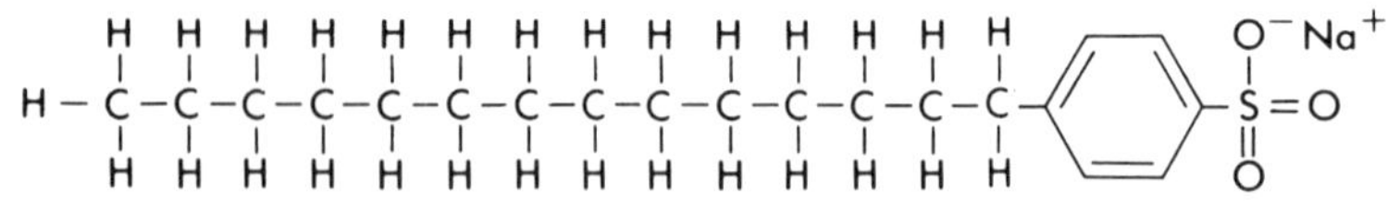

A detergent molecule

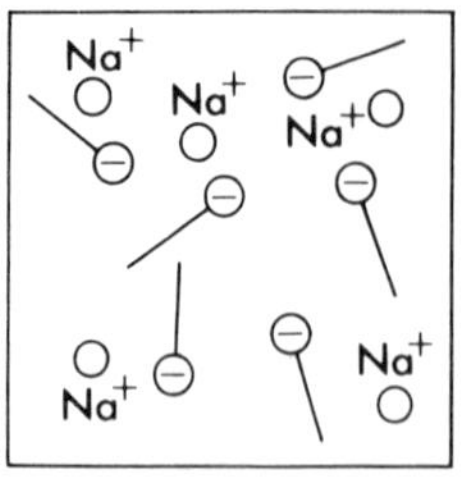

Detergent molecules
in water

Fig. 12.13 A typical soapless detergent.

HARD AND SOFT WATER

Tap water often contains dissolved salts, depending on what type of rock the rain water has washed through. Water in different parts of the country will contain different salts, and in different amounts. The types of water are known as *hard* or *soft.*

Hard water contains either magnesium or calcium salts (ie Mg^{2+} or Ca^{2+} ions).
Soft water contains none, or only very few, dissolved magnesium or calcium salts, although it may contain other dissolved salts.

The problem with hard water is that the calcium ions or magnesium ions in it will react with soaps. They attach themselves to soap molecules, forming an insoluble 'scum' on the surface of the water. The soap can no longer emulsify grease, so more soap has to be added to hard water than to soft water to do the same job. Soapless detergents do *not* behave in this way. No scum is formed with hard water, and hence no detergent is wasted.

Fig. 12.14 The reaction between soap and ions in hard water

sodium stearate + calcium ions → calcium stearate + sodium ions

2NaSt(aq) + Ca^{2+}(aq) → $CaSt_2$(s) + $2Na^+$(aq)

Note: St represents the stearate part of the molecule ($C_{17}H_{35}COO^-$)

Removing hardness in water

Hard water can cause more serious problems than wasting soap, so it is important to be able to remove the hardness. The common salts which cause hardness are calcium hydrogen carbonate, calcium sulphate, magnesium hydrogencarbonate and magnesium sulphate. When hard water is heated, a chemical reaction occurs, producing insoluble carbonates. This is the fur or limescale that appears inside hot water pipes and kettles.

$$Ca(HCO_3)_2(aq) \xrightarrow{\text{heat}} CaCO_3(s) + H_2O(l) + CO_2(g)$$

This furring up of pipes can cause damage and reduces the efficiency of hot water heating systems. The hardness of water can be removed by boiling, but this is expensive and not always convenient, so alternative methods have been developed. *Water softeners* are chemicals that can be added to water to remove calcium ions from solution by precipitating them out. Sodium carbonate is an example. *Ion exchange resins* are the active components in water softener units that are built into many dishwashing machines. The ion exchange resins work by replacing calcium ions with sodium ions, so they need to be regularly topped up with salt (sodium chloride).

9 NATURAL AND SYNTHETIC POLYMERS

Polymer molecules are very long chains consisting of repeating *monomer* units. There can be between 1000 and 50 000 monomers in a chain. The chemical reaction in which monomers combine is called *polymerisation.*

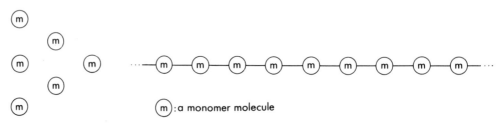

(m): a monomer molecule

Fig. 12.15 A polymer molecule: polymers are made by joining together many small molecules called monomers.

There are two ways in which monomers can react to form polymers:

■ addition polymerisation

■ condensation polymerisation

Addition Polymerisation

Unsaturated monomers which have a double carbon-carbon bond join together to form a polymer. For example, ethene, an unsaturated hydrocarbon forms poly(ethene), i.e. polythene, a saturated hydrocarbon.

Fig. 12.16
$$n \left(\begin{array}{c} | \ \ | \\ C = C \\ | \ \ | \end{array} \right) \longrightarrow \left(\begin{array}{c} | \ \ | \\ -C - C- \\ | \ \ | \end{array} \right)_n$$

Condensation Polymerisation

Condensation polymers are formed when small molecules are lost when the monomers react together. These small molecules are usually water or hydrogen chloride. For example, nylon – a polyamide; terylene – a polyester.

NATURAL POLYMERS

Starch

Starch is a natural polymer, which is made by green plants. It consists of long chains of *glucose* molecules (the monomer) joined together. Starch is a carbohydrate (contains carbon, hydrogen and oxygen atoms only) and as a food is a useful source of energy. The starch molecule is too large, however, to pass through the gut wall into the blood system and must be converted into smaller units in the digestive system.

 Digestion.

 Hydrolysis involves adding water

Starch can be broken down by reaction with water into smaller units; the process is called hydrolysis. *Salivary amylase* (the enzyme in saliva) catalyses the hydrolysis of starch into a sugar called maltose (which is effectively a double glucose molecule). *Acids* can also catalyse the hydrolysis, but this time the product is glucose. In the stomach, hydrochloric acid breaks down any unconverted starch or maltose molecules into glucose molecules, which are small enough to pass through the gut wall.

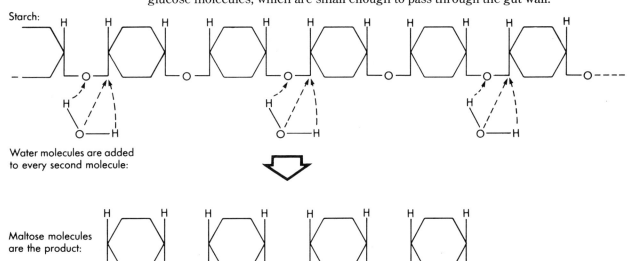

Starch:

Water molecules are added to every second molecule:

Maltose molecules are the product:

Fig. 12.17 Salivary amylase catalyses the breakdown of starch by hydrolysis (adding water).

Proteins

These are polymers which are made up of different combinations of monomer units called *amino acids*. There are twenty different naturally occurring amino acids. Each amino acid contains a nitrogen atom. Amino acids are essential for cell growth and repair. Proteins are also broken down in the digestive system to the monomer units (amino acids) by the action of enzymes.

Other natural polymers include wool, cotton, cellulose and rubber.

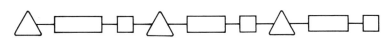

Each acid contains   – NH₂ group (amino)   eg H₂N ▭ COOH

and   – COOH group (acid)   or H₂N △ COOH

The different shapes represent different amino acids

A typical protein

Fig. 12.18 Proteins are polymers, the monomer units are amino acids.

SYNTHETIC POLYMERS

Plastics

Plastics form a group of synthetic polymers which have a wide range of mouldability, particularly at high temperatures. In plastics the polymers do not all have the same chain lengths. Polymers are manufactured with the object of building up compounds which have predicted properties (they can be tailor-made to suit a purpose). Since the properties depend on the degree of polymerisation (length of the chain) it is necessary to stop the polymerisation when desired. This may be done in various ways, eg by varying the concentration of the catalyst. These plastics are supplied by a manufacturer in a variety of forms, eg powder, granules or sticky liquids. These are then converted into the final product, often by heating and moulding in some way.

There are two main types of plastics:

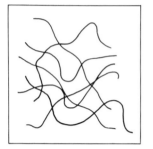

Fig. 12.19 Structure of thermosoftening plastics.

- *Thermosoftening plastics*: these are plastics which can be softened when heated and harden again when they cool down. This can be repeated many times. *Nylon*, for example, can be melted and extruded through tiny holes to produce a fibre, or moulded to produce an object of any desired shape. The molecules in thermosoftening plastics are separate from each other and are held together by weak intermolecular forces. Heating provides the molecules with more energy, so they slip past each other more easily. On cooling, they lose this extra energy, and the weak forces of attraction take over again, so the plastic becomes rigid.

  Some of these plastics can have different densities, eg *high-* or *low*-density polythene. The molecules in high-density polythene are much closer together, and lie almost parallel to each other. This type of polythene stands up to more wear and tear and softens at a higher temperature.

  Examples of thermosoftening plastics are nylon, polythene, polypropylene, PVC and polystyrene.

- *Thermosetting plastics*: these are plastics which can be heated and moulded only once, since when they cool and harden they cannot be remoulded by heating. They are manufactured in two stages. In stage 1, a resin is produced of long chains, which is heated and moulded. In stage 2, cross links between the molecules are formed. The cross links are strong chemical bonds which hold the shape rigid, and are not broken down by reheating.

  Examples of thermosetting plastics are bakelite, epoxy resin and melamine-formaldehyde.

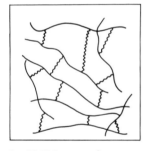

Fig. 12.20 Structure of thermosetting plastics.

The uses of plastics are shown in Figure 12.21

Advantages of plastics

- They are cheap and easy to mould into shapes.
- They are not corroded and can resist chemical attack.
- They are waterproof.
- They can easily be coloured.
- They are light weight.

Disadvantages of plastics

- Their manufacture uses raw material derived from oil (a non-renewable resource).
- They are flammable and give off toxic fumes when they burn.
- They cannot easily be disposed of; plastics waste in land fill sites will not break down in the soil.

Thermosoftening plastics

Plastic	Uses
Polyethene (Polythene)	bags, films for packaging toys, household goods, insulation for electrical wiring
Polypropylene	tableware, chair seats, toilet seats, heels for shoes, filaments for brushes
PVC	water pipes, drain pipes, packaging gramophone records, coating fabrics, rainwear, floor tiles
Polystyrene	household containers, toys, expanded foam insulating material, packaging
Polyester	clothes, sheets, ropes, tents, sails, safety belts

Thermosetting plastics

Plastic	Uses
Bakelite	electrical switch and plug covers, bottle and container tops, door handles, ash trays
Urea-formaldehyde resins	adhesives, surface coatings of metal, laminating timbers
Melamine-formaldehyde resin	moulding, laminated sheet, table ware
Polyester resin	reinforced with glass fibres used in boat and car body production, crash helmets, varnish and paint
Polyurethanes	in foam form for sponges, cushions, buoyancy in boat hulls

Fig. 12.21 Uses of plastics

10 ▸ PROPERTIES AND USE OF MATERIALS

Materials have different properties which allow them to be used for different purposes. For example Fig.12.2 shows how metals are used for different functions. Other materials which you may have studied are: ceramics, glass, plastics, man-made fibres and composite materials. The summary shows the properties of these materials:

- **ceramics**, minute crystals bonded by glass, such as pottery, porcelain and enamels, usually made from clay which has been heated to very high temperatures

    - very hard and brittle
    - strong in compression, weak in tension
    - are electrical insulators
    - have high melting points
    - are unreactive and resistant to most chemicals.

- **glass**, made from a mixture of sand, sodium carbonate; an irregular giant structure of silicon and oxygen atoms held together by strong covalent bonds

    - when molten can be moulded into shapes or rolled into sheets
    - similar to ceramics but usually transparent and with a lower melting point
    - very brittle and weak in tension
    - special glass such as heat resistant glass (Pyrex) can be made with a higher melting point and low thermal expansion

- **plastics**, long molecules joined by strong covalent bonds (see Section 9 above)

    - usually strong but soft and flexible
    - easily soften and melt or burn when heated
    - are electrical and thermal insulators

- **man-made fibres**, made by pulling out plastics into long fibres

    - similar properties to plastics by greater tensile strength along the length of the fibre
    - the resulting fibres are usually made into strong hard-wearing fabrics which are water resistant.

- **composite materials**, such as reinforced concrete, glass-reinforced plastic

    - these materials combine the advantageous properties of more than one material, for example in reinforced concrete the tensile strength of concrete is improved by inserting steel rods through the concrete. The resulting product is strong in both compression and tension; in asbestos concrete the resulting material is strong, lightweight, fireproof and weather resistant

EXAMINATION QUESTIONS

QUESTION 1

The first humans used stones to make their tools. Our history has been influenced by metals and their discovery. The dates are shown in Table 1 below.

Table 1

Metals	Dates of Discovery
Gold	Before 6500 BC
Bronze	6500 BC
Iron	1750 BC
Aluminium	
Sodium	} After AD 1800
Magnesium	

a) Gold was discovered very early. Why was this? (4 lines available)   *(1)*

b) Bronze, a mixture of copper and tin, was used early in human history. The copper and tin were extracted by heating their ores (oxides) with carbon.

   Complete the word equation for the extraction of copper and tin (bronze)

Copper oxide + tin oxide	+		→		+	

(3)

c) The next metal to be extracted from its ore (oxide) by heating with carbon was iron. Figure 1 shows the furnace that is now used.

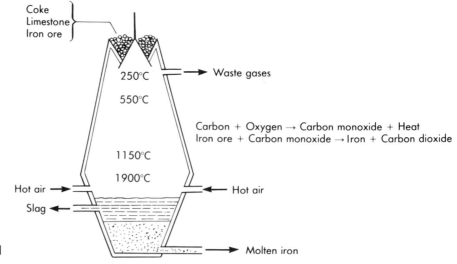

Fig 1

Use the diagram to find **two** reasons why this discovery took place so long after the discovery of bronze.

Reason 1 (3 lines available)

Reason 2 (3 lines available)   *(4)*

d) Aluminium, sodium and magnesium could only be extracted from their ores after we began to use electricity. Why was this? (4 lines available)   *(2)*

(10 marks total)
(ULEAC)

QUESTION 2

There are more atoms of aluminium in the Earth's crust than of any other metal. Until about 100 years ago it was rare and expensive, but now it has many uses. It is the lightest of the common metals and is easily shaped.

a) i) Aluminium can be made easily from bauxite (aluminium oxide) by heating it with a more reactive metal. Give **one** example of a metal which might be used.

_____
(1)

ii) Suggest **one** reason why this method is not widely used.

_____

_____
(1)

iii) Bauxite is found in the Earth's crust. What name do we give to compounds such as this?

_____
(1)

Aluminium is usually extracted by passing electricity through a cell containing molten *alumina* mixed with molten *cryolite*. The diagram below shows the main parts of the cell used.

b) What is the name of this type of extraction process?

_____
(1)

c) The temperature in the cell stays at about 1000 degrees Celsius (°C) but it is not heated from outside at all.

Suggest how this temperature is maintained. (3 lines available)   *(2)*

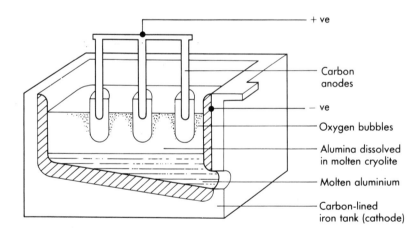

d) Suggest and explain why aluminium was so expensive one hundred years ago.

Suggestion _____
(1)

Explanation (2 lines) _____
(1)

e) Aluminium appears to be unreactive. This is because a coating of aluminium oxide quickly forms on the outside of the metal. Without its oxide layer, aluminium is reactive and burns easily.

Aluminium has replaced other metals in a number of uses. It is used for overhead power cables instead of copper, and because it is a good reflector of heat it can be used to trap heat inside an area or keep it out.

i) Suggest **one** property which aluminium **must** have if it is used for overhead power cables.

_____

(1)

ii) Suggest and explain **one** reason, apart from cost, for the use of aluminium instead of copper for these cables.

Reason _____

(1)

Explanation (2 lines) _____

(1)

iii) Tiny babies are sometimes wrapped in a blanket made from polyester fabric coated with a thin film of aluminium. Suggest and explain one reason why this is done.

Reason _____

(1)

Explanation (2 lines) _____

(1)

iv) Many cars are now partly made of aluminium, but the main frame is still made of steel. Apart from cost, suggest why they are made this way. (4 lines available) *(3)*

(SEG)

QUESTION 3

When iron rusts, it combines with the oxygen of the air to form iron dioxide. The rusting of seven identical nails was investigated by treating each nail as shown in the table below. All seven nails were left exposed to the atmosphere for a few months. (One of the results in the table is incorrect.)

Nail	Treatment given to each nail	Cost of Treatment	Mass of the nail and coating before exposure	Mass of the nail and coating after exposure
A	waxed	cheap	5.0 g	5.3 g
B	oiled	cheap	5.0 g	4.1 g
C	chromium plated	expensive	5.0 g	5.0 g
D	painted	cheap	5.0 g	5.4 g
E	galvanised	fairly expensive	5.0 g	5.1 g
F	dipped in salt	cheap	5.0 g	6.7 g
G	untreated	NIL	4.9 g	6.1 g

a) By reference to the table, say which nail has received

i) the coating which gives the best protection

_____

(1)

ii) a treatment that could be used to protect steel car bumpers from rusting

_____

(1)

iii) a treatment which would be the most practical to use to protect iron railings from rusting

_____

(1)

iv) in which case is there an obvious mistake in the mass of the nail and coating after the experiment?

_____

(1)

b) Give the name of another naturally occurring substance that with oxygen will cause iron to rust.

_____

(1)

c) Give the name of the process that takes place when any metal reacts with oxygen to form an oxide.

_____

(1)

(WJEC)

QUESTION 4

Table A below shows the action of heat on six metal oxides.

Table A

Metal oxide	Appearance of oxide	Change on heating	Change on cooling after heating
Copper (II) oxide CuO	black powder	none	none
Mercury (II) oxide HgO	red powder	turns black oxygen evolved	silver droplets of mercury formed
Zinc oxide ZnO	white powder	yellow powder	white powder
Lead (IV) oxide PbO$_2$	chocolate brown powder	melts oxygen evolved	yellow powder
Calcium oxide CaO	white powder	none	none
Lead (II) oxide PbO	yellow powder	melts, no oxygen	yellow powder

a) Which element is present in all of the metal oxides in the table?

_____

(1)

b) Using the table, name
   i) **two** metal oxides chemically unchanged by heating.

   _____ and _____

   (2)

   ii) **one** metal oxide which changes on heating but changes back on cooling.

   _____

   (1)

   iii) **two** metal oxides that decompose on heating

   _____ and _____

   (2)

c) How would you test whether oxygen was produced when the oxides were heated? (2 lines)

   (1)

d) Five common gases are carbon dioxide, chlorine, nitrogen, hydrogen and oxygen.

   i) Which one of these gases is

   (1) a compound _____

   (2) coloured? _____

   (2)

ii) Name **two** of these gases which extinguish a lighted splint without burning.
(2 lines) *(2)*

e) A scientist wished to test a mineral. When dilute hydrochloric acid was added to the mineral, a colourless gas was produced which extinguished a lighted splint and turned limewater cloudy.

When the mineral was heated, carbon dioxide was produced and the solid remaining was yellow in colour when hot and white when it cooled down.

i) Use the table of metal oxides (Table A) to identify the solid formed when the mineral was heated.

The solid formed was _____
(1)

ii) Which chemical compound does the mineral mainly consist of?

_____
(2)
(Total marks 14)
(ULEAC)

QUESTION 5

a) Starch molecules consist of long chains of smaller glucose molecules.

i) Suggest **two** ways by which starch molecules can be broken down. *(2)*

ii) What is the name of this process? *(1)*

iii) Name another product of this reaction. *(1)*

b) In industrial brewing processes yeast is added to glucose solution and left to ferment at 25°C.

i) What does the yeast do to the glucose molecules? *(1)*

ii) What are the products of fermentation? *(3)*

iii) What will be the effect of raising the temperature to 35°C? *(1)*

iv) Explain why boiling the yeast/glucose mixture stops the reaction. *(2)*

c) Describe how animals obtain and use glucose. *(4)*
(MEG)

QUESTION 6

The diagrams below show a range of everyday objects which can be made from polymers.

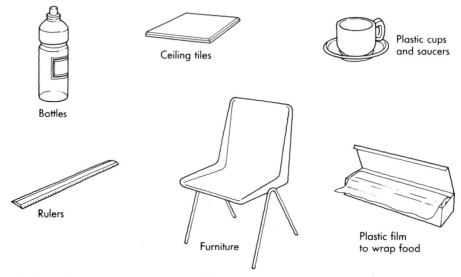

Bottles

Ceiling tiles

Plastic cups and saucers

Rulers

Furniture

Plastic film to wrap food

a) Describe what you understand by the term 'polymer'. *(3)*

b) Draw a diagram to show the general structure of polymers. *(2)*

A student tested three types of polymers and made the following observations.

Type	Observations
A	hard and rigid, did not melt at low temperatures
B	stretchy, returns to original shape
C	melts on heating, easily moulded

c) Suggest which one of these types is a thermosetting plastic, and state your reasoning.
(2)

d) Suggest what property of elastomers distinguishes them from thermoplastic and thermosetting polymers. (1)

e) For **each** of the following jobs, explain why a particular plastic has been used:
   i)   covering electric cables – polyvinyl chloride; (2)

   ii) making shirts and blouses – nylon; (2)

   iii) packaging for TV sets – polystyrene (2)

f) Some metal frying pans are coated with an unusual thermoplastic called PTFE (polytetrafluorethylene), commonly known as teflon.

   i) Suggest why PTFE is an unusual example of a thermoplastic. (2)

   ii) Suggest **two** advantages of using PTFE to coat metal frying pans. (2)
   (MEG)

QUESTION 7
(Levels 8–10)

In part (a) you are given information in the form of a table and asked questions based on that information. Part (b) tests your knowledge and understanding.

a) Study the information given below, and then answer the questions which follow.

Type of material	Typical properties
Metals	Strong; hard; malleable; high density; conduct heat and electricity well; some react with air, water and acids.
Ceramics	Hard; strong when compressed, weak when stretched; brittle; high melting points; heat resistant; chemically unreactive.
Glasses	Same as ceramics but also transparent.
Plastics	Flexible; easily melted and moulded; wide range of properties depending on the specific plastic; some burn when heated in air.
Fibre	Structures are long, strong, hair-like strands; flexible; some burn when heated in air.

Explain which **one** of the above types of material would be best for making each of the following. (4)

   i) An oven door: (3 lines) _____

   ii) A dustbin: (3 lines) _____

b) Explain the difference between a compound and an element. Use the examples of sodium, chlorine and sodium chloride to illustrate your answer. (10 lines) (6)
[Science SEG]

QUESTION 8
(Levels 8–10)
The diagram here provides the introduction to the question. Study the diagram for a few minutes to help you answer the question.

The diagram below shows a simplified flow chart of an industrial process to make polyethene, (polythene) from crude oil.

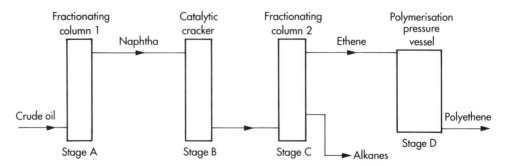

a) What is the purpose of the catalytic cracker? (3 lines)   (1)

b) Why is fractionating column number 2 necessary? (3 lines)   (1)

c) Which stages in the process require energy? (3 lines)   (1)

d) The table below contains information about three common plastics.

Name of monomer	Formula of monomer	Name of polymer	Formula of polymer
Ethene	$\begin{array}{c} H \quad\quad H \\ \diagdown \quad\quad \diagup \\ C = C \\ \diagup \quad\quad \diagdown \\ H \quad\quad H \end{array}$	polyethene	$\left(\begin{array}{cc} H & H \\ \mid & \mid \\ -C - C - \\ \mid & \mid \\ H & H \end{array} \right)_n$
w	$\begin{array}{c} H \quad\quad H \\ \diagdown \quad\quad \diagup \\ C = C \\ \diagup \quad\quad \diagdown \\ H \quad\quad Cl \end{array}$	polychlorethene	z
Tetrafluoroethene	x	y	$\left(\begin{array}{cc} F & F \\ \mid & \mid \\ -C - C - \\ \mid & \mid \\ F & F \end{array} \right)_n$

Complete the table by filling in the blank spaces.   (4)

e) Explain why thermosetting plastics and thermosoftening plastics behave differently when heated (10 lines).   (4)

[Co-ordinated Science, NEAB, WJEC, ULEAC]

ANSWERS TO EXAMINATION QUESTIONS

STRUCTURED QUESTIONS

ANSWER 1
a) Gold is not combined with other elements in the Earth's surface.

b) copper oxide + carbon   →   copper + carbon dioxide
            +   tin oxide   + tin

c) Reason 1 – very high temperatures are required to extract the iron from iron ore.
Reason 2 – a way of making carbon monoxide had to be found which would remove the oxygen from the iron ore.

d) Very large amounts of energy are required to separate the metals from their ores.

ANSWER 2

a) i) magnesium (or sodium)
   ii) magnesium is very reactive and expensive
   iii) ores

b) electrolysis

c) heat generated by electric current passing through the cell during electrolysis, which balances heat loss to surroundings.

d) Because the method of extraction was being developed and large amounts of electricity were required.

e) i) conduct electricity
   ii) Reason - they are much lighter.
   Explanation - the metal is less dense.
   iii) Reason - babies lose a lot of body heat.
   Explanation - aluminium reflects heat.
   iv) Aluminium is very lightweight but may dent easily. Steel is used for the main body of the car, as it is stronger.

ANSWER 3

a) i) C
   ii) C
   iii) D
   iv) B

b) water

c) oxidation

ANSWER 4

a) oxygen

b) i) copper oxide and calcium oxide
   ii) zinc oxide
   iii) mercury oxide and lead oxide

c) Hold a glowing splint near the test tube. The splint should relight if oxygen is evolved.

d) i) 1 carbon dioxide
   2 chlorine
   ii) carbon dioxide and nitrogen

e) i) zinc oxide
   ii) zinc carbonate

ANSWER 5

a) i) By boiling in acid; by mixing with amylase
   ii) hydrolysis
   iii) maltose

b) i) They break it down to release energy.
   ii) carbon dioxide + alcohol + energy
   iii) to increase the rate of the reaction
   iv) Enzymes which are proteins are destroyed by boiling.

c) Animals eat other animals or plants, and digest food into small molecules, which are transported to cells of body via blood stream. Cells release energy from glucose during respiration.

ANSWER 6

a) long chains of repeating small units

b)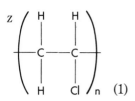

c) type A, because it did not melt at low temperatures

d) They return to their original shape after stretching.

e) i) very flexible; non-conductor
   ii) can be made into threads and woven into fabric; very hard-wearing
   iii) can be made into foam which contains air to absorb shocks on impact

f) i) It has a very high melting point.
   ii) Food does not stick to the pan; it protects the pan from chipping and going rusty.

ANSWER 7

a) select a type of material and a suitable property from the table
   i) for example: metal (1) strong (1) or glass (1) transparent (1)
   ii) plastic (1) easily moulded (1) or metal (1) strong (1)

b) in an element the atoms are all the same (1)
   e.g. sodium metal contains sodium atoms/ions (1)
   chlorine contains pairs of chlorine atoms (1)
   in a compound there are more than one type of atom (1)
   combined together / chemically bonded (1)
   in fixed proportions (1)
   e.g. sodium chloride contains sodium and chloride ions (1)

ANSWER 8

a) to break the large molecules down into smaller molecules (1)

b) to separate ethene from the alkanes (1)

c) stages A, C and D (1)

d) look for the pattern shown for ethene to help you complete the rest of the table

W polychlorethene (1)

X

$$\begin{matrix} F & & F \\ & \diagdown \quad \diagup & \\ & C = C & \\ & \diagup \quad \diagdown & \\ F & & F_{\text{/}} \end{matrix}$$ (1)

z

$$\left(\begin{matrix} H & H \\ | & | \\ -C - C - \\ | & | \\ H & Cl \end{matrix} \right)_n$$ (1)

y polytetrafluoroethene (1)

e) this answer expects some extended writing;
   think carefully about the four points you want to make for the 4 marks, and make it clear which plastic you are describing. For example, you might make some of the following points:

   thermosoftening plastics (thermoplastics) consist of long polymer molecules twisted together, but the bonds between these molecules are weak (1)
   on heating the chains move further apart and the forces of attraction are reduced so that the plastic can change shape (1)
   thermosetting plastics consist of long polymer molecules which are cross-linked by strong bonds (1)
   the polymer is rigid as heating does not affect the bonds (1)

A STUDENT'S ANSWER WITH EXAMINER'S COMMENTS

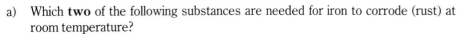

a) Which **two** of the following substances are needed for iron to corrode (rust) at room temperature?

    A carbon dioxide
    B nitrogen
    C oxygen
    D sodium chloride (salt)
    E water

66 Good. 99

C oxygen   E water

(2)

b) The rate at which iron corrodes depends upon the climate and the location. Table 3 gives information about the climate and location of cities, and the amount of corrosion that occurs.

City	Temperature	Amount of moisture in the atmosphere	Location	Rate of corrosion
Birmingham	moderate	moderate	inland	moderate
Bogota	high	high	inland	high
Nairobi	high	low	inland	low
Seattle	moderate	moderate	coastal	high
Singapore	high	high	coastal	very high
Sydney	moderate	high	coastal	high
Vladivostok	low	moderate	coastal	moderate

Table 3

i) In which of the above cities is the rate of corrosion the slowest?

Nairobi

(1)

66 Good. You have used the information and selected 'low'. 99

66 But in a) you state water is necessary; so a better answer is that sea coastal air holds more moisture. 99

ii) Explain why corrosion is faster at coastal places than inland.

More salt in the air.

(2)

c) Figure 1 gives some information about different ways of preventing iron corroding.

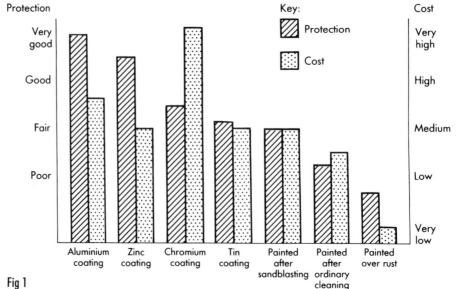

Fig 1

Suggest the most suitable method for protecting an iron bridge in the following cities. Give reasons for your choices.

i) Singapore: _aluminium coating as Singapore has a very high rate of corrosion and this method gives the best protection although expensive._

Good. You have made 3 points for 3 marks.

ii) Birmingham: _tin coating. there is only a moderate rate of corrosion and tin coating is quite good enough._

Yes. Include medium cost as well for 3rd mark.

(6)
(Total marks 11)
(ULEAC)

R E V I E W   S H E E T

 List four useful properties of metals

1. _____
2. _____
3. _____
4. _____

All metals are _____ and are grouped on the _____ side of the periodic table.

The common everyday metals are found in the block referred to as the _____ metals.

Metal atoms react to form _____ ions. The charge on the ion depends on the _____ in the periodic table.

Complete this table.

Group	Charge on ion	Example
1	1 +	
2	2 +	
3	3 +	

_____ are solid mixtures of metals formed by melting together two or more different metals.

List four alloys. For each alloy describe its important properties and uses.

Alloy	Property	Uses
1.		
2.		
3.		
4.		

A highly reactive metal has a _____ tendency to form ions. Potassium is a _____ reactive metal.

List four uses of the reactivity series.

1. _____ 3. _____
2. _____ 4. _____

List three things present in a simple cell.

1. _____ 2. _____ 3. _____

If the metals are far apart in the reactivity series then a _____ voltage is produced.

Complete this table. Say whether a 'large' or 'small' voltage will be produced in each case.

Metal pair	Voltage produced
magnesium/copper	
iron/zinc	

List four things which might affect the rate of corrosion of a metal.

1. _____
2. _____
3. _____
4. _____

✎ Suggest three ways of protecting metals from corrosion

1. _____

2. _____

3. _____

✎ _____ is the most abundant metal in the earth's crust.

✎ Name 2 methods for extracting metal from its ore.

1. _____   2. _____

✎ Fill in the labels on this diagram of a blast furnace.

250°C

550°C

Carbon + Oxygen → Carbon monoxide + Heat

Iron ore + Carbon monoxide → Iron + Carbon dioxide

1150°C

1900°C

✎ List four consequences of the molecules in a hydrocarbon getting larger

1. _____   3. _____

2. _____   4. _____

✎ Carbon atoms joined by a single carbon–carbon bond are called _____ hydrocarbons, whereas carbon atoms joined by a double bond are called _____ hydrocarbons.

✎ Large hydrocarbon molecules can be broken down by a process called _____

✎ Macromolecules consisting of long chains of smaller molecules linked together and forming a repeating pattern are called _____. The smaller molecules which form the pattern are called _____.

✎ Starch is a natural polymer, made by _____

✎ List three other natural polymers.

1. _____   2. _____   3. _____

✎ Plastic is a type of _____ polymer. There are two main types of plastics;

_____ plastics and _____ plastics.

✎ List three advantages of using plastics in industry and three disadvantages.

Advantages	*Disadvantages*
1. _____	4. _____
2. _____	5. _____
3. _____	6. _____

THE SOLAR SYSTEM, THE WEATHER, AND ROCKS

GETTING STARTED

Every day the Sun rises and sets, at night the stars 'appear' in the sky, and the Moon seems to change its shape during the month. To understand how some of these events take place you need to know how the Earth orbits around the Sun, and how the Moon orbits around the Earth.

To investigate conditions in outer space, man has sent both manned and unmanned rockets on voyages of discovery. One day it is possible that people could be living in a space station instead of living on Earth.

Satellites are already in everyday use for observing the Earth and its atmosphere, and making a major contribution to weather forecasting. In Britain, as in many countries, a very common topic of conversation is the weather. People generally enjoy warm, sunny weather more than cold, wet weather. Although the weather in Britain seems very changeable, we are not usually affected by the extremes experienced in some parts of the world, where floods, droughts, earthquakes and volcanoes cause great suffering to many people.

1 ▷ THE SUN

The Sun is one of billions of stars which make up a galaxy known as the Milky Way. There are billions of galaxies like the Milky Way in the Universe. The Sun is about half-way through its life cycle of 9600 million years and is about a million times larger than the Earth. It is made of hydrogen and helium gas, and its temperature is about 6000° C at its surface. At the centre of the Sun the temperature is much higher, and this is where nuclear fusion is taking place as the hydrogen is being converted to helium. Figure 13.1 shows the life cycle of a star such as the Sun.

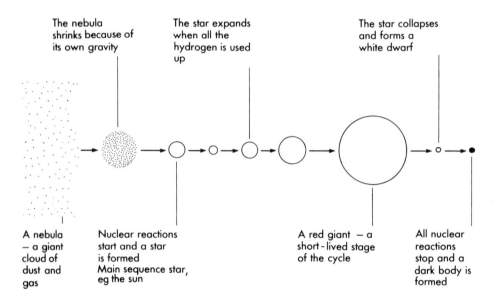

Fig. 13.1 The life cycle of a star.

The 'big bang' theory of the origin of the Universe suggests that an explosion may have occurred about 15 thousand million years ago to create the Universe. At one time the galaxies must have been much closer to each other and may even have been one big mass. It would seem that the galaxies are moving away from each other, possibly as a result of a massive explosion or 'big bang'. Evidence for this is suggested by the fact that the light from other galaxies has shifted to the red end of the spectrum and the further away galaxies are, the bigger this 'red shift'. The cause of the 'big bang' is not known.

2 ▷ THE SOLAR SYSTEM

Nine planets, of which Earth is one, orbit around the sun, which is at the centre of our *solar system*. The force of gravity between the planets and the Sun is smaller the further the planets are away from the Sun. Planets are visible because planets reflect light from the Sun whereas stars emit their own light. Figure 13.2 shows the arrangement of the *planets* (not to scale).

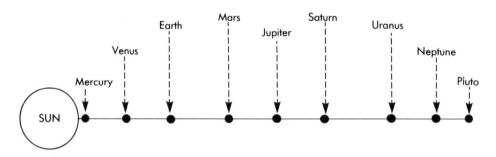

Fig. 13.2 How the planets are arranged.

Try and understand general patterns in the planets

There are two basic groups of planets. The planets nearer the Sun - Mercury, Venus, Earth and Mars - have small diameters and high density; the planets further away - Jupiter, Saturn, Uranus, Neptune and Pluto - have large diameters but low density. Planets which are further away from the Sun take longer to orbit the Sun and generally have lower mean surface temperatures than planets nearer the Sun.

THE MAIN MEMBERS OF THE SOLAR SYSTEM										
Body	**1** Diameter	**2** Mass	**3** Surface gravity	**4** Density, in Kg m^{-3}	**5** Period of spin			**6** Angle of tilt between axis and orbit	**7** Average distance from Sun (Sun–Earth=1)	**8** Period of orbit, in years	**9** No. of moons (*=plus rings)
(Earth=1)	(Earth=1)	(Earth=1)			days	hours	mins.				
Sun	109.00	333 000.00	28.00	1400	25	9		97°			
Mercury	0.40	0.06	0.40	5400	58	16		90°	0.4	0.2	0
Venus	0.95	0.80	0.90	5200	244	7		267°	0.7	0.6	0
Earth	1.00	1.00	1.00	5500		23	56	113°	1.0	1.0	1
Moon	0.27	0.01	0.17	3300	27	7		91°	1.0	1.0	0
Mars	0.53	0.10	0.40	4000		24	37	114°	1.5	1.9	2
Jupiter	11.18	317.00	2.60	1300		9	50	93°	5.2	11.9	16*
Saturn	9.42	95.00	1.10	700		10	14	116°	9.5	29.5	15*
Uranus	3.84	14.50	0.90	1600		10	49	187°	19.2	84.0	5*
Neptune	3.93	17.20	1.20	2300		15	48	118°	30.1	164.8	2
Pluto	0.31	0.0025	0.20	400	6	9	17	?	39.4	247.7	1

Fig. 13.3   Figure 13.3 shows you some data about the nine planets in the Solar system.

PROBLEMS OF COLONISATION

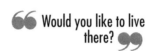 Would you like to live there?

When considering the problems of living on any planet other than Earth, you have to think about factors such as the availability of oxygen and water, temperature, pressure and radiation. Conditions on the surface of the planets, with the exception of the Earth, are generally fairly hostile. For example, *Jupiter,* the largest planet in the solar system, has a solid rock core surrounded by layers of liquid hydrogen, and is covered in a thick layer of hydrogen gas. The atmosphere is very cold since the planet is so far away from the Sun, and the planet is surrounded by zones of radiation. Trying to colonise this planet would cause astronauts several problems, such as protecting themselves from radiation and from the low temperatures, carrying sufficient oxygen to breathe, and moving about.

One of the factors which limit space travel includes providing the amount of fuel required to accelerate to high speeds to escape from the Earth's gravitational field. Also most journeys to other planets could take a number of years and problems of providing basic human needs such as water, food, oxygen, warmth and sanitation have to be solved.

3 > THE EARTH

Some important facts:

- A year is the time taken for the Earth to orbit the Sun, about 365 days.

- A day is the time taken for the Earth to spin on its own axis, about 24 hours.

Figure 13.4 shows how the Earth is tilted as it orbits the Sun.

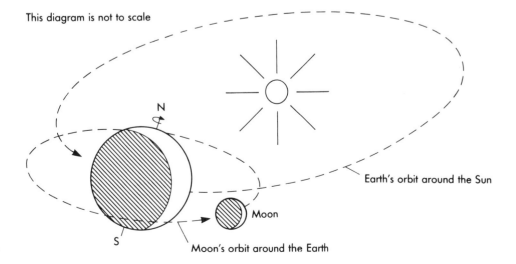

Fig 13.4 How the Earth orbits the Sun.

THE SEASONS

The 23° tilt of the Earth's axis means that different parts of the world get different amounts of sunlight, and this causes the seasons. Winter occurs in the half of the Earth which is tilted *away* from the Sun; summer occurs in the half of the Earth which is tilted *towards* the Sun. When it is summer in the Northern hemisphere, it is winter in the Southern hemisphere (see Figure 13.5). This means that at places which are tilted towards the Sun the weather is warmer because more energy is received from the Sun. The period of daylight is longer than that of the nights and the Sun rises higher in the sky.

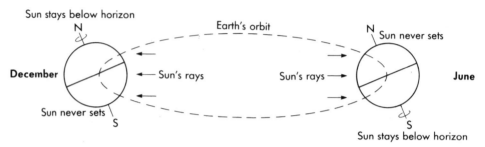

Fig. 13.5 How the seasons are caused.

4 > THE MOON

The Moon is a *satellite* of the Earth which takes 28 days to orbit the Earth. This is known as a *lunar month*. The Moon also rotates on its own axis every 28 days, so the same side of the Moon faces the Earth all the time.

Figure 13.6 shows how the different phases of the Moon appear when the Moon is viewed from Earth. When the Earth is between the Sun and the Moon we can see all the light from the Sun which is reflected by the Moon, and the Moon therefore appears to be a full Moon.

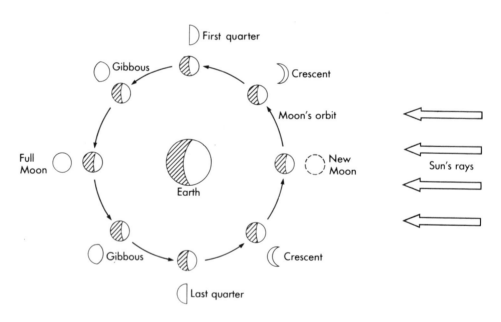

Fig. 13.6 How the different phases of the Moon are caused.

 Try to sort out the difference between an eclipse of the moon and an eclipse of the sun

A LUNAR ECLIPSE

An *eclipse of the Moon* happens when the Earth stops the Sun's rays from reaching the Moon, as shown in Figure 13.7.

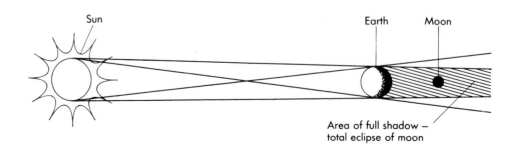

Fig. 13.7 In an eclipse of the moon, the Earth blocks the light from the Sun

A SOLAR ECLIPSE

An *eclipse of the Sun* happens when the Moon passes between the Sun and the Earth, so the Sun appears to be covered, as shown in Figure 13.8.

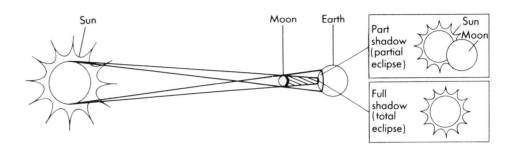

Fig.13.8 In eclipse of the sun, the Moon blocks the light from the Sun

THE TIDES

The Moon exerts a gravitational pull on the water on the Earth's surface. The effect of this on the side nearest the Moon is to pull the water towards the Moon and thereby produce a high tide. Another high tide happens on the side of the Earth furthest away from the Moon. Owing to the rotation of the Earth, these high tides happen every 12 hours.

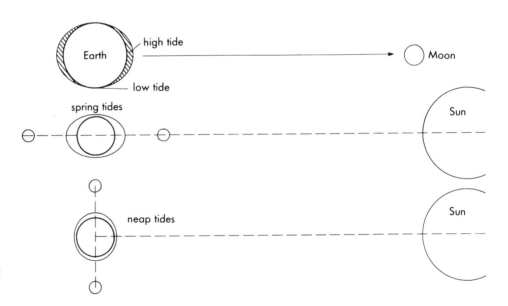

Fig. 13.9 How 'spring' tides and 'neap' tides are caused.

Spring and neap tides

Spring tides don't only happen in the Spring

Although the Sun is much further away from the Earth, it too has a gravitational pull on the Earth. When the Sun and Moon are *in line*, about twice a month, their combined gravitational pull causes a very high tide or 'spring' tide. These tides have very large tidal ranges, this means that they have 'very high' high tides and 'very low' low tides.

When the Sun and Moon are *at right angles* with each other, which happens about twice a month, the gravitational effect is cancelled out and weak tides, called 'neap' tides, with small tidal ranges, are produced. These tides have 'low' high tides.

THE ATMOSPHERE

The surface of the Earth is surrounded by a thick layer of gases called the *atmosphere*. It is held to Earth by gravitational attraction and is densest at sea level and thins out rapidly at higher altitudes. About 97% of the atmosphere is within 30 km of the Earth's surface, but the upper limit is about 10 000 km. The atmosphere is essential in keeping the Earth's surface temperature more or less constant. In comparison the Moon, which is the same distance from the Sun as the earth and has no atmosphere, has surface temperatures ranging from as high as 100°C in the sunlight falling to – 150°C at night.

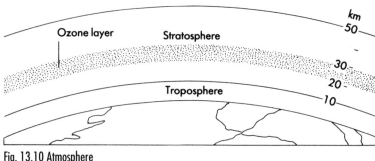

Fig. 13.10 Atmosphere

Composition of the Atmosphere

The composition of the Earth's atmosphere is fairly uniform in terms of the proportions of gases it contains and is maintained by the action of living organisms, mostly green plants and micro-organisms

The proportion of gases in the atmosphere is shown below:

- nitrogen about 78%
- oxygen about 21%
- carbon dioxide about 0.03%
- inert gases mostly argon less than 1%
- impurities such as dust particles and very small amounts of other gases
- water vapour which varies from nil to about 5%

Evolution of the atmosphere

It is thought that volcanic activity during the evolution of the Earth released gases which formed the original atmosphere. This atmosphere probably consisted mainly of carbon dioxide, with some water vapour, methane and ammonia.

Changes due to the following processes are thought to have occurred which have resulted in the present atmosphere:

- the carbon from the carbon dioxide became 'trapped' in sedimentary rocks as carbonates and fossil fuels
- the amount of oxygen increased due to colonisation by plants and the ozone layer developed to filter out harmful ultraviolet radiation from the sun and allow development of new organisms
- methane and ammonia reacted with oxygen
- nitrogen gas was released into the air from reactions of denitrifying bacteria.

The ozone layer

The *ozone layer* surrounds the Earth in the part of the upper atmosphere known as the stratosphere. The stratosphere is vital to life on Earth as it shields us from most of the harmful types of ultra violet radiation from the Sun. Increased exposure to UV radiation may cause damage to crops and increase the incidence of skin cancer in humans.

Ozone is a form of oxygen which has three atoms in each molecule (O_3) compared with the usual form of oxygen molecules which has only two atoms (O_2). In simple terms ozone protects us by a series of chemical reactions. Some types of UV radiation will split the oxygen molecules (O_2) to form oxygen atoms. These are very reactive and combine with oxygen molecules to form ozone (O_3). The ozone then absorbs other types of UV radiation which can convert ozone back into oxygen molecules (O_2) and atoms. These reactions normally prevent harmful UV radiation but this balance is being upset by the release of chemicals such as chlorofluorocarbons (CFCs) from aerosols and other sources, as well as nitrous oxides from car exhausts. These substances react with the ozone making fewer molecules available at any time to absorb the UV radiation. The result of this is to create 'holes' in the ozone layer through which harmful UV radiation can pass.

AIR PRESSURE

The Earth's gravitational pull holds the layer of gases around the surface of the Earth, and the weight of air above any part of the Earth is described as *air pressure*. For example, the weight of air pressing down on 1 centimetre square is 10 Newtons. Atmospheric pressure is therefore about 10 N/cm^2. This unit is also described as *one bar* or 1000 millibars . Look at the weather map shown in Figure 13.11.

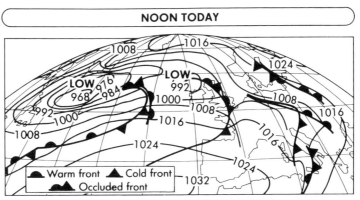

NOON TODAY

Information supplied by London Weather Centre

Fig 13.11 The isobars link places which have equal pressure.

The lines on the weather map are pressure contours called *isobars*, which join points of equal pressure. When the isobars are close together, the pressure gradient is steep, and winds will be very strong. Wind generally moves from an area of high pressure to an area of low pressure.

Watch the weather news on TV to help you understand weather maps

You can see the isobars or pressure bars on the map. For instance, those labelled as 1024 millibars indicate a 'high' pressure of just over 10 N per centimetre square. Pressure is usually measured with a barometer, but in an aeroplane a pilot uses a sensitive barometer, called an *altimeter*, which measures atmospheric pressure and height.

Increasing and decreasing pressure

If air is compressed, the molecules are closer together in a smaller space; as the air becomes denser in this way, the pressure is increased. Pressure decreases with altitude because as you go higher up, there is less air above you pressing down on you. If you go about 6 kilometres high, the pressure drops to about half as the air molecules thin out.

6 ▷ WATER VAPOUR

Usually we cannot see *water vapour* until it condenses and falls as precipitation: rain, snow, hail, sleet. We do however feel the effects of water vapour. When there is a high moisture content the air feels sticky and damp and we find it difficult to cool down.

HOW CLOUDS ARE FORMED

1 Water is constantly evaporating from the surface of water masses such as rivers, lakes, seas and oceans, and from soil and plants.
2 When the air has absorbed the *maximum amount* of water vapour which it can hold at that temperature, it is said to be *saturated*. Colder air can hold less water vapour than warmer air.
3 The energy from the Sun heats up masses of air and causes the air molecules to spread out, so that the air becomes less dense and rises.

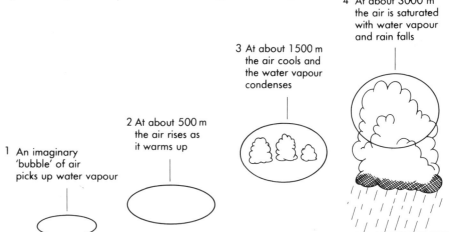

4 At about 3000 m the air is saturated with water vapour and rain falls

3 At about 1500 m the air cools and the water vapour condenses

2 At about 500 m the air rises as it warms up

1 An imaginary 'bubble' of air picks up water vapour

Fig. 13.12 How clouds are formed

4 As the air rises, it cools down; any water vapour in the air begins to condense and form clouds.

5 When the cloud rises higher, the air in the cloud becomes saturated with water vapour, which is then released as rain.

A good example of technological application

Britain is covered by a network of stations whose function is to detect falling rain by radar. In the near future it is hoped that these will be linked with radar stations across Europe. Meteorologists can then predict where rain is likely to fall in the next few hours. This is of especial benefit to people such as air traffic controllers, farmers and organisers of outdoor events, such as Wimbledon tennis.

DIFFERENT TYPES OF CLOUDS

The chart below shows information about three common types of cloud: cumulus, cirrus, and stratus clouds.

Name	Height ('000m)	Description
cirrus	8	wispy white threads
cumulus	2.5	thick white clouds with flat base and rounded tops
stratus	0.5–2.5	continuous sheet of low cloud

7 **GLOBAL WEATHER**

A number of different factors affect how air masses move around to cause global weather patterns. However, two important factors are as follows:

1 The air at the Equator is heated up more than the air at the Poles, as the Equator receives more of the Sun's radiation.

2 The Earth spins on its axis, at a speed of approximately 2 000 km per hour at the Equator, but at a speed of zero at the poles. This means that as air moves *towards the Poles* the air speed is slowed down, but as air moves *towards the Equator* the air speed is increased.

Figure 13.13 shows the net effect of these two factors on how air masses move around. The winds move in a clockwise direction in the Southern hemisphere, and in an anticlockwise direction in the Northern hemisphere.

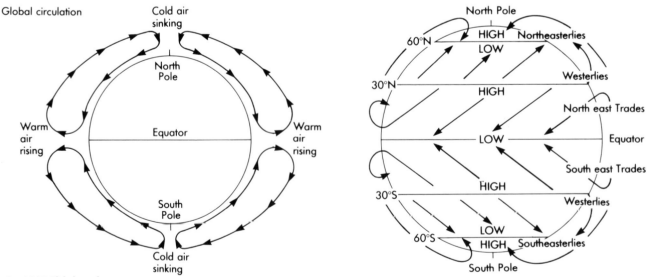

Fig. 13.13 Global weather patterns.

COLD FRONTS AND WARM FRONTS

Figure 13.13 shows a belt of low pressure at about 50° N. This region of low pressure is the boundary between two large air masses: the cold, dry *Polar Continental* and the warm, moist *Tropical Maritime*. The warm air is less dense than the cold air and rises over it, creating a front called the *Polar Front*. Figure 13.14 shows how 'kinks' develop in this Polar Front, creating warm and cold fronts.

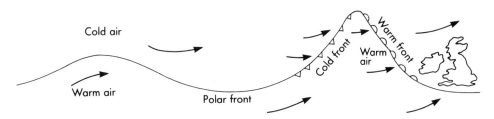

Fig 13.14 An imaginary aerial view of the polar front.

A *warm front* develops as warm, moist air rises over the cold, dry air. A *cold front* develops as cold, dry air pushes underneath the warm, moist air.

The weather map in Figure 13.15 shows a typical depression or LOW, with a cold front and a warm front.

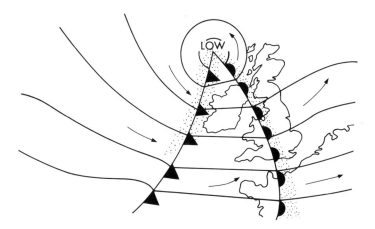

Fig 13.15 A typical depression or LOW will bring rain to Britain

As the *warm front* passes over, the weather pattern will show increasing wind and cloud cover, light rain or drizzle and a fall in pressure. As the *cold front* passes, the rain becomes much heavier, the wind becomes very strong and the temperature drops. The pressure then rises and the rain ceases as the sky clears.

Many weather maps also show wind speed and direction in the form of wind direction arrows.

THE WEATHER

The weather is described by factors such as temperature, rainfall, wind speed and direction. It is possible that on a local scale you may have taken measurements of:

- the highest and lowest temperature
- the number of millimetres of rainfall
- the speed and direction of the wind
- the numbers of hours of sunshine

WEATHER FORECASTING

Satellite pictures, like the ones shown in Figure 13.16 and on the TV weather news, are able to show the position and speed of the changing weather patterns. For example, a satellite could show the development of a cold front, or the position of a depression as it moved across the Atlantic Ocean, and how temperature varies vertically through the atmosphere. The information from satellites is used together with other information from more conventional methods of collecting data, such as using hydrogen-filled balloons which float in the atmosphere, and computer weather forecasts. Meteorologists are then able to pass information to national and local news stations as well as to aeroplanes and shipping.

 These satellites are also used in communication

The type of satellite used is a *geostationary satellite* whose speed is the same as that of Earth. The satellite is held in orbit by the Earth's gravitational field. Some satellites are able to use both infra-red and visible light to collect data. This means that data can be collected during a 24-hour period as a frontal system develops.

Fig. 13.16 A satellite picture showing a frontal system approaching Britain

8 > **THE STRUCTURE OF THE EARTH**

EVIDENCE FOR THE STRUCTURE OF THE EARTH

The Earth is an almost spherical body about 6400 km in radius. Much of the evidence for the layered structure of the Earth comes from the behaviour of earthquake shock waves as they reach different zones. There are two types of earthquake waves:

i) the P waves which travel very quickly and will pass through liquids and solids, including the core; they travel more quickly through the core than the mantle; and

ii) the slower moving S waves which only travel though solids. An analysis of the behaviour of these shock waves has indicated the main regions of the Earth as shown in Fig. 13.17.

As can be seen in Fig 13.17, at the centre of the Earth is the *core*, a spherical zone about 3500 km in radius. The core is divided into an *inner core*, thought to be a solid metallic substance which has a radius of approximately 1340 km. The *outer core* is thought to be a liquid mass of nickel-iron with a radius of approximately 2160 km. This outer core is thought to create the electric currents which gave rise to the Earth's magnetic field.

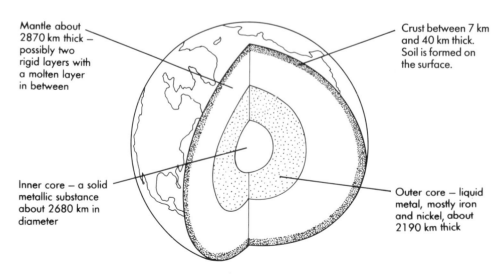

Mantle about 2870 km thick — possibly two rigid layers with a molten layer in between

Crust between 7 km and 40 km thick. Soil is formed on the surface.

Inner core — a solid metallic substance about 2680 km in diameter

Outer core — liquid metal, mostly iron and nickel, about 2190 km thick

Fig. 13.17 The structure of the Earth.

The average density of the Earth is about 5.5 g/cm^3 whereas the surface rocks average 3 g/cm^3. This observation means that the density increases towards the centre where it may be as high as 10–15 g/cm^3. Temperatures in the Earth's core are thought to be around 2500°C.

Outside the core is the *mantle*, a layer about 2870 km thick thought to be composed of the mineral olivine.

The thinnest, outer layer of the Earth is the *crust*, about 7 km to 40 km thick. It is composed mostly of igneous and metamorphic rocks many of which contain minerals which exist as pure elements or as mineral ores. Earthquake waves change velocity very sharply at the boundary between the crust and mantle. Evidence indicates that the crust beneath the continents consists of two rock layers about 40 km thick whereas beneath the oceans there is only one thin layer, mostly basalt, a few kilometres thick.

PLATE TECTONICS

It is thought that the Earth's crust consists of a number of large 'plates' and it is the interaction of these plates which is described as *plate tectonics*. The plates are thought to be moving at relative speeds of a few centimetres per year.

There are basically three ways the plates can move in relation to each other.

Movement of the plates

- The plates can slide *past* each other along a common boundary. The plane along which motion occurs is a vertical fracture or fault. Earthquakes can arise when there are sudden movements along these faults due to a build up of energy. For example, the San Andreas fault in Southern California.

- The plates can slide *towards* each other so that the thinner, denser ocean plates are pushed beneath the more buoyant continental plates, forcing the continental crusts upwards. Strong pressures build up giving rise to earthquakes and volcanoes. For example Chile, Japan and Alaska, as well as narrow zones around the Pacific Basin.

- The plates can *pull apart* from each other so that gaping cracks appear in the ocean crust. Magma continually rises to fill the gap and form new ocean crust. This is described as 'sea floor spreading'. Earthquakes can also occur but are usually too small to be of significance, for example in the mid-Atlantic ocean ridges.

CONTINENTAL DRIFT

It can be seen from Fig. 13.18 that the edges of the continents have shapes which appear to fit closely together, even though they are now separated by oceans.

The theory that best explains this observation is that over 300 million years ago the land masses formed a super continent called Pangaea. The Americas fitted closely against Africa and Europe, and the continents of Antarctica and Australia and the subcontinents of India and Madagascar were closely grouped around the Southern tip of Africa. 200 million years ago the separation of the continents began as the Americas pulled away from the rest of Pangaea, leaving a great rift that became the Atlantic Ocean. Later other fragments pulled away from Africa and from each other. The theory of *plate tectonics* helps to explain how the continents have moved apart in this way.

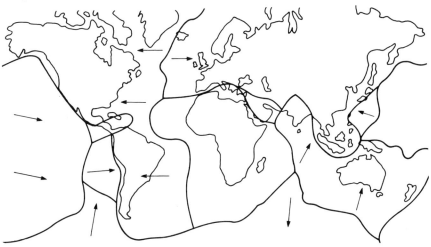

Fig. 13.18 The large plates of rock which form the Earth's crust.

EARTHQUAKES

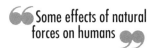 Some effects of natural forces on humans

Some of the visible effects of *earthquakes* are buildings falling down and large cracks appearing in the roads. In mountainous regions earthquakes can be responsible for causing avalanches of snow, and in the oceans very large tidal waves can be produced. In 1988 a very powerful earthquake in Armenia destroyed whole towns and killed many thousands of people.

Fig. 13.19

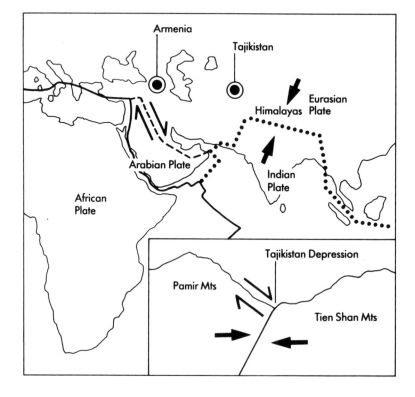

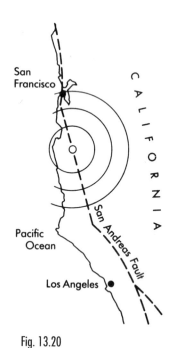

Fig. 13.20

In 1989 the second worst earthquake to hit the United States occurred in the San Francisco area of northern California along the San Andreas fault, causing roads and bridges to collapse, landslides and gaping cracks in roads.

VOLCANOES

A *volcano* is a large cone-shaped mountain which is formed when steam, lava, rocks and gases are pushed out from inside the Earth by the pressure of the gases and steam. The magma which flows out on the surface at a temperature of 1000°C is a mixture of lava and volcanic gases (Fig. 13.21). Some eruptions produce large amounts of volcanic dust particles which enter the atmosphere and cause cloud formation. It is thought that the volcanic ash in the atmosphere may also cause cooling of the Earth as the particles prevent radiation from the Sun reaching the Earth. Some of the effects of volcanoes are the destruction of towns and villages, and the removal of agricultural land and forests. A major volcanic eruption took place in 1976 in China where over 1 million people were killed. On the beneficial side: volcanic ash forms a very fertile soil; and molten rock underground heats underground water forming steam which can be used to generate electricity.

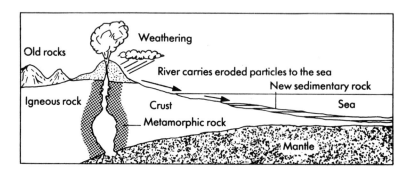

Fig. 13.21

9 ⟩   ROCKS

The most important zone of the Earth for Man is the thin outer crust which contains the continents and ocean basins and is the source of the soil, the gases of the atmosphere and all the free water of the oceans, atmosphere and land. Fig. 13.22 shows the eight most abundant elements of the Earth's crust.

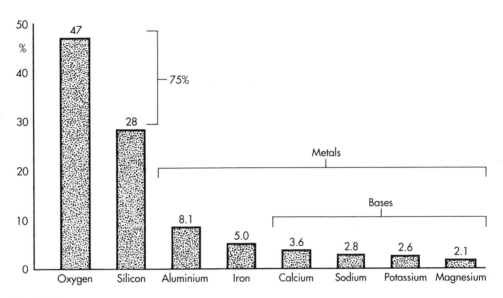

Fig. 13.22

The oxygen which accounts for almost half the total weight is combined with silicon, and is also a major element in organic substances.

The elements of the Earth's crust are present in minerals, usually as compounds. A great variety of minerals exists and are usually found in different combinations in rocks. Most rocks in the Earth's crust were formed millions of years ago but some are being formed now as lava from volcanic eruptions solidifies on contact with the atmosphere.

IGNEOUS, SEDIMENTARY, METAMORPHIC ROCKS

There are three major categories of rocks in the Earth's crust:

Igneous rocks

❝ Look at some samples of rocks such as granite. Can you see the crystals? ❞

Igneous rocks are formed when molten magma from the mantle cools and solidifies. The size of the crystals which can be seen in igneous rocks indicates the rate of cooling of the magma. Small crystals are formed when the magma cools rapidly. Volcanoes occur when the molten rock forces its way to the surface, often through a weak part of the crust. Granite and basalt are examples of igneous rocks.

Sedimentary rocks

There are accumulations of particles from existing rocks formed in many different ways:

- by the action of moving water;
- by wind, ice and frost;
- by changes of temperature;
- by chemical action, such as acidic rainwater on limestone;
- by the action of living organisms, such as worms and plant roots.

These factors cause the existing rock to disintegrate physically or chemically and form small particles. Some of these particles become mixed with the remains of dead animals and plants and form *soil*. The soils formed will differ in their drainage properties, texture, acidity and mineral composition. Other particles such as gravels and sands are transported by streams, rivers, wind and ice and are deposited by streams and rivers as sediments on the sea bed, in estuaries, swamps and marshes where they form successive layers known as *sedimentary strata* over millions of years. These layers are usually laid down horizontally but as a result of movements in the Earth's crust they become faulted and folded as you can see in Fig. 13.23. You can sometimes see strata at the coast where uplifting of the ocean floor may have occurred.

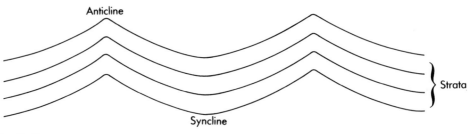

Fig. 13.23

Larger, heavier particles settle out first and this fact affects the type of sedimentary rock which is formed; for example a mixture of particles of salt and clay with some sand forms the sedimentary rock mudstone. Other examples include shale – the most abundant sedimentary rocks, sandstone, and limestone.

Metamorphic rocks

■ These are igneous or sedimentary rocks which have been physically or chemically changed by the tremendous pressures and very high temperatures which accompany mountain building movements in the Earth's crust. The metamorphic rock is so changed in appearance and may have formed new structures and minerals compared with the parent rock. For example shale, a sedimentary rock is altered into slate which further changes into schist; limestone is changed into marble, and so on.

The different rock types can be identified by their appearance:

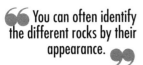
You can often identify the different rocks by their appearance.

■ Rocks which have random interlocking crystals are usually igneous rocks. If the crystals are very small then the magma from which the rock is formed will have cooled quickly. These rocks will probably have originated from a volcano. If the crystals are larger then the magma will have cooled more slowly, probably within the crust.

■ Rocks composed of bands of interlocking crystals are usually metamorphic.

■ Rocks composed of layers of cemented grains or fragments are usually sedimentary. Fossils may also be present in sedimentary rocks with different layers of rocks containing fragments of plants and animals that lived at the time the sediments were laid down.

THE ROCK CYCLE

All three types of rocks are continually being transformed from one rock to another over millions of years in a process known as the *rock cycle*. There is no record of the 'original' rocks that first formed the earth's crust as they will have been recycled millions of years ago.

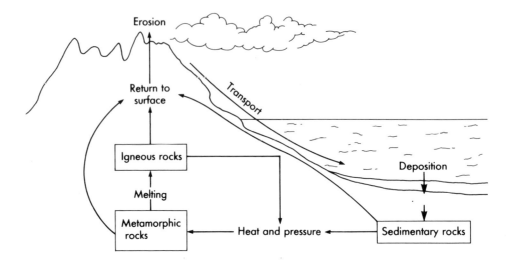

Fig. 13.24

- The igneous rocks are continually being affected by weathering and erosion.
- The resulting sediments are transported and deposited to form sedimentary rocks.
- High pressures and temperatures may cause some of these sedimentary rocks to be changed into metamorphic rocks, some of which may melt and form magma.
- The magma may rise into the crust where it cools and forms igneous rocks.

EXAMINATION QUESTIONS

MULTIPLE CHOICE

QUESTION 1

What is a year?
A the time taken for the Earth to rotate on its axis
B the time taken for the Moon to orbit the Earth
C the time taken between two solar eclipses
D the time taken for the Earth to orbit the Sun
E the time taken between summer and winter.

QUESTION 2

The flow chart below shows the possible life cycle of our Sun, a middle-aged star.

clouds of dust and gas → star contracts → main sequence star → star expands → X
white dwarf → dark body

Which one of the following should be at X?
A black hole   D neutron star
B galaxy   E red giant
C nebula

QUESTION 3

Which one of the following phases of the Moon occurs during a 'spring' tide?
A crescent moon   D gibbous moon
B first quarter   E last quarter
C full moon

QUESTION 4

What happens during a total eclipse of the Moon?
A The Moon goes behind the Sun.
B The Moon is between the Earth and the Sun.
C Mars moves between the Sun and the Moon.
D The Earth is between the Sun and the Moon.
E The Sun is between the Earth and the Moon.

QUESTION 5

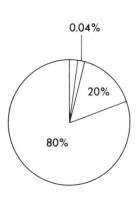

The diagram shows the approximate percentage of gases in the atmosphere.
What gas is present in the largest percentage?
A carbon dioxide   D nitrogen
B hydrogen   E sulphur dioxide
C oxygen

QUESTION 6

The diagram below shows a weather map.

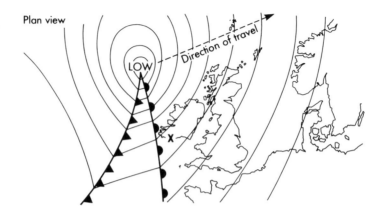

What type of weather is happening at area X?
A cold with very heavy rain
B cold with clear blue skies
C a very strong wind
D warm, sunny, dry weather
E warm and raining.

QUESTION 7

The diagram opposite shows the structure of the earth.

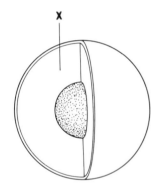

What does area **X** represent
A crust
B inner core
C mantle
D outer core
E continental plates

QUESTION 8

Which one of the following describes how igneous rocks are formed?
A Existing rocks are broken down by changes of temperature.
B Existing rocks are eroded by the action of water.
C An earthquake cracks the Earth's crust.
D Existing rocks are changed by high temperature and pressure.
E Hot magma from the mantle cools and solidifies.

QUESTION 9

The diagram below shows the rock cycle.

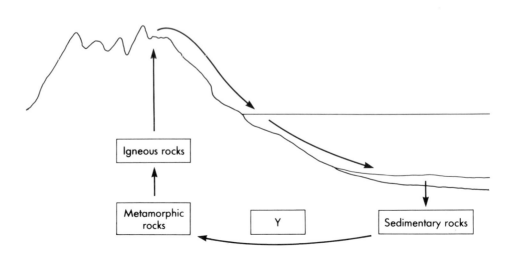

Which one of the following should be in box Y?
A deposition
B erosion
C evaporation
D melting
E heat and pressure

STRUCTURED QUESTIONS

QUESTION 10

The diagram below, which is not drawn to scale, shows the relative positions of the Sun, Moon and Earth.

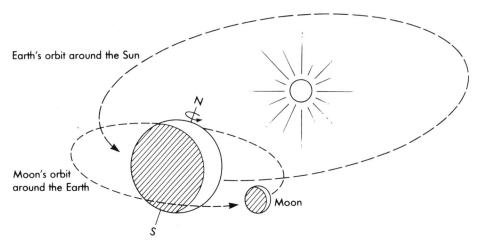

Earth's orbit around the Sun

Moon's orbit around the Earth

Moon

a) State how the motion of the Moon and Earth gives us
   i) a year (2 lines) *(1)*
   ii) a lunar month (2 lines) *(1)*
   iii) a day (2 lines) *(1)*

b) Draw labelled diagrams showing the positions of the Sun, Moon and Earth when:
   i) spring tides occur _____
   (1)

   ii) neap tides occur _____
   (1)

   iii) What phase of the Moon would you expect to see when there are spring tides?

   _____
   (1)

c) A list of planets is given below.
   Mercury
   Pluto
   Mars
   Saturn
   Venus
   From the list choose which planet

   i) has the most moons _____
   (1)

   ii) is the smallest planet _____
   (1)

   iii) has the longest year _____
   (1)

d) If you attempted to live on Venus, describe two problems you might encounter other than those of getting there.

1 _____

(1)

2 _____

(1)

(MEG)

QUESTION 11

A study of some planets in a solar system has produced the following observations. They are listed in Table A.

PLANET	Mass compared with Earth	Atmosphere	Nature of surface	Average temperature (°C)
A	one tenth	None	Very hard and rocky	−25
B	half	Traces of oxygen. Little carbon dioxide. Little clouds	Soft sand, some water	2
C	four times	Traces of oxygen. Nitrogen. Dense clouds.	Mainly water. Swamp land.	28

Table A

a) i) Suggest which planet may have the highest gravity.

_____

(2)

ii) Give a reason. (3 lines available)   *(2)*

b) i) Suggest which planet may support plant life.

_____

(1)

ii) Give **two** reasons. (7 lines available)   *(2)*

c) i) Which planet is **most unlikely** to support life?

_____

(1)

ii) Give **two** reasons. (7 lines available)   *(2)*

d) i) What would happen to water spilled by an astronaut on planet A? (2 lines)   *(1)*

ii) Give a reason for your answer. (2 lines)   *(1)*

e) Describe **five** benefits of space exploration to society. (10 lines available)   *(5)*

f) State **two** disadvantages of space exploration.

1 _____

2 _____

(2)

(Total marks 19)

(ULEAC)

"Oh dear!"

Astronaut drops insulated flask of water

Flask stopper comes off

Figure I

QUESTION 12

Figure 1 is a map of California showing the San Andreas fault.

a) i) What is meant by a 'fault' in the Earth's surface? (2 lines)   *(1)*

ii) The San Andreas fault is known as a 'tear' fault. Draw a labelled diagram to illustrate how such a fault occurs in the Earth's surface.   *(3)*

San Francisco

Pacific Ocean

Los Angeles

CALIFORNIA

San Andreas Fault

iii) Explain why earthquakes are common in this area. (6 lines available) *(3)*

iv) Explain why volcanic eruptions are likely in areas of the Earth's crust like this. (6 lines available) *(3)*

b) Earthquakes and volcanoes can give rise to destruction and enormous loss of human life. However, the San Andreas fault is in an area which is densely populated by people. Much of San Francisco was destroyed in 1906, and there is constant fear of further major earthquakes, yet still it is a densely populated region.

Write a scientific account of why such active regions of the Earth's crust are still attractive for humans to live in. (12 lines available) *(6)*

QUESTION 13
(Levels 6-8)

This question, based on the diagram of the volcano, is aimed at level 6.

The diagram below shows a section through a volcano.

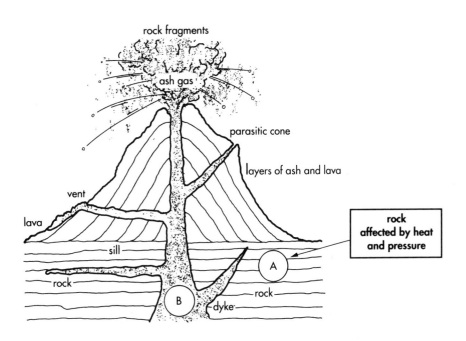

a) Name a type of rock you would expect to find at (A).

_____

(1)

b) i) What type of rock will eventually be formed at (B)?

_____

ii) Explain how this type of rock is formed. (2 lines) *(1)*

[Co-ordinated Science, NEAB, ULEAC, WJEC]

QUESTION 14
(Levels 8-10)

This question presents you with data in the form of a weather map and gives you opportunity for extended writing. It is aimed at level 9.

The map below shows the weather conditions at 0600 h on 15 January.

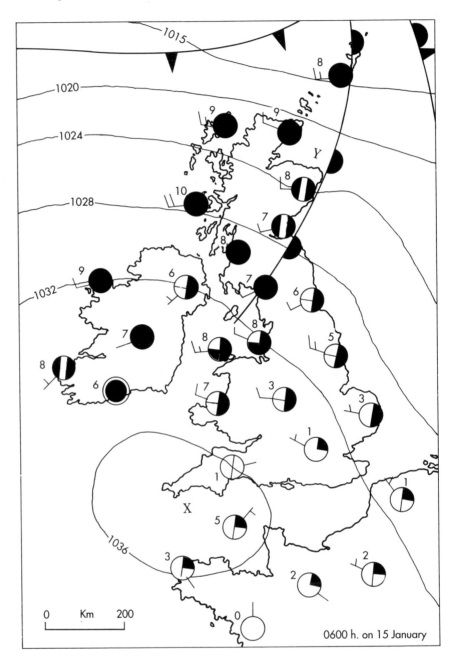

0600 h. on 15 January

Describe and explain the weather conditions which will be experienced over the next few hours at:

1   point X. (10 lines and [4] marks)

2   point Y. (10 lines and [4] marks)

[Co-ordinated Science NEAB, ULEAC, WJEC]

QUESTION 15
(Levels 8–10)

This question provides you with data in the form of a map and gives you opportunity for extended writing. Note you are asked to use the theory of plate tectonics; the diagram gives you a clue to help you here by showing you the shape of the 2 continents.

The map below shows two of the continents bordering the Atlantic Ocean.

Africa

South America

KEY

——— = Plate Boundary

 = Continental Shelf

It is believed that 150 million years ago these two continents were joined.

Use the theory of plate tectonics to explain how these continents could have moved apart to reach their present positions. You may use diagrams if you wish.

Marks will be given both for showing knowledge and understanding and for the way in which your account is organised and expressed.

(space and 10 lines for the answer, and [10] marks)

[Co-ordinated Science NEAB, ULEAC, WJEC]

ANSWERS TO EXAMINATION QUESTIONS

MULTIPLE CHOICE

ANSWER 1

Key D. Option A is a day, option B is a lunar month.

ANSWER 2

Key E, red giant. Option C, nebula, is the name of the gas cloud at the start of the life cycle. Option B is the name for a collection of many stars. Option D, a neutron star, is formed by some massive stars when they have exploded after becoming red super giants, but the question refers to the Sun.

ANSWER 3

Key C, full moon.

ANSWER 4

Key D. Remember, the Moon never goes behind the Sun as in option A, as the Moon is a satellite of the Earth.

ANSWER 5

Key D, nitrogen. Option C, oxygen, is only present about 20%.

ANSWER 6

Key E, warm and raining. This type of weather is typical of a warm front. Option A is typical of a cold front.

ANSWER 7

Key C, the mantle.

ANSWER 8

Key E describes the formation of igneous rocks. Options A and B are both descriptions of sedimentary rocks, and option D describes metamorphic rocks.

ANSWER 9

Key E. Heat and pressure lead to the formation of metamorphic rocks.

STRUCTURED QUESTIONS

ANSWER 10

a) i) A year is the time taken for the Earth to go once around the Sun.
   ii) A lunar month is the time taken for the Moon to go once around the Earth.
   iii) A day is the time taken for the Earth to spin once on its own axis.
b) i) diagram with the Sun, Moon and Earth in line
   ii) diagram with the Moon at right angles to line of Earth and Sun
   iii) full or new Moon
c) i) Saturn
   ii) Mercury (or Pluto)
   iii) Pluto
d) 1 no oxygen for breathing, so I would have to carry oxygen in cylinders
   2 very hot, so I would have to wear protective clothing

ANSWER 11

a) i) planet C
   ii) four times the mass of Earth
b) i) planet C
   ii) 1 traces of oxygen for respiration
      2 temperature similar to Earth
c) i) planet A
   ii) 1 no atmosphere
      2 very low temperatures
d) i) It would freeze.
   ii) temperature below freezing point of water, $0°C$
e) 1 minerals may be discovered
   2 more space available for people to live
   3 new sources of food may be discovered
   4 alternative energy sources may be found
   5 better understanding of effects of gravity if research carried out where there is little gravity
      (Any similar answers acceptable.)
f) 1 very expensive, the money could be used to cure diseases on Earth
   2 dangerous: rockets explode and kill astronauts

ANSWER 12

a) i) The pressure of the Earth causes the rocks in the crust to break or fault.

ii)

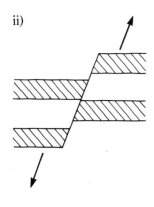

iii) Earthquakes happen near large faults, as two plates in the Earth's crust move past each other, aided by lubrication of a small proportion of molten material. Sudden fracturing releases energy, causing vertical and horizontal vibrations.

iv) Volcanic eruptions occur at weak places in the Earth's crust, as molten rock forces its way to the surface. In this area, lava runs from long fractures or fissures to form basalt plateaus.

b) The region may be very fertile and produce good crops. Other safer areas may be less fertile. The region may be on the coast and be accessible for trading, whereas other safer areas may be inland. There may be valuable minerals in the area which can offer employment to people involved in mining industries. The risk factor of earthquakes is being reduced, owing to their predictability. Buildings are being constructed to withstand the shockwaves.

(Any valid scientific suggestion would be acceptable here.)

ANSWER 13

a) the clue on the diagram is the label 'rock affected by heat and pressure' so the answer is metamorphic rock (1)

b) i) igneous rock (1)

ii) magma cools and crystallises (1)

ANSWER 14

As with all these opportunities for extended writing, look at the number of marks and try to list the four key points you hope to establish for each area. Remember to 'describe' and 'explain' the weather conditions.

1 Point X

the isobar shows an area of high pressure (1)
this leads to clear weather (1)
usually calm (1)
settled weather (1)

2 Point Y

a warm front is passing over Y (1)
warm air rises over cold air (1)
unsettled weather (1)
possibly rain (1)

ANSWER 15

This question is targeted at level 10. The diagram should help you to remember the theory of plate tectonics. Note 10 marks are allocated but at least 3 of these will be for organising a logical account so you need to think about establishing 7 points in your answer.

A possible answer would include the following:

the Earth's crust is formed from a number of plates (1)
these are moving (1)
at a few centimetres per year (1)
as a result of convection currents (1)
these two continents are moving apart (1)
evidence comes from the formation of mid-Atlantic ridges (1)
formed from basaltic magma (1)

logical, concise, scientific account (3)
logical and concise but lacking in scientific terms (2)

A STUDENT'S ANSWER WITH EXAMINER'S COMMENTS

Some facts about four planets in a different solar system are given in the table below.

Planet	Temperature range °C	Atmosphere	Surface conditions	Mass compared with Earth = 1
Helios	0 to 50	Nitrogen, oxygen, some carbon dioxide and cloud	Water and sandy soil	1.4
Rheagos	−25 to −10	Hydrogen, some CO_2. No cloud	Very hard rock with some powdered material	4.6
Solos	−10 to 12	Mainly CO_2 with a lot of cloud	Swampland and water	3.2
Carmel	−45 to 40	None	Very hard rock	0.9

a) Study the table and then answer the following questions.

  i) Which planet is most likely to support plant and animal life as we know it?

    <u>Helios</u> ✓

    (1)

 *Good.*

  ii) Give **three** reasons for your answer to part i).

    1 <u>water available on Helios</u>

    (1)

    2 <u>the temperature ✓ is like Earth</u>

    (1)

 *Look at the information. What about oxygen?*

    3 _____

    (1)

 *Look carefully. Carmel has a 95° range.*

  iii) Which planet has the greatest temperature variation?

    <u>Helios</u> X

    (1)

  iv) Why do you think Solos has a lot of cloud in its atmosphere?

    <u>due to the CO_2 and water.</u>

    (1)

    (WJEC)

R E V I E W   S H E E T

✎ The sun is a _____, one of billions which make up the _____ known as the Milky Way.

✎ Fill in as many labels as you can for the nine planets which orbit around the sun.

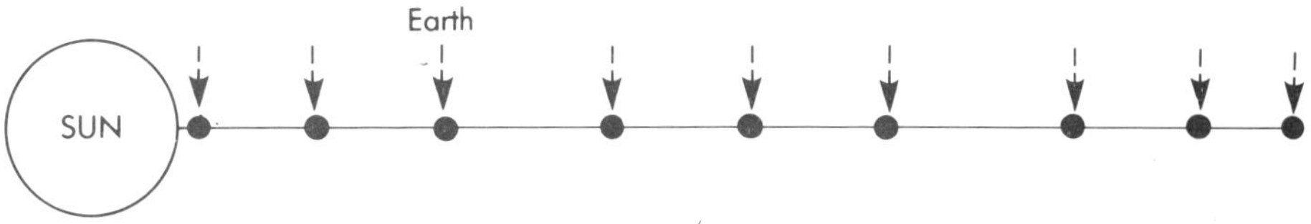

Earth

SUN

✎ Planets nearer the sun have _____ diameters and _____ density; planets

further away from the sun have _____ diameters and _____ density.

✎ List, in descending order, the three main gases of the atmosphere.

1. _____   2._____   3. _____

✎ The _____ has developed 'holes' in recent years through which harmful radiation can pass.

✎ The weight of air above any part of the Earth is described as _____

✎ Points of equal air pressure are described on weather maps by lines called _____

✎ Wind generally moves from an area of _____ pressure to an area of _____ pressure.

✎ A barometer is an instrument for measuring _____

✎ Fill in the boxes for each of the four stages in this diagram, describing how clouds are formed at each stage

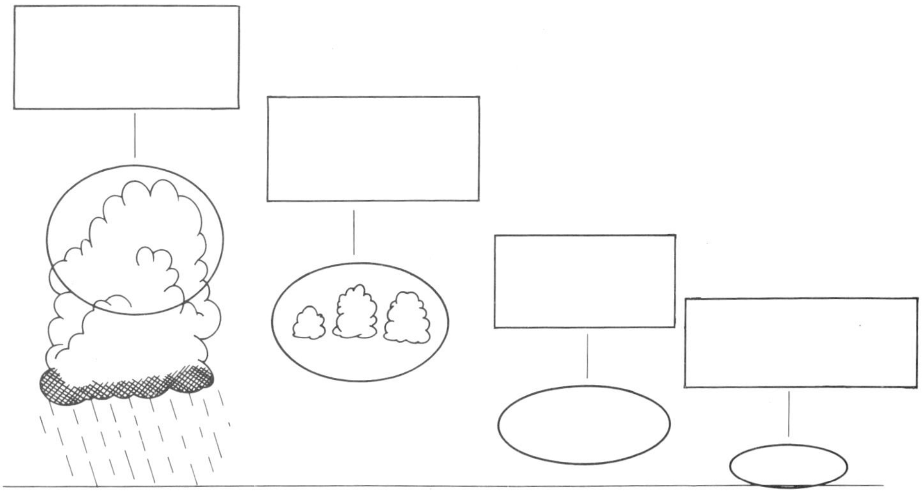

✎ Complete the table of cloud names below:

Name	Height)'000m)	Description
	8	wispy white threads
	2.5	thick white clouds with flat base and rounded tops
	0.5–2.5	continuous sheet of low cloud

✎ Fill in the label lines for this diagram of the earth's structure. Try to describe each part you have labelled.

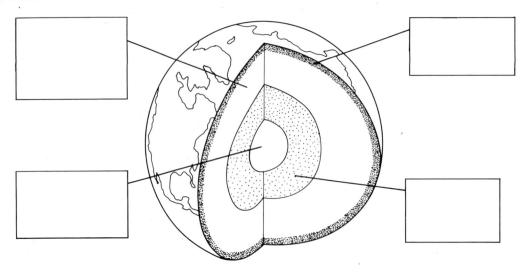

✎ List three ways in which the 'plates' of the earth's crust can move in relation to each other

1. _____

2. _____

3. _____

✎ During the eruption of a volcano, _____ flows out on the surface at a temperature of 1000°C, being a mixture of lava and volcanic gases.

✎ _____ is the most abundant element of the earth's crust.

✎ _____ rocks are formed when molten magma cools and solidifies.

✎ _____ rocks are accumulations of particles from many different rocks formed by things such as the action of moving water, changes of temperature, etc.

✎ _____ rocks have been physically or chemically changed by the tremendous pressures and high temperatures which occur during mountain building movements in the earth crust.

✎ Fill in the boxes in this diagram of the rock cycle

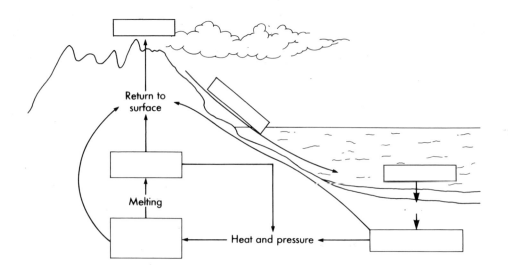

ENERGY AND FUELS

GETTING STARTED

Chapters 14 to 18 of this book will take you through the main topics and points needed to cover Attainment Target 4: Physical Processes.

One of the most important topics in GCSE Science is the study of energy and fuels. In your home and at school you are using energy to heat and light the buildings you live and work in, to cook food and to make electrical appliances work. In industry, energy is being used to drive machinery to make many different types of consumer goods, such as cars and household items. Most of the energy which is used in this way is in the form of electricity which has been generated in a power station from a primary source of energy, such as the fossil fuels or nuclear fuel.

The *type* of fuel you use to heat your home may be affected by many different factors, such as how much a fuel costs, whether it is easy to store, and how cheap it is. Most people try to save money by reducing the amount of energy which is lost from their homes as heat, and you probably already know something about loft insulation and double glazing.

Fossil fuels, such as coal and oil, are finite and will eventually run out, so scientists and technologists are investigating *alternative* energy sources such as solar energy, tidal energy, wave energy and wind power.

ENERGY TRANSFER

IMPORTANCE OF THE SUN

FOSSIL FUELS

WHAT MAKES A GOOD FUEL?

USING FUELS TO GENERATE ELECTRICITY

ENERGY LOSSES AND INSULATION

ALTERNATIVE ENERGY SOURCES

GREENHOUSE EFFECT

ESSENTIAL PRINCIPLES

1 ENERGY TRANSFER

Whenever you see something moving or happening you know that energy is being transferred from one form to another. Things only move or happen when energy is transferred. For example, a clockwork toy moves because the potential energy from the wound up spring is transferred to kinetic energy which turns the wheels of the toy.

There are many examples of energy sources, such as chemical energy in fuel and batteries, and gravitational potential energy in objects lifted above the ground. When a fuel is burned the chemical energy stored in it is transferred to heat (thermal energy). When an object falls to the ground the potential energy it had because of its position is transferred to kinetic energy.

One of the most useful sources of energy at home and in industry is electrical energy which is easily transferred into light, sound, movement (kinetic energy) and heat (thermal energy). You have many electrical devices at home which transfer electrical energy into other forms of energy, for example:

> **Devices which transfer electrical energy into other forms of energy**

- an electric lamp converts electrical energy into heat (thermal energy) and light energy
- an electric kettle converts electrical energy into heat (thermal energy)
- an electric razor converts electrical energy into kinetic energy and sound energy
- a radio converts electrical energy into sound

During the transfer of energy, some of the energy is transferred to where it is needed and some is wasted, for example as thermal (heat) energy or sound energy. In any device the *proportion* of energy which is usefully transferred is called the 'efficiency' of the device. For example an electric motor transfers electrical energy into kinetic energy but some heat and sound are produced as well. The efficiency can be calculated using the formula:

$$\text{efficiency} = \frac{\text{useful energy transferred by device (energy output)}}{\text{total energy supplied to the device (energy input)}}$$

This can also be considered as:

$$\text{efficiency} = \frac{\text{power output}}{\text{power input}}$$

> **Energy cannot be created or destroyed**

For example, if a motor is supplied at 100 W and the power output is 60 W then its efficiency is 60/100 = 60%. Note that when energy is transferred, the *total amount* of energy is unchanged but some energy is eventually transferred to the surroundings as thermal or sound energy where it is spread out and unavailable for further energy transfers. It is in this sense that the 40% of energy can be regarded as 'wasted' in the motor example above.

2 THE IMPORTANCE OF THE SUN

The Sun is ultimately the major source of energy for Earth. Almost all the available energy comes from, or has come from, the Sun. Some of the Sun's energy is used by green plants in the process of photosynthesis. Over millions of years the remains of these plants and the animals which fed on them were changed into fossil fuels by the action of heat and pressure.

3 FOSSIL FUELS

Fossil fuels are stores of chemical energy which is converted into thermal energy when the fuel burns. These fuels, such as coal and oil, were formed millions of years ago by the effect of heat and pressure on decaying plants and animals. Fossil fuels are described as *non-renewable* energy sources because once they are used up they cannot be replaced. Chemical energy is released as heat and light when the fuel is burned.

fuel + oxygen → carbon dioxide + water + heat

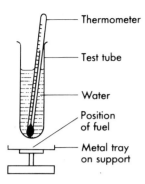

- Thermometer
- Test tube
- Water
- Position of fuel
- Metal tray on support

Fig. 14.1 You may have used equipment like this to compare the amount of heat energy released by different fuels.

A *chemical equation* for this reaction would be :-

$$CH_4 + 2O_2 \rightarrow CO_2 + 2H_2O + heat$$

When fuels burn they may also produce oxides of sulphur, or oxides of nitrogen, as well as carbon monoxide. These waste products are one of the main causes of pollution. For example, sulphur dioxide dissolves in water vapour in the air to cause 'acid rain', which damages trees, and harms animal life in rivers and lakes.

You may have compared the amount of heat energy released by different fuels by measuring the rise in temperature of a known volume of water in a test tube.

4 > WHAT MAKES GOOD FUEL?

 **Which factor is most important to you as a consumer?**

You should be aware of some of the factors which affect *why* a certain fuel is used for a particular job.

Some of these factors are:

1 How much it costs to obtain, and consequently the cost to the consumer.
2 How easy it is to transport and to store, which depends on whether it is solid, liquid or gas.
3 How easily it catches alight and burns.
4 How much pollution is caused, poisonous gases and dust particles being released into the atmosphere.
5 How much energy is released when it burns.

For example the chart below shows how much energy is released when 1 kilogram of fuel is burned:

Gas	55 MJ per kg
Oil	44 MJ per kg
Coal	29 MJ per kg
Wood	14 MJ per kg

Although gas may be the 'best' fuel as it releases the most energy, 1 kilogram of gas takes up much more space than 1 kilogram of oil, and is more bulky to transport and to store. So you have to take account of *all* the factors mentioned above, and the main interests of the *user* of the fuel, before you can make a decision as to the 'best' fuel for a particular task.

5 > USING FUELS TO GENERATE ELECTRICITY

Fuels such as coal and oil are used in a power station to heat water and convert it into high pressure steam. The steam is then used to turn huge turbines which spin around and in turn drive a generator, causing it to rotate very rapidly, at around 50 times per second. It is the *generator* which produces an alternating current at a frequency of 50 Hertz. The electricity is generated at a high voltage of about 25 000 volts, and it is usually increased using a transformer to 400 000 volts when it is passed through the overhead transmission lines of the National Grid. The high voltages mean that a *low current* is used and, as a result, very little power is lost during transmission to people's homes. The voltage is then decreased to the 240 volts required for the home.

Any fuel can be used to produce the steam in a power station. In nuclear power stations, nuclear fuel is used to heat carbon dioxide gas, which in turn converts water into steam.

In power stations the process of generating energy is inefficient and some energy is lost to the environment as heat. The *efficiency* of the power station can be calculated using the formula

 **Keeping warm uses energy**

$$efficiency = \frac{useful\ energy\ out \times 100}{total\ energy\ in}$$

Fig. 14.2 Electricity can be generated in coal fired power stations.

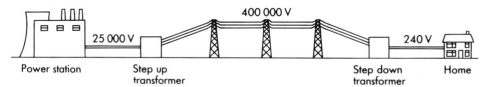

Fig. 14.3 How electricity gets from the power station to your home.

6 ⟩ ENERGY LOSSES AND INSULATION

During cold weather, about a third of the energy produced in Britain is used to heat people's homes to a comfortable temperature of about 20°C. Some of this heat energy may come from using coal, oil or gas to heat up water in radiators in a central heating system, or from burning a fuel in a fireplace in the room. Some houses are warmed using heaters, which in turn use electricity that has been generated in a power station from burning fuels. Figure 14.4 shows the ways in which heat energy is lost from an ordinary house.

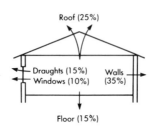

Fig. 14.4 How heat is lost from a house.

WAYS OF REDUCING HEAT LOSS

a) *Roof insulation*: laying an insulating fibre material which traps air in tiny spaces between the fibres. Air is a poor conductor of heat and reduces the heat escaping from the house.

Fibre fill material

66 All these cost money but keep heat in 99

Fig. 14.5 How to reduce loss of heat from a house.

a) Insulation in the roof.

b) *Double glazing of windows*: putting a second pane of glass in each window, so that a layer of air is trapped between the two panes, greatly reduces the amount of heat which can escape. In most new houses the windows are *installed* as sealed double glazed units. These already consist of two panes of glass with a trapped layer of air to prevent heat escaping.

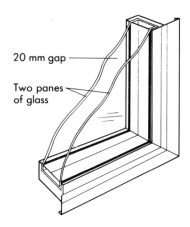

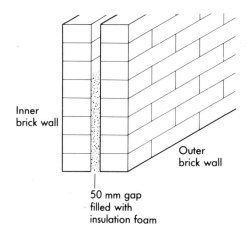

Fig. 14.5b) Double glazing of windows.

c) *Cavity wall insulation*: most recently built houses have walls which are made of two layers of bricks with a gap in between. This gap can be filled with insulating foam, which again traps pockets of air and reduces heat escaping from the house.

d) *Draught excluders*: putting strips of draught-excluding material around doors and windows can prevent warm air escaping and stop cold air from coming into the room. However, people who burn fuel in a fireplace need to check that there is a good flow of air to keep the fire burning, and to prevent the build up of poisonous fumes within the room.

Heat escapes from buildings in **three** ways:

Causes of heat loss

1 *Convection* – moving air carries heat away.
   During convection gases and liquids flow and carry energy away from places where the temperature is higher to where the temperature is lower.

2 *Conduction* – walls and roofs transfer heat to the surroundings.
   During conduction energy is transferred by a substance from places where the temperature is higher to where the temperature is lower. The substance itself does not move. Metals are good conductors whereas non metals and gases are poor conductors.

3 *Thermal radiation* – all hot objects lose heat to their surroundings.
   During radiation, energy is transferred to and from all objects. The hotter an object is, the more energy it will radiate. Dark, matt surfaces emit more radiation than light shiny surfaces.

7 ⟩ ALTERNATIVE ENERGY SOURCES

The supply of fossil fuels is limited and there is a need to obtain energy from *renewable* natural resources, such as the Sun as solar energy, the wind, tides, the rise and fall of waves, the flow of water from a higher to a lower level as hydro-electric power, and from the heat of the Earth itself.

SOLAR ENERGY

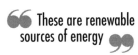

These are renewable sources of energy

A common use of solar energy is to heat up water which is inside a solar panel. These panels are usually painted black so that they absorb as much heat as possible. The solar heated water is then pumped to a normal hot water tank where it can be used to pre-heat the cold water. The warmed up water can then be further heated electrically. It is obviously much cheaper to heat water which has already been warmed up than to heat water from cold.

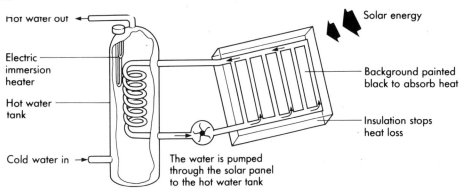

Fig. 14.6 A hot water system which uses solar energy.

Solar cells

These are devices which absorb the sun's energy and convert it into electricity. However, many thousands of cells are needed to produce useful amounts of electricity. One of their main uses is in satellites, where conventional batteries would be difficult to replace!

 **Pollution free**

HYDRO-ELECTRIC POWER

Hydro-electric power (HEP) is the result of fast-flowing water driving turbines in a hydro-electric power station and thereby producing electricity. There is no pollution, and the source of energy is free. The only costs involved are in the building of the power station and in maintenance.

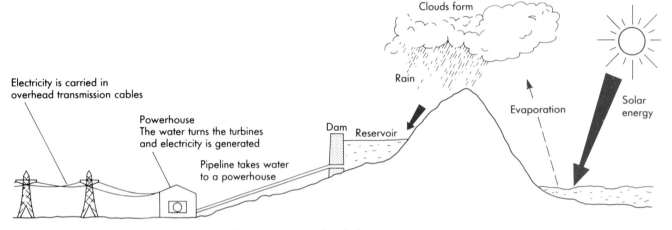

Fig 14.7 How electricity is generated from hydro-electric power.

WAVE POWER

Waves are produced as the wind blows across the surface of the sea. A wave power machine converts the up and down movement of the waves into electricity. The potential for generating electricity is very great but there are many technological problems to be overcome.

TIDAL POWER

The gravitational effect of the Sun and Moon on the Earth cause regular tidal movements of the oceans. These tidal movements can be used to push water into reservoirs, which can then be used to drive turbines and so produce electricity.

WIND ENERGY

Windmills which turn to generate electricity are called aerogenerators. A typical aerogenerator, capable of generating enough electricity for a small village, would need to have blades 20-25 metres long.

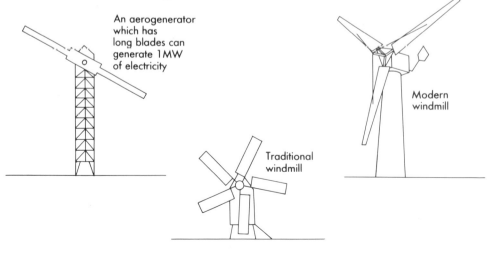

Fig. 14.8 Using wind energy to generate electricity.

GEOTHERMAL POWER

Heat which is trapped in hot rocks deep in the Earth can be used to heat up water and convert it into steam. The steam can then be used via a heat exchanger to drive generators and produce electricity.

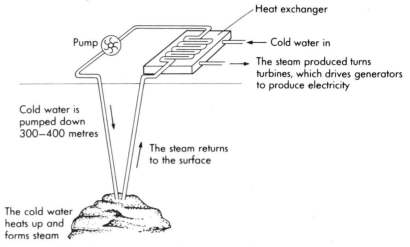

Fig 14.9 Using hot water from the Earth to generate electricity.

WHY ARE ALTERNATIVE ENERGY RESOURCES BEING DEVELOPED?

Why are alternative energy supplies being developed? There are three main reasons:
1 Fossil fuels are 'finite'. It has been predicted that in 600 years' time the known supplies of coal will have been used up.
2 Burning fossil fuels can cause pollution, especially acid rain.
3 There is an increasing demand for electricity from industry and from consumers. This may exceed the supply from existing power stations burning fossil fuels.
The chart below summarises the main alternative sources of energy, and their advantages and disadvantages:

ENERGY SOURCE	ADVANTAGES	DISADVANTAGES
Wind	■ will not run out ■ no fuel costs ■ no pollution ■ useful for isolated communities	■ windmills can spoil the environment ■ wind speeds may vary, so the generation of electricity is varied
Solar	■ will not run out ■ no fuel costs ■ no pollution	■ cloud cover blocks the sun ■ difficult to store energy produced ■ huge solar panels needed
Tidal	■ no fuel costs ■ no pollution	■ expensive to build power stations ■ may cause silting up of rivers
Geothermal	■ long-term supplies can provide hot water	■ not easily available ■ costly to obtain
Wave	■ will not run out ■ no pollution	■ many technological problems ■ hazard to shipping

ENVIRONMENTAL PROBLEMS

There are however environmental problems associated with all the different sources of energy. For example, burning fossil fuels generates pollution on a large scale (for one example of the pollution caused by burning fossil fuels: see Acid Rain, chapter 11 . However using renewable energy sources such as wind power and wave action may seem environmentally 'friendly' but there is a huge cost of developing the technology to obtain energy in this way and to build the equipment required. The amount of electricity produced may be much smaller than that produced from a conventional power station so the cost per unit of electricity is relatively high.

NUCLEAR POWER

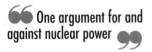

One argument for and against nuclear power

Nuclear power is another important source of energy. One of its main disadvantages is that the waste products are highly radioactive and are very difficult to dispose of safely. An advantage of nuclear power is that there are adequate supplies of uranium, and the nuclear power station does not release potentially harmful gases such as sulphur dioxide. Of course there is the disadvantage of the possible accidental release of radioactive substances into the atmosphere. Generally speaking, it can be said of nuclear power that although the fuel costs are relatively low, the costs of building nuclear power stations and the costs of de-commissioning them at the end of their useful life can be very high. See page 146.

8 GREENHOUSE EFFECT

The Earth is surrounded by an atmosphere which acts as a 'blanket' keeping it warm. On Earth the average surface temperature is $+15°C$, whereas on the Moon, which has no atmosphere, the surface temperature is $-18°C$.

Evidence has shown that the Earth is slowly warming up, caused by changes in the atmosphere. This gradual warming is called the *'Greenhouse effect'*.

During the last century man has been adding to the amount of *carbon dioxide* in the atmosphere as a result of burning fossil fuels (coal, oil, gas) and burning trees (as a result of deforestation to provide land for growing crops). This has disturbed the balance of carbon dioxide in the atmosphere; it has been estimated to have increased over the last century from a 'pre-industrial' level of 0.275% to 0.350% today. This is turn has resulted in a slight warming of the Earth. In addition, other man-made gases have been released into the atmosphere which have been shown to add to the problem, for example chlorofluorocarbons (CFCs), methane, nitrous oxide and ozone. (Be careful – this is an increase in ozone in the lower atmosphere – do not confuse it with the ozone layer.)

How the greenhouse effect works

The Earth is warmed by solar radiation which passes through the atmosphere and is absorbed by the ground and oceans, warming them up. This energy is re-radiated (at a different wavelength) as *heat* into the atmosphere. Carbon dioxide, water vapour and the other gases mentioned absorb this heat energy and then re-radiate it *back* to the surface. Any increase in the amount of carbon dioxide will therefore increase the amount of heat 'trapped', resulting in a gradual warming (Fig. 14.10).

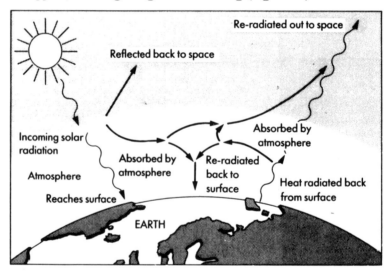

Fig. 14.10

Implications

Many predictions have been made as to the effect that a slight warming of the Earth ($1°C$ to $2°C$) will produce, using many different computer models. Some of the suggestions put forward include:

- a change in climate; some areas will become dryer, some wetter, some warmer. Drought may occur in parts of the Earth and floods in others.
- Polar ice caps will melt, and this will itself affect the climate.

No one is certain what will happen – only that there will be changes.

The tables and charts used in many of the questions which follow provide extra detail on a number of the *principles* we have considered. This is true throughout the book. So, as well as answering the questions, take note of the relevant information.

EXAMINATION QUESTIONS

QUESTION 1

MULTIPLE CHOICE

Which one of the following is a fossil fuel?

A coal
B paper
C the Sun
D uranium
E wood

QUESTION 2

What gas is released when coal is burned?

A carbon dioxide
B hydrogen
C methane
D nitrogen
E oxygen

QUESTION 3

Which one of the following is an advantage of using coal, instead of wind energy, to generate electricity?

A It is very cheap.
B It will not run out.
C It does not cause pollution.
D It is very easy to obtain.
E It can generate a lot of electricity.

QUESTION 4

The chart below shows some data on five different fuels. Which fuel, A, B, C, D, or E, costs the most to release 1000 units of energy?

Fuel	Price per 100g	Energy released per 100g
A	10p	2000
B	12p	3000
C	18p	6000
D	24p	4000
E	25p	5000

STRUCTURED QUESTIONS

QUESTION 5

a) Why is oil described as a fuel?

____________________ *(2)*

b) Suggest two reasons why gas is used to heat houses instead of solid fuel.

1 ____________________

2 ____________________ *(2)*

c) Fossil fuels are non-renewable and will eventually run out. Name two sources of alternative energy which can be used to slow down the rate at which fossil fuels are being used.

1 ____________________

2 ____________________ *(2)*

QUESTION 6

The table below gives some information about reducing heat loss in the home.

Method of reducing heat loss	% of heat saved	Typical cost in £'s	Approx. time to recover cost (years)
Double glazing	15	1000	30
Carpet underlay	20	200	8
Draught proofing	25	50	1
Roof insulation	30	150	3
Cavity wall insulation	35	300	5

a) Which single method of reducing heat loss saves most energy?

_____

(1)

b) Which is the most effective method of reducing heat loss at the smallest relative cost? Explain your answer.

Method _____

Explanation _____

(3)

c) How much money do you save each year by using roof insulation?

_____

(2)

(NICCEA)

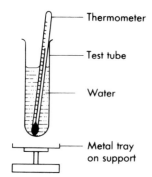

Thermometer

Test tube

Water

Metal tray on support

Fig. 14.11

QUESTION 7

a) Describe how you would use the apparatus shown opposite to compare the amount of heat released by three different samples of solid fuel. (7 lines available)   *(5)*

b) State **three** factors which should be considered when choosing the best fuel to heat a house.

1 _____

2 _____

3 _____

(3)

c) When fossil fuels burn they form sulphur dioxide gas. Describe and explain **one** effect that this gas has on the environment. (3 lines available)   *(2)*

QUESTION 8

a) Name **two** fossil fuels.   *(2)*

b) Explain briefly how **one** of these fuels is formed and how it is extracted.   *(2)*

c) When fossil fuels are burned in power stations sulphur dioxide and carbon dioxide are produced. These gases appear to be having an effect on our environment especially with regard to the greenhouse effect and acid rain.
Explain how these gases affect our environment.   *(4)*

d) Some varieties of plants have begun to show remarkable tolerance to high levels of sulphur dioxide in the air. Describe the mechanism that could lead to the evolution of these plant varieties.   *(3)*

e) Nuclear power stations do not use fossil fuels.
   i) Name a fuel that they use.
   ii) Give **three** different environmental arguments for or against the use of nuclear fuels.   *(3)*

(MEG)

QUESTION 9

The diagram below shows the main parts of a solar heating system designed to provide hot water for a house. Heat energy from the Sun warms the water in the solar panel. This water is then pumped through a spiral of copper tube inside the hot water tank so that it can transfer its heat to the water in the tank.

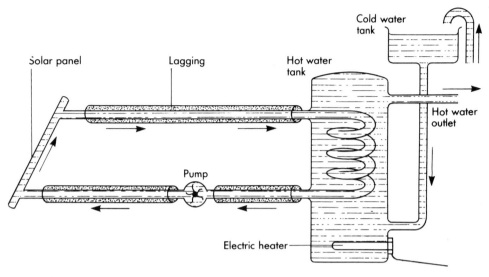

Fig. 14.12

a) i) State one reason why copper is used to make the spiral.

_____

ii) State one reason why a spiral tube is used and not a straight tube.

_____

(2)

b) The pipes between the solar panel and the hot water tank are lagged.

i) Name a suitable material for the lagging.

_____

ii) State one reason why this should be done.

_____

(2)

c) Explain why the hot water outlet pipe is at the top of the hot water tank. (3 lines available) *(2)*

d) The electric heater in the hot water tank is rated at 240 V, 2 400 W. Electrical energy is sold in units called kilowatt hours (kWh). Each unit costs 5p.

i) Calculate the electric current which will pass through the heater when it is switched on. (2 lines available)

ii) How much energy is supplied by the heater if it is switched on for one hour? (2 lines available)

iii) What is the cost of using the heater for two hours? (2 lines available)

(6)
(SEG)

QUESTION 10

a) i) Explain the difference between renewable and non-renewable sources of energy. (4 lines available) *(2)*

ii) Explain briefly why it is important to continue the development of renewable energy sources. (4 lines available) *(2)*

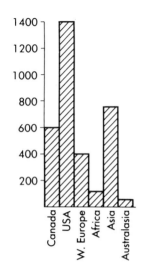

Fig. 14.13

Fig. 14.14

The bar graph shows the reserves of coal of several areas of the world.

b) What are the reserves of coal in

   i) USA? _____ billion tons

   ii) Africa? _____ billion tons

   iii) Western Europe is using coal at the rate of four billion tons per year. If this rate continues, for how long will its coal stocks last?

_____

(3)

c) The dying bird below was photographed in a French bay following the wreck of the oil tanker 'Torrey Canyon' in 1967.

   i) Had the bird been rescued suggest one step which could have been carried out to remove oil from its feathers. (2 lines available)

(1)

   ii) What risk does your removal method carry for the bird? (2 lines available)

(2)

(NICCEA)

QUESTION 11

Levels 6–8

In this question notice how sub-questions (a), (b) and (c) can be answered independently so if you are unable to answer (a), go straight on to (b). Part (a) is targeted at level 6, part (b) at level 7, part (c) at levels 7 and 8.

a) The diagram below (Fig. 14.16) shows the position of a hydro-electric power station.

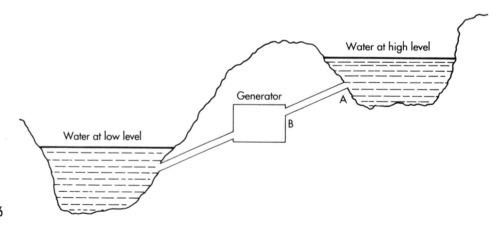

Fig. 14.16

   ı) What form of energy does the water have at the position marked A on the diagram?

_____

(1)

   ii) What forms of energy does the water have at the position marked B on the diagram?

_____ and _____

(1)

iii) Give three advantages of a hydro-electric power station over a coal-fired power station.

1 _____

2 _____

3 _____

(3)

b) The diagram below (Fig. 14.17) shows an electrically heated hot water storage tank.

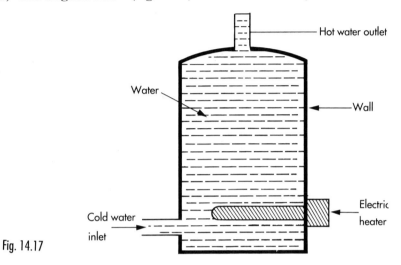

Fig. 14.17

i) Explain why the heater is plated at the bottom of the tank rather than at the top. (4 lines available) *(2)*

ii) Explain how you would reduce the heat energy loss through the walls of the tank, naming any materials you might use. (4 lines available) *(2)*

c) The diagram below (Fig. 14.18) shows a microwave oven.

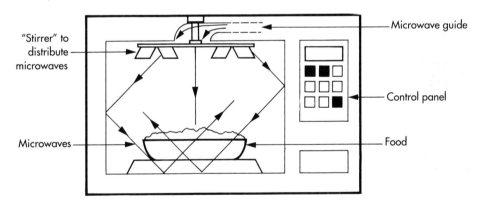

Fig. 14.18

Microwaves are absorbed by the water in the food. The specific heat capacity of water is 4.2 kJ/kg/°C.

i) A plastic jug containing 500 g of water at 20°C was placed in the microwave oven. The oven was switched on at full power. After two minutes in the oven the temperature of the water had risen to 44°C. Calculate how much energy had been transferred to the water in two minutes. (4 lines available) *(3)*

ii) The output power of the oven is rated at 650 W. How much energy does the cooker transfer from the electricity supply in two minutes? (2 lines available) *(2)*

iii) Compare the amounts of energy you have calculated in (i) and (ii). Account for any difference. (3 lines available) *(2)*

iv) The microwaves produced by the oven have a frequency of 2 450 MHz and a velocity of 300 000 km per second.
Calculate their wavelength. (4 lines available) *(2)*

[Co-ordinated Science, NEAB, ULEAC, WJEC]

OUTLINE ANSWERS

ANSWER 1

Key A, coal, is the only fossil fuel. A common distractor is option E, wood, which is a fuel made from trees but not a fossil fuel. Option D 'uranium' is a nuclear fuel, and options B and C are other *distractors*.

ANSWER 2

Key A, carbon dioxide, is always formed when a fuel burns. Option C, methane, is the name for a fuel, natural gas, and option E, oxygen, is what all fuels need in order to burn.

ANSWER 3

Key E, coal, produces a lot of electricity. All the other options, A to D, are advantages of wind energy, and disadvantages of fossil fuels.

ANSWER 4

Key D is correct, as 1000 units of energy at this rate would cost a quarter of 24, which is 6p. Options A and E cost 5p, option B costs 4p, and option C costs 3p.

ANSWER 5

a) Oil is a fuel because it releases heat and light when it burns.
b) easy to transport through pipes to the house; less dust, soot or ash.
c) i) wind power;   ii) tidal power.

ANSWER 6

a) cavity wall insulation;
b) Method - draught proofing. Explanation - cheapest method, recovers cost in 1 year, and 25% of heat saved. The most efficient method which saves 35% costs 6 times as much and takes 5 years to recover costs.
c) about one third of the heating bill.

ANSWER 7

a) These key points should appear in your answer:
   same mass of fuel used each time;
   same volume of water used at the same temperature;
   temperature of water measured before and after heating;
   method mentioned of preventing heat escaping;
   safety precautions such as wearing safety goggles;
   recording results in a chart;
   calculating and comparing temperature change.
b) 1 the cost of the fuel;
   2 whether it is a solid, liquid or gas;
   3 how easy it is to transport and store.
c) Sulphur dioxide dissolves in the water vapour and forms acid rain. Acid rain can destroy trees and make water in lakes very acid, so killing the fish.

ANSWER 8

a) coal, oil
b) Coal was formed millions of years ago from trees and ferns which died and decayed, forming layers of peat. The peat layers were covered with mud and sand, and usually covered by the sea. This process was repeated many times over millions of years and the layers were pushed down. Owing to the pressure and the heat, the peat changed into coal seams.

c) Sulphur dioxide forms acid rain when it dissolves in water vapour. The acid rain destroys trees and makes water in lakes very acid, so killing fish. Carbon dioxide in the atmosphere prevents heat escaping and produces the 'greenhouse effect', with a possible warming of the temperature of the Earth's surface.

d) A few plants may be more resistant to sulphur dioxide, and these grow well and form seeds which in turn produce plants which are resistant. By a process of natural selection those plants best adapted survive and others die.

e) i) uranium
   ii) nuclear fuels produce radioactive waste which is difficult to dispose of safely; nuclear fuels do not pollute the atmosphere with harmful gases like fossil fuels, which produce sulphur dioxide; there is always the danger of an explosion which would be difficult to control in a nuclear power station.

ANSWER 9

a) i) copper metal is a good conductor of heat;
   ii) to increase the surface area for exchange of heat.

b) i) any material which has lots of air trapped in it, such as insulating foam, woollen cloth, spongey tubing.
   ii) to reduce the amount of heat loss from the water on its way to the tank.

c) Due to convection currents, hot water rises to the top of the tank and denser cold water sinks to the bottom of the tank, where it can be heated.

d) i) Use the formula W = V x A (remember West VirginiA, i.e Watts = Volts x Amps)
      So, to find the current, use $\dfrac{W}{V}$ = A

$$\frac{2400}{240} = 10 \text{ amps}$$

   ii) Energy supplied = power x time = 2.4 kW x 1hr = 2.4 kWh.
   iii) In 2 hours the energy used = 4.8 kWh. 1 kWh costs 5p. The cost of using the heater is 5p x 4.8 = 24p.

ANSWER 10

a) i) Renewable resources are those which will always be available, such as the sun, the wind and the tides. Non-renewable resources are those which have taken a long time to form, such as fossil fuels, and are being used up. They cannot be replaced.
   ii) It is important to continue developing renewable energy resources as supplies of coal and oil are being used up, and there is an increasing demand for energy in the form of electricity, especially for industry. Also fossil fuels cause pollution, whereas renewable energy resources such as wind power do not cause pollution.

b) i) 1400, ii) 100, iii) 100 years

c) i) Use detergent to remove the oil from the feathers.
   ii) This substance may be harmful to the bird, and destroy natural oils in the feathers.

ANSWER 11

a) i) At position A the water has gravitational potential energy. *(1)*
   ii) At position B the water has kinetic energy and gravitational potential energy. *(1)*
   iii) non-polluting *(1)*
       cheaper running costs *(1)*
       uses renewable energy source *(1)*

b) i) A liquid expands and becomes less dense when it is heated (1), so the liquid at the bottom of the tank therefore rises up towards the hot water outlet, creating a warm convection current. (1) The cold water coming into the tank replaces the warm water. *(2)*
   ii) The tank could be insulated (1) by wrapping padded fibre material around it (1) *(2)*

c) i) energy transferred = specific heat capacity x mass x change in temperature *(1)*
       = 0.5 kg x 4200 J x 24° *(1)*
       = 50.4 kJ *(1)*
   ii) 650W x 120 s (1) 78 kJ (1) *(2)*

iii) More energy goes into the cooker than is transferred to the water. (1)

Energy may be absorbed by the inside of the cooker, or be released to the surroundings (1)   *(2)*

iv) $\underline{\text{300 000 km/s}}$ (1)
   2450 MHz
   $= 1.2 \times 10^{-4}$ m   (1)   *(2)*

A STUDENT'S ANSWER WITH EXAMINER'S COMMENTS

1 a) George and Sybil live in adjoining semi-detached homes. George has an open coal fire and Sybil has an electric storage heater.

   i) In what way does most of the heat travel into George's room?

   by radiation
   (1)

   ii) Sybil tells George that his fire is a nuisance to the environment. State two reasons why this may be true.

   when coal burns it produces carbon dioxide.
   (2)

   iii) Explain how **most** of the heat will travel around Sybil's room.

   by convection currents, hot air rises and cold air sinks.
   (1)

b) The word equations below show what happens when natural gas burns under different conditions:

   natural gas + plenty of air → heat + water + carbon dioxide.
   natural gas + limited air → heat + water + carbon monoxide.

   i) Explain why it is dangerous to use a gas fire in a badly ventilated room.

   the gas fire can produce poisonous gases if there is not enough air present.
   (3)

   ii) Explain why it is foolish to try to save money by not having gas fires and boilers serviced regularly.

   If the fire is not serviced it may not be burning the fuel properly and not enough heat will be given out.
   (2)

   (WJEC)

You were asked for *two* reasons. You could also mention the dust and soot which are formed.

Good

You could have identified carbon monoxide from the information given in the question. You might mention how carbon monoxide joins with haemoglobin and prevents oxygen reaching the cells.

Also state that carbon monoxide could be formed, which is poisonous.

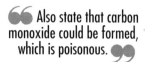

Overall some good points made, but lacking in detail to gain still higher marks.

R E V I E W   S H E E T

✎ List 4 different sources (types) of energy

1. _____   3. _____

2. _____   4. _____

✎ Things only move or happen when _____ is transferred.

✎ The _____ of a device refers to the proportion of energy which is transferred.

✎ The major source of the earth's energy is the _____. Some of its energy is used by green plants in the process of _____ .

✎ Fossil fuels are _____ energy sources, since once used they cannot be replaced.

✎ Complete these equations for the release of chemical energy when fuel is burned.

fuel   +   oxygen   →

A *chemical equation* for this reaction would be:–

CH_4 + $2O_2$ →

✎ List four factors which might influence the choice of fuel to use.

1. _____

2. _____

3. _____

4. _____

✎ Rank these four fuels in terms of how much energy is released when 1 kilogram of fuel is burned

oil   wood   gas   coal

1. _____

2. _____

3. _____

4. _____

✎ Fill in the labels on this diagram showing how electricity gets from the power station to your home.

✎ List three ways in which heat can escape from a building. Briefly describe what happens in each case.

1. _____

2. _____

3. _____

✎ Suggest four practical ways of reducing heat loss in a building.

1. _____   3. _____

2. _____   4. _____

✎ Suggest three reasons why energy users are being encouraged to consider alternative energy sources to the fossil fuels.

1. _____

2. _____

3. _____

✎ Complete the following table on renewable energy sources.

ENERGY SOURCE	ADVANTAGES	DISADVANTAGES
Wind		
Solar		
Tidal		
Geothermal		
Wave		

✎ Name one advantage and one disadvantage of using nuclear power as a source of energy.

1. advantage _____

2. disadvantage _____

✎ The _____ effect has played a part in raising the average temperature at the earth's surface.

✎ _____ is one of the main gases involved in trapping heat against the earth's surface.

✎ Suggest two likely consequences of increasing the earth's average temperature.

1. _____

2. _____

CHAPTER 15

CURRENT ELECTRICITY

GETTING STARTED

Imagine a day in your life without electricity and you have some idea of how important electricity is to everyone, at home, at school and in offices and factories. Most people come home from school or work in the colder months of the year to a warm, well lit house, and sit in front of the fire to watch TV, with a cup of tea or coffee. At the same time dinner is being cooked in an electric oven, and an electric washing machine is doing the family wash!

So why do you need to know anything about electricity? Clearly a basic knowledge of how electricity can be used safely and how much it costs and an understanding of electrical circuits can be very important for you in your everyday life, as well as in a Science examination! For example, you may have seen all the decorative lights on the Christmas tree go out, just because of one faulty lamp, but other rows of decorative lights appear to work even though more than one of the lamps may be faulty. You may also have wondered why electricity is transmitted by overhead power cables at very high voltages, when the voltage used at home is only 240 V. Is the reason so that every house gets a share of the voltage, or is there a more correct, technical explanation?

ESSENTIAL PRINCIPLES

1 > CURRENT ELECTICITY

Conductor	Insulator
Copper	Wood
Iron	Sulphur
Aluminium	Polythene
Carbon	Rubber
Sea-water	Paraffin
Sulphuric acid	Propanone

Fig. 15.1

2 > SERIES CIRCUITS AND PARALLEL CIRCUITS

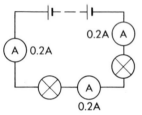

Fig. 15.2 Current in a series circuit.

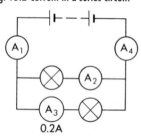

Fig. 15.3 Current in parallel circuits.

Parallel circuits are useful for Christmas tree lights

3 > CURRENT AND CHARGE

An electric current is a flow of charged particles around a circuit. Strictly speaking, it is the flow of negatively charged electrons around a circuit, from the negatively charged terminal to the positively charged terminal of the electrical supply. The conventional direction of conventional current flow is often shown by an arrow on a circuit diagram and is opposite to that of the electron flow. Current is measured in amps (A) by using an ammeter in the circuit. All circuits require an energy supply to push the particles around the circuit. All circuits should be made from good conductors, such as metals, as these allow the charged particles to pass through easily. Some substances are poor conductors or insulators, such as plastic and glass, and these do not allow significant amounts of current to pass through.

SERIES CIRCUITS

Figure 15.2 shows a simple *series circuit*, using the conventional symbols for circuit diagrams. (These symbols are shown at the end of the chapter to remind you.) As you can see, an ammeter is used to measure the amount of current flowing in the circuit. The *same* amount of current flows at any point in the series circuit, as no current is used up in the circuit.

We look at voltage in more detail below. However, we can say here that the energy given to the charged particles (electrons) by the battery to push them round the circuit is the *voltage* across the battery. The voltage is measured by a voltmeter. An ordinary battery or dry cell which you may have used in the lab has a voltage of 1.5 V. In a series circuit the battery voltage is split between each lamp. The voltage across each lamp adds up to the voltage across the battery.

PARALLEL CIRCUITS

Figure 15.3 shows two lamps connected in *parallel*.

Each lamp glows brightly, as it has the total voltage of the battery across it. If the lamps each take 0.2 A (the readings on A2 and A3 will be 0.2 A), then the total current drawn from the battery will be 0.4 A (the readings on A1 and A4 will be 0.4 A). Most household power sockets are connected in parallel with the mains supply so that if one appliance is switched off the others remain working. Each appliance receives the mains voltage of 240 V.

Advantages of a parallel circuit

■ If one lamp is faulty, the others stay alight. This is especially useful in wiring decorative lights, for example on a Christmas tree, or along a street. In a series circuit, if one lamp is faulty, all the lamps go out.

Disadvantages of a parallel circuit

■ The circuit can be more difficult to set up and uses more wire, which can be expensive.

The amount of electrical charge which flows is related to current and time as shown in the equation.

$$\text{charge (coulombs)} = \text{current (amperes)} \times \text{time (seconds)}$$

$$Q = I \times t$$

$$I = \frac{Q}{t}$$

When an ammeter measures that 1 ampere of current is flowing it means that in one second a coulomb of charge is passing that point. One coulomb is the amount of charge transported by an electric current of one ampere in one second. It is about the same charge as 6.2×10^{18} electrons.

If 10 amps (I) flow for 5 seconds (t) then 50 coulombs (Q) have passed through a point in the circuit. If the current through a household electric fire is about 4 amps, this means that 4 coulombs are passing through a point in the circuit per second.

4 > VOLTAGE

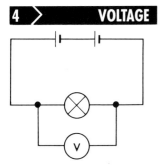

Fig. 15.4 The voltmeter is in parallel with the lamp.

The *voltage* is the potential difference between two points of a circuit measured in volts. A current only flows through an electrical device or component if there is a potential difference (p.d) or voltage across its ends. The bigger the potential difference across a device, the bigger the current that flows through it. Some devices or components resist a current flowing through them so that a bigger voltage is needed to produce a particular current.

A voltmeter is placed in a circuit in parallel with the component, i.e. the place where the energy is being converted. It is used to measure the potential difference (p.d) across a device or component in a circuit. The voltmeter measures the change of electrical energy into another form of energy. For example, in a lamp, energy is being converted into light and heat.

5 > CATHODE RAY OSCILLOSCOPE (CRO)

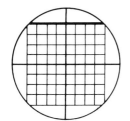

Fig. 15.5 The pattern produced by a DC supply (+ 4V).

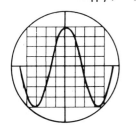

Fig. 15.6 The pattern produced by an AC supply.

A *CRO* can be used as a visual voltmeter for measuring voltage. A bright spot is produced on the oscilloscope screen by a beam of electrons. The vertical position of the spot can be altered by the voltage across the CRO. When the time base control is adjusted the dot moves across the screen and draws a visual graph of the voltage against time.

Figure 15.5 shows the waveform of a DC (*Direct Current*) supply. The gain control is set at 1 volt/cm and so the supply is positive + 4 V DC.

Figure 15.6 shows the waveform of an AC (*Alternating Current*) supply.

The gain control is set at 4 volts/cm, so the spot is deflected 1 cm upwards for every 4 volts across the input terminals. The amplitude of the waveform is 4 cm, so the *peak value*

= 4 cm x 4 V/cm = 16 V.

When a *diode* is placed in the circuit as shown in Figure 15.7, then the current only flows in one direction and halfwave rectification occurs.

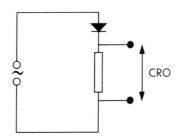 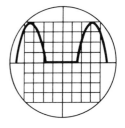

Fig. 15.7 The pattern produced when a diode is placed in the circuit.

6 > RESISTANCE

Fig. 15.8 A useful way of learning the formula.

Resistance is a force which opposes the flow of an electric current so that energy is required to push the charged particles around the circuit. The circuit itself can resist the flow of particles if the wires in the circuit are very thin and very long, as in the case of a filament in an electric light bulb. Due to this resistance, energy is given out as heat and light. Many household appliances, such as electric heaters, hair driers, toasters, ovens and electric fires use a high resistance wire in their elements so that heat is given out. Four factors affect the resistance of a wire:

1 *diameter*: thin wires have more resistance than thicker wires;
2 *length*: long wires have more resistance than shorter wires;
3 *the material used*: iron has more resistance than copper;
4 *temperature*: hotter wires have more resistance than cooler wires.

Resistance is measured in units called *ohms*, symbol Ω. A resistor has a resistance of one ohm if a voltage of one volt is required to push a current of one amp through it. The higher the resistance, the more voltage is required.

Single cell

Group of cells
(battery)

Lamp as indicator

Lamp for illumination

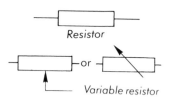

Resistor

or

Variable resistor

Fig. 15.9

To calculate the resistance you need to know the voltage and current, and use the formula:

$$\text{Resistance} = \frac{\text{Voltage}}{\text{Current}} \quad \text{or} \quad R = \frac{V}{I}$$

ie: expressed more fully

$$\text{Resistance (ohms } [\Omega]) = \frac{\text{Potential Difference (volts [V])}}{\text{Current (amperes [A])}}$$

Figure 15.8 is a useful way of using this formula. You may, for example, have to calculate resistance, given the voltage and current.

RESISTORS

Resistors are simply conductors which have a resistance. The diagram (Figure 15.9) shows the symbol for a resistor.
The value of a resistor is marked by colour bands on the outside which correspond to the value in ohms (Ω). These values can range from millions of ohms to a few ohms.
Resistors are devices which can be used to control the current flowing in a circuit, by offering resistance to the current. A *fixed* resistor is where there is a constant value of the resistor. A *variable* resistor (rheostat) is where the resistance can be changed, for example by sliding a contact along a length of wire to vary the resistance. For example in a food mixer, the control knob can increase or decrease the speed of the mixer (Fig. 15.10). The knob is acting as a variable resistor and letting different amounts of current through. When the knob is turned to a high setting, the resistance is decreased and more current flows to the motor so the speed increases.

Uses of resistors

Variable resistors are used, for example to control the volume on a television set. In a laboratory a variable resistor can be used as a rheostat to control the current in a circuit, or as a potential divider to control the voltage (potential difference) across a component.

Adjustable knob

Fig. 15.10

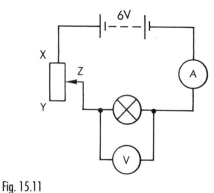

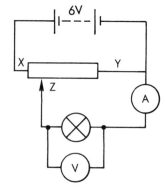

Fig. 15.11

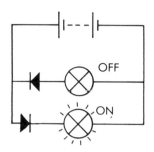

Fig. 15.12

Diodes

A special example of a device which uses resistance is a semiconductor diode which has a high resistance in one direction and a low resistance in the other direction allowing the current to flow.
Diodes are used to change alternating current to direct current. The diode only conducts during the part of the cycle when the current is flowing in the forward (positive) direction. This is known as half wave rectification. (See section 5 above, Figure 15.7.) Rectification or smoothing is necessary for many appliances which only use d.c., such as radios and car battery chargers.

Resistors in series

To calculate the resistance of resistors in *series* use the formula

$$R = R_1 + R_2$$

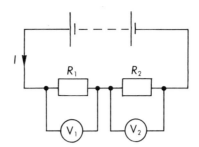

Fig. 15.13

The diagram (Figure 15.13) shows a circuit with a resistance of 30 ohms.

Resistors in parallel

To calculate the combined resistance in *parallel* use the formula:

$$\frac{1}{R} = \frac{1}{R_1} + \frac{1}{R_2}$$

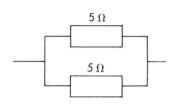

Fig. 15.14

Two resistors of equal value in parallel have the total resistance equal to half of one of them.

$$\frac{1}{R} = \frac{1}{5} + \frac{1}{5}$$

$$\frac{1}{R} = \frac{2}{5}$$

$$R = \frac{5}{2} = 2.5 \ \Omega$$

When calculating total resistance for resistors of unequal values (Fig. 15.15) use the formula above.

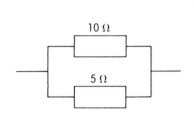

Fig. 15.15

$$\frac{1}{R} = \frac{1}{10} + \frac{1}{5}$$

$$\frac{1}{R} = \frac{1}{10} + \frac{2}{10}$$

$$\frac{1}{R} = \frac{3}{10}$$

$$R = \frac{10}{3} = 3.3 \ \Omega$$

Remember, more resistors in series *increase* the total resistance in a circuit. More resistors in parallel *decrease* the total resistance in a circuit.

Internal resistance of cells

The *internal resistance* of a cell is the amount of energy that a coulomb of electricity has to use to get through the cell. This means that some of the electrical energy supplied by the cell is converted into heat in the supply and is not converted usefully in the circuit, and so becomes 'lost volts'.

energy available = energy converted externally + energy converted internally

In practice most power packs and batteries have very low internal resistance.

Thermistor

The *thermistor* is a semiconductor device that changes its resistance as the temperature changes. The resistance gets smaller as it gets warmer. This change can be quite large, but the actual values depend on the type chosen.

The shape and size can vary from a small bead to a rod 10 mm long (Fig. 15.16). A large thermistor will obviously take more heat to change its temperature and might be unsuitable as the sensor for a thermometer, but would be stronger and cope with bigger currents.

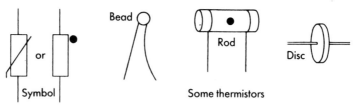

Fig. 15.16   Symbol   Some thermistors

Light Dependent Resistor (LDR)

LDR stands for *Light Dependent Resistor.* It is a resistor that will change its resistance depending on the brightness of the light that falls on its window (Fig. 15.17). It will have a smaller resistance in brighter light. Different types from the different manufactures vary in the amount of charge produced, but one common type varies from a few hundred ohms in bright light to 100 kΩ in the dark.

There are many uses for these devices, including light meters for photographers and automatic switches for security lights outside homes and factories. Usually the rest of the electronic circuit will need an output voltage that changes with the light, and this is often produced by putting the LDR in series with a suitable resistor to form a potential divider.

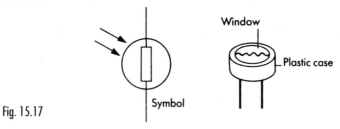

Fig. 15.17

Light Emitting Diode (LED)

LED stands for *Light Emitting Diode.* It is a semiconductor diode which behaves in a similar way to an ordinary diode but gives out light when it is conducting current (Fig. 15.18).

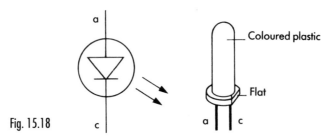

Fig. 15.18

The LED conducts current and gives out light only when it is *forward biased.* If a reverse bias is applied it must be kept small or the device will be damaged. The light produced is not very bright, but is very useful as a signal to indicate whether a circuit is on or off. The most common colour is red, but the devices are available in green and yellow and in a variety of different shapes.

When the LED is used it must have a suitable resistor connected in series that will limit the current passing through the diode. In most cases a current of about 10 mA will make the diode bright enough and the diode will be designed to work with about 2 V across it. This makes it possible for you to use our earlier formula to work out the value of the resistor required.

The circuit diagram in Fig. 15.19 shows an LED being used as a signal lamp to show when the 9 V supply is switched on. When it is on, the diode will have 2 V across it, leaving 7 V across the resistor. The current is 10 mA.

$$\text{Resistance} \quad = \quad \frac{\text{p.d.}}{\text{current}}$$

$$= \quad \frac{7}{0.01}$$

$$= \quad 700\Omega$$

This does not need to be an exact value and a resistor of 1 kΩ would do nicely.

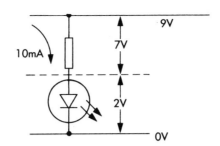

Fig. 15.19

OHM'S LAW

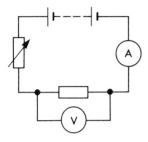

Fig. 15.20 You may have used a circuit like this to investigate Ohm's Law.

You may have carried out a practical investigation to compare the relationship between the voltage and amount of current flowing in a resistor. Figure 15.20 shows the circuit you may have used.

The current flowing is *proportional* to the voltage (at constant temperature). This relationship is called Ohm's Law and is shown in Figure 15.21.

■ Ohm's Law can be written as:

$$I \propto V$$

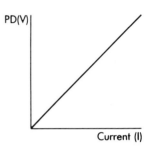

Fig. 15.21 This graph shows the relationship between current and voltage using a resistor in the circuit.

MAINS ELECTRICITY

Three key points to remember:

1. The voltage of the mains electricity in your home is 240 volts.
2. The direction of flow changes 50 times per second so its frequency is 50 Hertz.
3. Live and neutral wires carry the mains electricity, and the insulation around the wires is colour coded so you know which is which.

Mains electricity can be dangerous if used incorrectly. A person could receive an electric shock which is sufficient to kill them if basic safety rules are ignored. You should learn some of these essential safety rules:

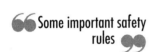
Some important safety rules

■ always have dry hands and keep all electrical appliances and sockets completely dry

■ always switch off the electricity before putting a plug into a socket or removing a plug

■ always check that the cable or flex is in good condition and is not worn or damaged

■ always use a plug which is correctly wired (see below) with the correct fuse

WIRING A THREE PIN PLUG

An important safety point here

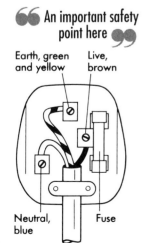

Fig. 15.22 Learn the colour code for the three-pin plug.

1. The live wire is coloured brown, and is connected to the live pin.
2. The neutral wire is coloured blue, and is connected to the neutral pin.
3. The earth wire is coloured green and yellow, and is connected to the earth pin at the top of the plug, as shown in Figure 15.22.

The purpose of the earth wire is to make sure that current flows to earth if, for any reason, the appliance becomes faulty. This may happen if the live wire touches part of the metal casing of the appliance. If the earth wire was not connected, then a current would flow to a person who touched the metal casing of the appliance.

FUSES

Each plug needs a *fuse* of the correct rating. The fuse is simply a thin piece of wire which melts and breaks the circuit if too much current is flowing. To find out the size of fuses use the following formula:

$$\text{current} = \frac{\text{watts}}{\text{volts}}$$

This is the same as:

   power = current x voltage   ie $P = I \times V$

For example, a 60 W table lamp uses a current of 60/240 or (60 ÷ 240) = 0.25 A, so a 3 amp fuse would be the correct one to use. However, an electric kettle using 2000 W would take a

current of $\dfrac{2000}{240}$ = 8.3 amps, so a 13 amp fuse is needed.

Magnetic circuit breakers

These are sometimes used instead of fuses. They have the advantage that they are very easy to reset after they have broken the circuit.

Double insulation .

Some electrical appliances have a plastic casing, so that there is no chance of someone getting an electric shock when they touch the appliance if it is faulty.

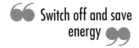 Switch off and save energy

BUYING ELECTRICITY

The amount of electrical energy an appliance uses depends on how long it is switched on for and how fast it uses energy (its power). The power is measured in watts (W) or kilowatts (1 kW = 1000W). How much you have to pay for electricity depends on:

1 how many electrical appliances are in use;
2 how long they are used for;
3 what the power rating is of each appliance.

The basic unit of energy used to calculate cost is the kilowatt-hour (kWh). This means 1 kW (l000 watts) being used for 1 hour, which costs approximately 6p.

- An electric fire, rated at 2 kW, which is used for 2 hours will use up 4 units or 4 kilowatt hours of electricity. The cost of using the fire for 2 hours is 4 x 6p = 24p.

- A table lamp, rated at 40 W switched on for five hours, uses 0.04 x 5 units = 0.2 kWh. The cost of using the table lamp is 0.2 x 6p = 1.2p.

Energy used (kilowatt hours)	=	power (kilowatts)	×	time (hours)

8 > TRANSMISSION OF ELECTRICITY

Electricity from a power station is *transmitted* across the country by the National Grid system. The commonest method is by overhead power cables, carried on pylons. Sometimes, underground transmission lines are used. The chart below summarises some of the main advantages (A) and disadvantages (D) of each method:

Overhead cables

- cheaper to install (A)
- easier to repair (A)
- unsightly (D)
- dangerous to people, especially those using kites, moving boats with high masts or carrying fishing rods (D)

Underground cables

- more expensive to install (D)
- more difficult to repair (D)
- hidden underground (A)
- no danger to people (A)

Electricity is transmitted from power stations at voltages of 400 000 V. The reason for using such high voltages is that there is a very low current, and the energy loss is very small. If electricity was transmitted at a lower voltage there would be a greater current, and more energy would be lost as heat. A simple model of this situation can be set up in the laboratory, using 12 V to represent a low voltage line, and 240 V to represent a high voltage line. A short piece of high resistance wire is used to represent the actual power lines which are used in the transmission of electricity. Two circuits are set up as shown below.

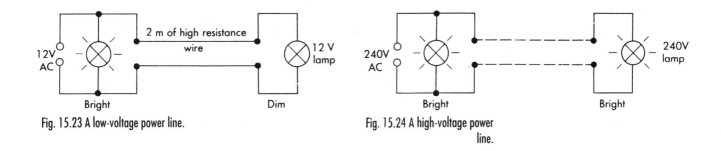

Bright — Fig. 15.23 A low-voltage power line. — Dim

Bright — Fig. 15.24 A high-voltage power line. — Bright

Energy is lost from the low voltage line as the second lamp glows only dimly. In the high voltage model the second lamp glows very brightly.

The *output power* equals the *input power minus the power loss.*

$$P_{OUT} = P_{IN} - P_{LOSS}$$

Power loss is I^2R, so low currents therefore reduce power loss. Step-down transformers (see chapter 16) are used to reduce the high voltages used in the transmission of electricity to the 240 V which is used in domestic electricity. The reason why alternating current (a.c.) is used in the transmission of electricity is that transformers only work on alternating current.

CIRCUIT SYMBOLS

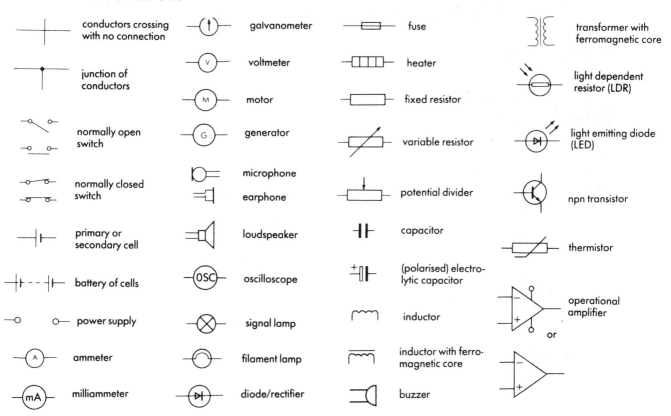

Fig. 15.25 Some of the conventional symbols for circuit diagrams

9 › SOME USEFUL DEFINITIONS

- **current** is a flow of charge, measured in amps
- **1 amp** = 1 coulomb of charge per second
- **voltage** is the measurement of the energy of each charge
- **1 volt** = 1 joule of energy per coulomb
- **power** is the rate of energy transfer, measured in watts
- **1 watt** = 1 joule of energy per second
- **power** = current x voltage
  $$P = I \times V$$
- **resistance** = $\dfrac{\text{voltage}}{\text{current}}$
- **power loss** = $I^2 R$
- **charge** = current x time
  $$Q = I \times t$$
- **Ohm's Law:** current flowing is proportional to the voltage
  $$I \, \alpha \, V$$

EXAMINATION QUESTIONS

MULTIPLE CHOICE

QUESTION 1

Which one of the following is the symbol for a switch in a circuit?

A —o o—

B —⬚—

C —⊣⊢—

D —⊖—

E —⊣⊢—

QUESTION 2

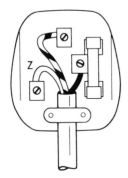

The diagram shows a three core cable connected to a three-pin plug.

What should be the colour of the cable labelled Z?

A blue   D green and yellow
B brown   E red
C green

QUESTION 3

Which of the circuits below would be suitable for measuring the resistance of a lamp?

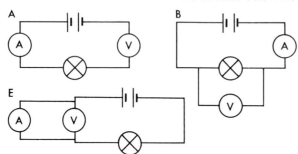

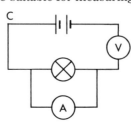

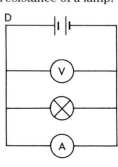

QUESTION 4

Which one of the following is a unit of power?
A Ampere   D Watt
B Joule   E Volt
C Newton

QUESTION 5

When wiring a house, the switches and fuses should be connected in only one arrangement. This arrangement has:
A switches in the live side and fuses in the neutral
B switches in the neutral side and fuses in the live
C switches and fuses both in the live wire
D switches and fuses both in the neutral wire
E switches and fuses both in the earth wire

QUESTION 6

The diagram below shows a circuit in which one of the lamps is faulty. None of the other lamps in the circuit can work because of the faulty lamp. Which of the lamps is faulty?

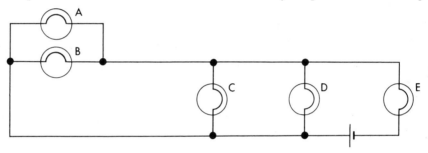

QUESTION 7

The diagram below shows a circuit. The resistor has a value of 2.5Ω and the reading on the voltmeter is 5 V.

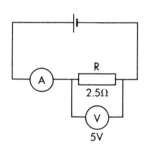

What is the reading on the ammeter?
A 0.5A   D 7.5A
B 2.0A   E 12.5A
C 5.0A

QUESTION 8

What is the frequency in Hertz of the mains electricity supplied to your home?
A 13; B 50; C 100; D 240; E 2500

QUESTION 9

What is the cost of using a 2 kW fire for 3 hours if a unit of electricity costs 6p per unit?
A 6p; B 12p; C 18p; D 24p; E 36p

STRUCTURED QUESTIONS

QUESTION 10

a) Decorative tree lights can be arranged in two ways, as shown in the diagrams below.

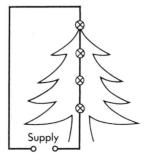

Circuit A: bulbs in series

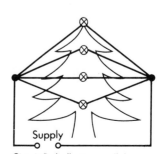

Circuit B: bulbs in parallel

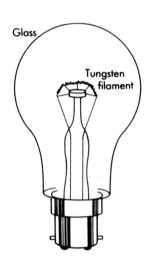

Glass

Tungsten filament

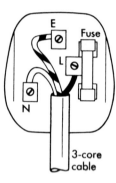

E

Fuse

L

N

3-core cable

i) If one bulb blows in each of the circuits, in which circuit will the remaining bulbs stay alight?

_____

(1)

ii) A set of lights has 20 bulbs in series, as in circuit A. Each is a 12 V bulb. What is the total voltage required for the set? (2 lines available) (1)

iii) Another set of lights has 20 bulbs in parallel, as in circuit B. The voltage supplied to the set is 240 V. What is the voltage across each bulb? (3 lines available) (1)

b) A diagram of a typical light bulb is shown opposite.

i) In the light bulb, electrical energy is converted to _____

and _____

(2)

ii) Suggest **one** property which makes tungsten a suitable metal to use for the filament.

_____

(1)

c) The diagram shows a three-pin plug.

i) What important safety feature, other than the top, is missing?

_____

(1)

ii) The fuse used in a plug should be suitable for the appliance connected to it. Using the following relationship,

Power measured in watts = Current in amps x Voltage in volts

Complete the table. Choose the most suitable fuse from 3 A, 5 A and 13 A.

(2)

Appliance	Power rating in watts	Voltage supplied in volts	Current rating of the most suitable fuse in amps
Kettle	3000	250	
Video recorder	50	250	

(MEG)

QUESTION 11

The kilowatt-hour is known as 1 unit of electricity. This is the amount of electricity used by a 1 kW appliance in 1 hour.. Suppose one unit costs 5p.

a) What is the cost of using
   i) a 1 kW heater for 2 hours?

_____

(1)

ii) a 3 kW fire for 10 hours?

_____

(1)

iii) a 1500 W iron for 2 hours?

_____

(1)

b) A student set up the circuit shown in the diagram below and then moved the contact to points **K, L, M, N** in turn.

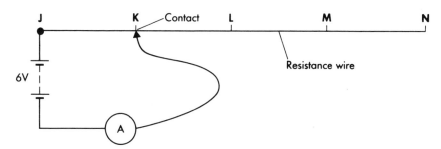

The current was measured by reading the ammeter, and the results are given below.

Contact made at	K	L	M	N
Ammeter reading	2	1	0.6	0.5

i) What units are missing from the results table?

_____

(1)

ii) As the wire under test becomes longer what happens to the electric current flowing in the circuit?

_____

(1)

iii) If resistance = $\dfrac{\text{voltage}}{\text{current}}$

what is the resistance of the wire between **J** and **K**?

_____

(1)

(MEG)

QUESTION 12

Study the diagram of the hot glue gun then answer the questions below.

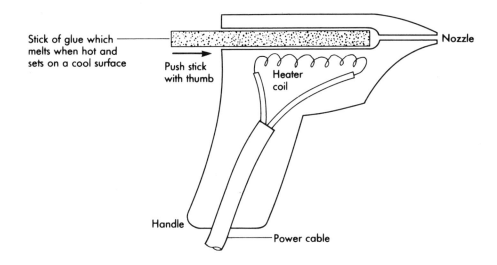

a) What happens to the solid stick of glue when the heater coil is switched on?

_____

(1)

b) What should come out of the nozzle when the glue gun is working?

_____

(1)

c) For the **wire** in the heater coil and the **wires** inside the power cable compare the following features and properties. Use words from the following list to complete the table below. You can use the words once, more than once, or not at all.

high   copper   quite thick   none   plastic   low   thin

Feature/property	Power cable wires	Heater coil wire
i) thickness		
ii) electrical resistance		
iii) covering insulation		

(3)

(d) The label on the handle of the glue gun includes the following information:

> **V** 240 ~
> **W** 100
> AC only 50 HZ

i) State what the following letters from the label stand for:

V _____   **W** _____

ii) A battery will not operate this glue gun. Give **one** reason for this, *using information from the label.* (2 lines available)

iii) Name a very common electrical household object which is also rated at 100 W.

_____

(3)

(WJEC)

QUESTION 13

a) The diagram shows a hydro-electric power station.

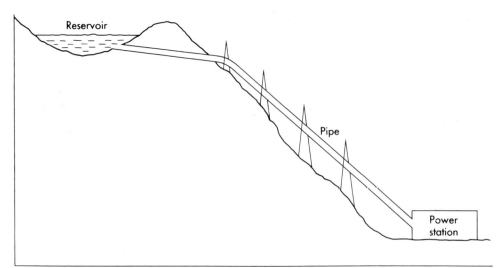

What kind of energy does the water have

    i) in the reservoir? *(1)*

    ii) just before it enters the power station? *(1)*

b) Electricity from power stations travels to your home, where it can be used for lighting. The diagram below shows part of a house lighting circuit. Each of the lamps carries a current of 0.25 A.

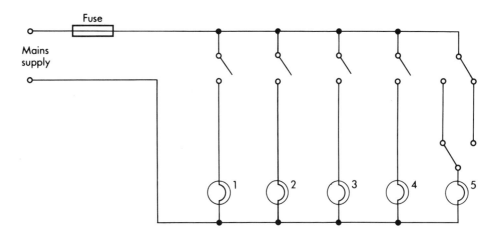

i) Explain why a fuse of 1 amp is not large enough for this circuit. *(1)*

Lamp 5 is controlled by two-way switches.

ii) Draw diagrams to explain how the switching system works. *(2)*

iii) What is the benefit of a two-way switching system? *(1)*

c) Electricity is also used to power appliances such as an electric kettle. Such an appliance is usually rated at 240 V 3 kW.
Calculate:
i) the current through the kettle, using the formula
Power (W) = Voltage (V) x Current (A) *(2)*

ii) the resistance of the kettle. *(2)*

iii) the cost of using the kettle for 5 minutes if electricity costs 6p per kWh. *(3)*

d) Explain why in some parts of the country water is hard and the insides of electric kettles become coated with mineral salt deposits. *(2)*

(MEG)

QUESTION 14

a) Maria's father has read a leaflet which tells him that his electric heating system should cost £400 per year to run. His annual bill totals £650.
Describe **four** ways by which he might save money on heating and still keep his house at a comfortable temperature. *(4)*

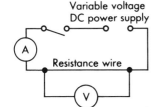

b) Maria was able to investigate the heating effect of an electric current at school. She used the circuit diagram opposite to connect her apparatus.

Using this apparatus, Maria took the following readings:

potential difference V (V)	0	1.0	2.0	3.0	4.0	5.0	6.0	7.0	8.0	9.0
current I (A)	0	0.30	0.68	1.00	1.30	1.55	1.64	1.72	1.78	1.82

i) Use the graph paper provided to plot a graph of potential difference V(V) (*y* axis) against current I(A) (*x* axis). *(4)*
ii) Use your graph to find the potential difference when the current is 1.7 A. *(1)*
iii) Calculate the resistance R of the wire at this value. *(2)*
iv) Explain what is happening to the resistance of the wire as the current increases. *(2)*

c) People often burn themselves on hot electric appliances like fires. Briefly describe how you would treat someone who had burned themselves badly on a hot electric fire.

(2)
(MEG)

QUESTION 15

In this question part (a) is targeted at level 6, parts (b) and (c) at level 7. and part (d) at level 8.

The diagram below shows an electric circuit.

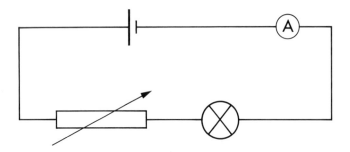

a) How could the voltage in this circuit be increased?

_____

(1)

b) Add a voltmeter to the circuit in a position where it could be used to measure the potential difference across the lamp. *(2)*

c) What would happen to the current in the circuit if another lamp was added in series?

_____

(1)

d) Explain what is meant by the term electrical current. (4 lines available) *(2)*

[Co-ordinated Science NEAB, WJEC, ULEAC]

A N S W E R S T O E X A M I N A T I O N Q U E S T I O N S

MULTIPLE CHOICE

ANSWER 1

Symbol A is the switch, B is a resistor, C is a capacitor, D is a lamp, and E is a cell.

ANSWER 2

Key A. The colour should be blue to the neutral pin.

ANSWER 3

Key B is the correct circuit. In option A the voltmeter is wrongly connected in series. In option C the ammeter is wrongly connected across the lamp. Remember a voltmeter should always be connected across the circuit component.

ANSWER 4

Key D.

ANSWER 5

Key C. The switches and fuses should both be in the live wire.

ANSWER 6

Key E. If any of the other lamps went out the electricity could 'bypass' the fault.

ANSWER 7

Key B. Use the formula current = voltage ÷ resistance.

ANSWER 8

Key B. Option D is the mains voltage, not the frequency. Option A is the maximum current of a three pin plug.

ANSWER 9

Key E. Remember a kilowatt hour is 1 kW for 1 hour. The fire uses 6 kW, so the cost is 6p x 6 = 36p.

STRUCTURED QUESTIONS

ANSWER 10

a) i) circuit B (this is the parallel circuit)
    ii) 240 V   (20 bulbs x 12 V = 240 V)
    iii) 240V
b) i) light and heat
    ii) it has a high resistance and glows when hot
c) i) the cable grip
    ii) kettle 13 A (current = watts ÷ volts, 3000 ÷ 250 = 12)
        video 3 A (current = watts ÷ volts, 50 ÷ 250 = 0.2).

ANSWER 11

a) i) 10p (1 kW x 2 x 5p)
    ii) £1.50 (3 kW x 10 x 5p)
    iii) 15p (1.5 kW x 2 x 5p)
b) i) amps or A
    ii) it decreases
    iii) 3 ohms (6 volts ÷ 2 amps).

ANSWER 12

a) The glue melts and is able to flow.
b) liquid glue
c) i) quite thick; thin
    ii) low; high
    iii) plastic; none
d) i) V is Volts W is Watts
    ii) The symbol on the label V 240 ~ means that an alternating current is needed. Batteries only supply direct current, at a much lower voltage.
    iii) a light bulb.

ANSWER 13

a) i) gravitational potential energy
    ii) kinetic energy
b) i) each lamp takes 0.25 A. There are 5 lamps, so the total current is 1.25 A. A 1 amp fuse would blow.
    ii)

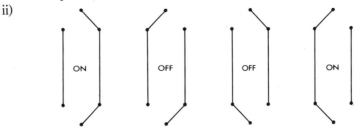

    iii) so that the lights can be switched on or off from either switch.

c) i) current = power ÷ voltage
$$= 3000 ÷ 240$$
$$= 12.5 \text{ A}$$

ii) resistance = voltage ÷ current
$$= 240 ÷ 12.5$$
$$= 19.2 \ \Omega$$

iii) cost for one hour is 6p x 3 kWh = 18p
cost for 5 minutes is 18 ÷ 12 = 1.5p

d) Hard water is caused by calcium salts which have dissolved out of limestone rocks. When hard water is boiled in a kettle the dissolved salts change back into limestone which is deposited inside kettles as 'scale'.

ANSWER 14

a) 1 By insulating the roof with insulating fibre material to trap air. Air is a poor conductor of heat.
2 By double glazing the windows, using a secondary pane of glass to trap air in between the two panes.
3 By having foam insulation put in the cavity walls.
4 By draught proofing around doors to prevent cold air coming in and warm air escaping.

b) i)

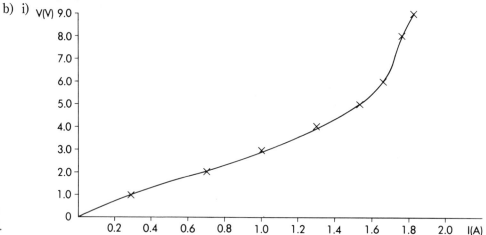

Graph to show heating effect of an electric current.

ii) 6.4V
iii) The resistance is 3.75 Ω.
iv) As the current increases the resistance increases.

c) 1 Place burned area under cold water.
2 Phone for doctor or take person to doctor or hospital.

ANSWER 15

a) by adding another battery   (1)
b) to gain the two marks you need to use the correct symbol for a voltmeter (1) and draw it in its correct position across the lamp (1), (see Fig 15.4)   (2)
c) the current would decrease   (1)
d) an electrical current is the flow of electrons (1)
from the negative charged terminal to the positive charged terminal (1)   (2)

REVIEW SHEET

✎ An electric current is a flow of _____ around a circuit.

✎ Current is measured in _____ by using an _____ in the circuit.

✎ All circuits should be made from _____ conductors.

✎ Identify each of these circuits

✎ List one advantage and one disadvantage of a parallel circuit

   1. advantage _____

   2. disadvantage _____

✎ Complete this equation

charge (coulombs) =

✎ The _____ is the potential difference between two points of a circuit and is measured

in _____

✎ A _____ only flows through an electrical device or component if there is a potential

difference across the device.

✎ _____ is a force which opposes the flow of an electric current. As a result energy is

given out as heat and light.

✎ List four factors which can affect the resistance of a wire

   1. _____

   2. _____

   3. _____

   4. _____

✎ Complete this equation

Resistance =

✎ A rheostat is a _____ resistor since the resistance can be changed.

✎ Diodes are used to change _____ current to _____ current.

✎ The _____ is a resistor that will change its resistance depending on the brightness of
the light that falls on its window.

✎ State Ohm's Law

_____

✎ The _____ in a plug is a thin piece of wire which melts and breaks the circuit if too much

current is flowing.

✎ List four important safety rules when dealing with mains electricity.

   1. _____

   2. _____

   3. _____

   4. _____

✎ The _____ is the basic unit of energy used to calculate the cost of electricity.

✎ Complete the following table on transmitting electricity by either overhead or underground cables.

Overhead Cables

1. Advantage _____

2. Advantage _____

3. Disadvantage _____

4. Disadvantage _____

Underground Cables

1. Advantage _____

2. Advantage _____

3. Disadvantage _____

4. Disadvantage _____

✎ A high voltage in electricity transmission means a _____ current, so that the energy loss is very small.

✎ The output power equals the _____ minus the _____

✎ _____ transformers are used to reduce the high voltages used in the transmission of electricity to the 240V which is used in domestic electricity.

✎ We use _____ current in the transmission of electricity since transformers only work on this type of current.

✎ Fill in the labels for these diagrams. Write the label in the boxes provided.

ELECTRO-MAGNETISM

GETTING STARTED

When a coil of wire is placed between two magnets, the coil turns when a current is passed through it. This effect was observed by Michael Faraday, who first realised that electric currents also have magnetic fields, just like ordinary magnets. When two magnetic fields interact, then movement can take place. This is the basis of the electric motor which is used in many household appliances, such as a record turntable, a hair drier, a food mixer, a vacuum cleaner and an electric oven fan. These motors have the ability to turn, owing to the *combined* effects of electricity and magnetism.

An electric current, flowing through a coil of wire, has the effect of making the coil act as a magnet, but when an iron bar is put inside the coil an *electromagnet* is made. The iron bar becomes a magnet only when the current is flowing, and so the magnetic effect can be switched on and off. Electromagnets are used in many machines, such as microphones, loudspeakers, radios, televisions and telephones.

ESSENTIAL PRINCIPLES

1 ▷ MAGNETS AND MAGNETIC FIELDS

The effect of a magnetic field around a magnet can be shown by using a plotting compass to find out which is the north-seeking or N pole of a magnet. If you place the plotting compass near the end of the magnet, the needle of the compass is repelled from the N pole, as shown in Figure 16.1.

You can also show the magnetic field by shaking iron filings around a magnet. The iron filings line up along the lines of force. Figure 16.2 shows the pattern produced.

These patterns show the lines of magnetic force. The magnetic field patterns produced between two attracting (unlike) poles and two repelling (like) poles are shown in Figures 16.3 and 16.4 respectively.

When two magnetic fields come together there is either a force of *attraction* or a force of *repulsion*, and as a result there is a possibility of movement. Magnets are usually made from magnetic alloys, and attract other magnetic metals such as iron and steel. Magnets do *not* attract non-magnetic metals such as copper, tin, and zinc.

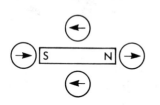

Fig. 16.1 The compass needle is repelled from the N pole of the magnet.

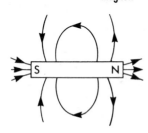

Fig. 16.2 The magnetic field pattern around a magnet.

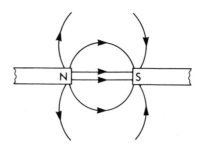

Fig. 16.3 Attraction between unlike poles of two magnets.

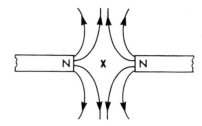

Fig 16.4 Repulsion between like poles of two magnets.

2 ▷ ELECTRO-MAGNETISM

A magnetic field is produced around a straight wire whenever an electric current flows through the wire. Plotting compasses or iron filings can be used to show this magnetic effect.

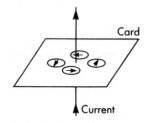

Fig. 16.5 Plotting compasses can be used to show the magnetic field around a current flowing through a wire.

Fig. 16.6. The pattern produced for a single wire carrying current. The current is flowing upwards out of the page.

Fig. 16.7 The pattern produced for a single wire carrying current. The current is flowing downwards into the page.

These magnetic fields are fairly weak, and the effect can be increased by using a coil of wire called a *solenoid*. The coil of wire acts like a magnet when an electric current flows through it. A soft iron bar placed inside the coil creates a more powerful magnetic effect and becomes an *electromagnet*. The strength of an electromagnet can be increased by:

- increasing the number of turns on the coil;
- increasing the size of current flowing through the coil.

Reversing the current in an electromagnet reverses the direction of the magnetic field around it.

Figure 16.8 shows the current flowing in a *clockwise* direction around the X end of the core. This end becomes the *south* pole.

When the current flow is *anti-clockwise* then X becomes a *north* pole as shown in Fig 16.9. So the *polarity is changed* by *reversing* the current direction.

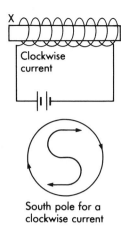

Clockwise current

South pole for a clockwise current

Fig. 16.8 The current flows in a clockwise direction around the X end of the core.

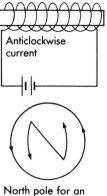

Anticlockwise current

North pole for an anticlockwise current

Fig. 16.9 The current flows in an anti-clockwise direction around the X end of the core.

ELECTROMAGNETIC RELAY

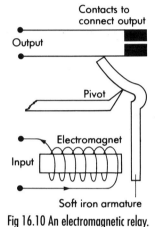

Contacts to connect output

Output

Pivot

Electromagnet

Input

Soft iron armature

Fig 16.10 An electromagnetic relay.

A simple application of this principle is in the *electromagnetic relay*. The relay is a simple switch, operated by an electromagnet, in which a small input current controls a larger output current. Stages 1 to 4 below describe how it works:

1. The input current causes the electromagnet to become magnetised.
2. The electromagnet attracts a soft iron armature, which closes the contacts and causes a greater current to flow through the output circuit.
3. The output circuit controls a device such as a motor.
4. When the input current stops then the output current is switched off and the motor stops.

3 | FORCES ON CURRENTS IN MAGNETIC FIELDS

When an electric current is passed through a length of copper wire which is placed in the field of a strong magnet, the wire moves at 90° to the direction of the magnetic field. If the *current direction* is reversed, then the *force on the current* is reversed and the wire moves in the opposite direction. The *direction* of force is always at right angles to the current direction and the field direction.

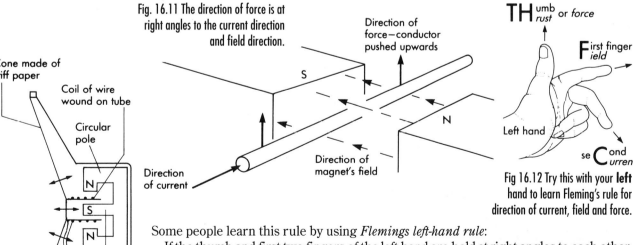

Fig. 16.11 The direction of force is at right angles to the current direction and field direction.

Direction of force—conductor pushed upwards

Direction of magnet's field

Direction of current

TH^{umb}_{rust} or *force*

First finger Field

Left hand

se**C**ond *current*

Fig 16.12 Try this with your **left** hand to learn Fleming's rule for direction of current, field and force.

Cone made of stiff paper

Coil of wire wound on tube

Circular pole

Central pole

Current supply

Fig 16.13 A moving coil loudspeaker.

Some people learn this rule by using *Flemings left-hand rule*:

If the thumb and first two fingers of the left hand are held at right angles to each other, then the *thumb* gives the direction of the force, the *first finger* points in the same direction as the field, and the *second finger* points in the direction of the current.

The *size* of the force can be increased by:

- increasing the strength of the magnetic field;
- increasing the size of the current.

One important application of this effect is in the moving coil loudspeaker.

MOVING COIL LOUDSPEAKER

Figure 16.13 shows the three main sections of the loudspeaker. When an alternating current is passed through the coil, the coil is pushed backwards and forwards, causing the paper cone to vibrate and give out sound waves. The frequency and amplitude of the alternating current which flows through the coil affect the type of sound produced.

4 ❯ **ELECTRIC MOTORS**

A simple motor contains several coils of wire, wound on a core which is pivoted on an axle between two permanent magnets, as shown in Figure 16.14.

The coil is connected to a power supply by two carbon contacts called *brushes*. These are held in position against two halves of the *commutator*, which is a split ring made of copper. When a DC current is passed through the coil, the magnetic field created is attracted to the opposite poles of the permanent magnets and this causes the coil to spin in a clockwise direction. When the N and S poles of the coil lie opposite the S and N poles of the permanent magnets, the coil should stop *turning*, but it carries on *spinning* because the two brushes now press against the opposite half rings of the commutator. The current now flows in the *opposite direction* and this results in the N and S poles of the coil being reversed. The coil then spins round to the S and N poles of the permanent magnets, and once again the current direction is reversed as the coil is about to stop.

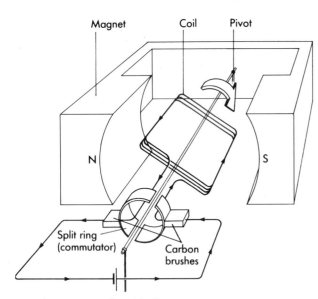

Fig. 16.14 The construction of a simple electric motor.

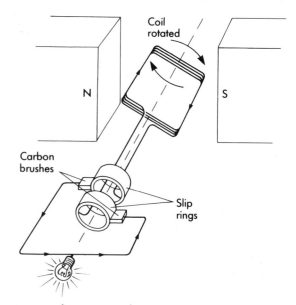

Fig. 16.16 The construction of a simple AC generator or alternator.

MORE COMPLEX MOTORS

Real motors which are used in everyday appliances such as electric drills, washing machines and food mixers usually have several coils, each of which may have its own commutator. The purpose of these is to produce a smoother and more powerful turning effect, and thereby allow the motor to run more evenly without stopping. The coils are usually wound on a soft iron core, called an *armature*. The effect of this is to increase the strength of the magnetic field.

GENERATORS

5 ❯ **GENERATORS AND ALTERNATORS**

You may have used a simple *generator* in the form of a dynamo to light the lamps on a bicycle. Generators transfer kinetic energy to electrical energy.

On an industrial scale, generators are used in power stations to supply mains electricity. Most generators work on the same principle that a current can be induced in a coil by electricity turning it in a magnetic field.

There are basically two types of generators:

❝ Generators produce electricity ❞

1 DC generators, which produce one-way direct current.
2 AC generators or *alternators*, which produce alternating current, such as those found in power stations and in cars.

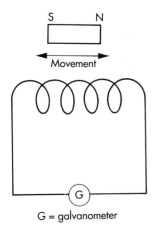

Fig. 16.15

INDUCED CURRENT

When a magnet is moved in and out of a coil of wire which is part of a complete circuit a voltage (potential difference) is produced between the ends of the wire. This induced voltage causes a current to flow (Fig.16.15). Similarly a voltage is induced when a coil of wire is moved in a magnetic field, i.e. the lines of magnetic force are cut by a conductor.

Three factors increase the size of the induced voltage:

- how fast the magnet or coil is moved
- how many turns there are on the coil
- the strength of the magnetic field

ALTERNATORS

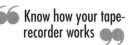

66 Alternators are generators which produce alternating current 99

The alternating current is induced as the coil rotates between the permanent magnets. The coil is linked to the outside circuit by two carbon brushes which press against two carbon slip rings which are fixed to the end of the coil, as shown in Figure 16.16 above.

The current can be increased by four factors:

1 having more turns on the coil;
2 using stronger magnets;
3 winding the coil on a soft iron armature;
4 rotating the coil at a higher speed.

TAPE RECORDING

66 Know how your tape-recorder works 99

An everyday application of electromagnetism is tape recording. Inside the recording head of a tape recorder is a small electromagnet, consisting of a coil wound on a circular iron core. There is a small slit at the front of the core, as shown in Figure 16.17.

The strength of the electromagnet changes as the current from the microphone changes. As a result there is a changing magnetic field across the slit, which magnetises the particles on the tape. The pattern of particles on the tape therefore reflects the pattern of the changing strength and frequency of the sound waves.

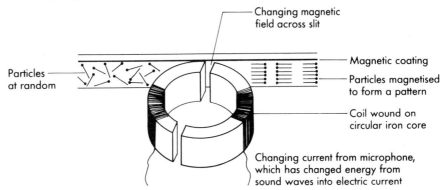

Fig. 16.17 The recording head is an electromagnet.

TRANSFORMERS

Three important facts to remember:

1 Transformers change voltage.
2 Transformers only work on alternating current.
3 Transformers contain an iron core and two coils of wire, a primary coil and a secondary coil.

Figure 16.18 shows a step-up and a step-down transformer.

Fig. 16.18

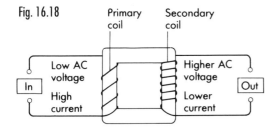

a) A step-up transformer gives out a higher voltage than the input voltage.

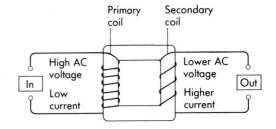

b) A step-down transformer gives out a lower voltage than the input voltage.

A *step-up* transformer gives out a higher voltage than the input voltage and has more turns on the secondary coil than the primary coil. A *step-down* transformer gives out a lower voltage than the input voltage, so there are more turns on the primary coil than the secondary coil.

When the primary coil is connected to an alternating current, it acts like an electromagnet which is switched on and off very quickly. This sets up a changing magnetic field in the iron core, which *induces* alternating current in the secondary coil. You can calculate the voltage induced in the secondary coil using the following formula:

Transformers change voltage

$$\frac{\text{voltage across secondary coil}}{\text{voltage across primary coil}} = \frac{\text{number of turns in secondary coil}}{\text{number of turns in primary coil}}$$

$$\text{In symbols} \quad \frac{V_2}{V_1} = \frac{N_2}{N_1}$$

For example, if a step-down transformer has 100 turns on the primary coil and 10 turns on the secondary coil, you can calculate the output voltage given that the input voltage is 240 V.

$$V_2 = \frac{10}{100} \times 240 = 24 \text{ V}$$

The output voltage is 24 volts.

One of the main uses of transformers is in the National Grid system, where *step-up* transformers increase the voltage and lower the current so that less electricity is wasted as heat. *Step-down* transformers are used in many household appliances, such as televisions, computers, radios and washing machines, in order to reduce the mains voltage to a lower voltage.

EXAMINATION QUESTIONS

MULTIPLE CHOICE

QUESTION 1

Which one of the following substances is used to make the core of a transformer?
A aluminium; B carbon; C copper; D iron; E steel

QUESTION 2

A step-down transformer has 300 turns on the primary coil and an input voltage of 240 volts. The secondary coil has an output voltage of 40 volts. How many turns must there be on the secondary coil?
A 40; B 50; C 100; D 250; E 400

QUESTION 3

What is the advantage of using an electromagnetic relay switch in a transistor circuit?

A A large input current controls a small output current.
B A large output current controls a small input current.
C A small output current controls a large input current.
D A small input current controls a small output current.
E A small input current controls a large output current.

QUESTION 4

Two bar magnets are placed so that their north poles are 2 cm apart. Which of the following diagrams best represents the resulting magnetic field?

  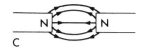

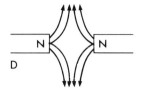 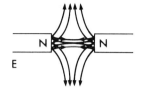

QUESTION 5

In the National Grid system, the transmission of electrical energy is by means of overhead conductors. These conducting wires carry
A alternating current at high voltage
B alternating current at high frequency
C alternating current at low voltage
D direct current at low voltage
E direct current at low frequency.

QUESTION 6

The circuit opposite was set up as shown and connected to an oscilloscope. Which one of the following traces was produced on the oscilloscope screen?

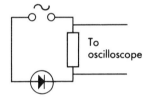

QUESTION 7

The diagram opposite shows a horizontal wire carrying a current, placed between the poles of two magnets.

In which direction is the force on the wire?
A vertical downwards between the two magnets
B vertically upwards between the two magnets
C the same direction as the current flows in the wire
D from the north pole to the south pole of the two magnets
E from the south pole to the north pole of the two magnets.

STRUCTURED QUESTIONS

QUESTION 8

a) Some students set up the apparatus shown in the diagram opposite to show that a current flowing through a wire produces a magnetic field.

   i) State **two** methods of detecting the magnetic field around the wire that they could have used.

   1 _____
   (1)

   2 _____
   (1)

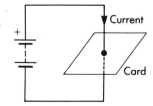

   ii) Sketch the magnetic field obtained. *(1)*

b) The teacher then challenged the students to see if they could obtain electricity from magnetism. The students set up the apparatus opposite.

   The apparatus was left lying on the bench but no reading was seen on the milliammeter.

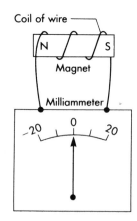

Coil of wire

N   S

Magnet

Milliammeter

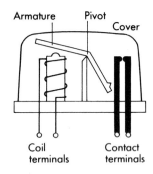

Armature   Pivot

Cover

Coil
terminals

Contact
terminals

i) What should the students do to get a reading on the milliammeter?

_____

_____
(1)

ii) State **two** ways in which they could increase the milliammeter reading.

1 _____

(1)

2 _____

(1)

c) A useful application of electromagnetism is the electromagnetic relay which is shown opposite.

i) What is the armature made of?

_____
(1)

ii) Describe how the relay works when a current flows in the coil. (3 lines available)
(3)

iii) Explain why relays are used in some electrical circuits. (3 lines available) *(2)*
(MEG)

QUESTION 9

The diagram shows a simple motor which has been made by a student in a laboratory.

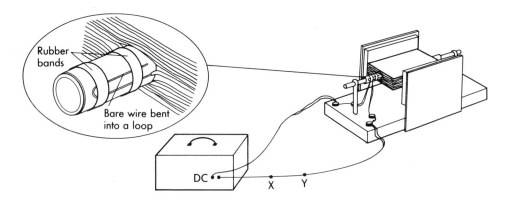

Rubber
bands

Bare wire bent
into a loop

DC

X   Y

a) Describe what happens when the motor is connected to a DC supply. (2 lines available)
(1)

b) What would happen to the speed of the motor if a resistor was added to the circuit between points X and Y? (2 lines available) *(1)*

c) Many modern electrical appliances, such as the food mixer shown opposite, have variable speeds.

Explain how turning the knob on the mixer causes the speed of the motor to increase. (4 lines available) *(3)*

Adjustable knob

d) Explain the purpose of a commutator in an electric motor. (6 lines available) *(3)*

e) Why do motors used in electrical appliances usually have at least three commutators and complex coils? (3 lines available) *(2)*

f) When a tape recording is made, the microphone converts the energy in sound waves into changing electrical currents. Name the electrical device which receives these electrical currents and magnetises the particles on the tape.

_____

(1)
(MEG)

QUESTION 10

The figure shows the main parts of a meter designed to measure electric current. There are two iron bars inside a coil. One bar is fixed and the other is on the end of a pivoted pointer.

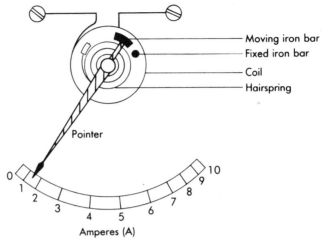

a) i) Apart from heat, what will be produced inside the coil when electricity passes through it?

_____

(1)

ii) Explain what effects this will have on the two iron bars. (6 lines available) *(4)*
Suggest what the hairspring does. (2 lines available) *(1)*

Another way of detecting electric currents is to use an oscilloscope. The diagrams below show two possible traces on the oscilloscope screen. Explain what each trace represents.

Trace 1 (3 lines available)

(2)

Trace 2 (3 lines available)

(2)
(SEG)

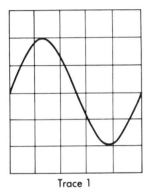

Trace 1

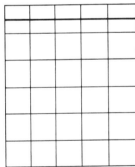

Trace 2

QUESTION 11
Levels 8-10

In this question notice how parts (a), (b) and (c) can be answered separately so if you are unable to do part (a), go onto (b).

Part (a) is targeted at level 7, part (b) at levels 8 and 9, and part (c) at level 10.

a) The relay circuit shown is used to switch on a car starter motor.

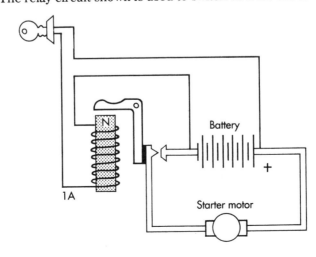

    i) Explain how this relay works when the key is turned. (6 lines available)   *(3)*

    ii) Name **two** other devices that use an electromagnet.

    _____ and _____

    (2)

b) Another part of the car electrical circuit is used to light a 12 V lamp. A constant current of 3 A circulates around the circuit.

    i) Explain what happens to the energy of the electrons as they flow through the lamp wire. (5 lines available)   *(4)*

    ii) How much energy is converted (used) by the lamp in 20 seconds? (Energy = watts x seconds). (4 lines available)   *(2)*

    iii) If the current flows for 20 s, what is the **charge passed** in the circuit during this time? (3 lines available)   *(3)*

c) Explain what is meant by **electromagnetic induction** and state the factors that affect electromagnetic induction when moving a magnet into a coil. (10 lines available)

    (6)

Coil of insulated wire

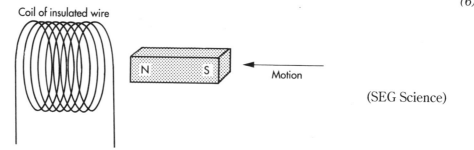

Motion

(SEG Science)

ANSWERS TO EXAMINATION QUESTIONS

MULTIPLE CHOICE

ANSWER 1

Key D, iron. The core of a transformer has to become magnetised and demagnetised very quickly. Iron is easily magnetised and loses its magnetism easily.

ANSWER 2

Key B, 50 turns. The ratio of the input voltage to the output voltage is 6:1. So the number of turns is $300 \div 6 = 50$.

ANSWER 3

Key E. In using a relay switch in a transistor circuit, a small input current, such as that triggered by an electron sensor, controls a large output current, such as that used by a motor.

ANSWER 4

Key D. The poles are both N poles so they repel each other. Option C shows the pattern of attraction which would be produced by two unlike poles.

ANSWER 5

Key A. The National Grid carries AC, and high voltages are needed to produce a low current and prevent loss of heat.

ANSWER 6

Key D. The diode has the effect of half wave rectification.

ANSWER 7

Key B. The force on the wire is upwards. Remember Fleming's left hand rule. Hold the thumb and first and second finger of the left hand at right angles to each other. The second finger points in the direction of the current, the first finger points in the field direction, and the thumb gives you the direction of movement.

ANSWER 8

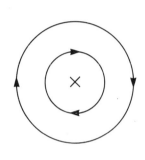

a) i) 1 iron filings sprinkled on the card   2 a plotting compass placed on the card
    ii) see diagram

b) i) move the magnet in and out of the coil
    ii) 1 put more turns on the coil   2 use a stronger magnet

c) i) soft iron
    ii) a magnetic field is produced when the current flows in the coil which attracts the armature. As the armature moves, it closes the contacts and completes the circuit.
    iii) a relay is used because a small current controls a larger current.

ANSWER 9

a) the motor spins
b) the speed would slow down
c) the knob is linked to a variable resistor. As the knob is turned, the resistance is decreased and more current flows, so the motor gets faster.
d) the commutator changes the direction of the current flowing through the coil, so that the coil keeps on spinning.
e) so that the motor is more efficient and runs smoothly
f) an electromagnet

ANSWER 10

a) i) a magnetic field
    ii) The iron bars become magnetised temporarily and repel each other. The moving iron bar is fixed to a pointer, which moves along the scale. The higher the current the further the iron bars repel each other.

b) The hairspring resists the rotation of the coil and prevents the pointer moving off the scale.

c) Trace 1 shows an alternating current. The top of the wave shows the maximum forward current. The bottom of the wave shows the maximum reverse current. Trace 2 shows a direct positive current. The height of the line above the zero can indicate the voltage if the scale is known.

ANSWER 11

a) i) When the key is turned the circuit is complete (1)
        the electromagnet is switched on (1)
        and attracts the armature (1)   *(3)*
    ii) any device such as a tape-recorder, an electric bell   *(1)*

b) i) The electrons flow through the lamp wire due to the potential difference (1)
        There is resistance to the flow of electrons in the lamp wire (1)
        Some of the potential energy (1)
        is transferred to heat and light (1)   *(4)*

    ii) Energy = volts x amps x seconds (1)
                 = 12 x 3 x 20 (1)   *(2)*

    iii) Q = I x t (1)
            = 3 amps x 20 seconds (1)
            = 60 Coulombs (1)   *(3)*

c) There are 4 marks allocated for the explanation.

Electromagnetic induction occurs when an electric current is induced (1)
by a changing magnetic field (1).
The size of the current depends on the number of turns on the coil (1)
and the rate of change of the magnetic field (1)   *(4)*

There are 2 marks allocated for giving this explanation in a logical sequence (1) and
for being precise (1).   *(1)*

STUDENT'S ANSWER WITH EXAMINER'S COMMENTS

A student was working in a laboratory and needed to produce a 3 V AC electrical
supply to light a lamp. The only power pack available was set at a fixed output of
12 V AC.
The student drew a sketch of a transformer which could be made from two iron
C-cores and some insulated wire.

a) i) How many coils of wire should there be on each C-core?   *(2)*
    ii) Explain how you calculated the number of coils on each C-core. *(2)*

b) Draw a diagram to show how the student could use the 12 V AC supply, together
with two iron C-cores, two lengths of insulated wire and the 3 V lamp to produce
a 3 V supply and light the lamp.

                                                                     (4)

c) Explain how an output is produced from the secondary coil of the transformer.
                                                                     (3)

d) Why is it necessary to use an AC supply for a transformer instead of a DC
supply?

                                                                     (2)
                                                                     (MEG)

Version 1: maximum marks

**Correct formula**

a) i) 40 on the primary coil, 10 on the second coil

**Good, over 10 coils used.**

    ii) using the formula $\dfrac{V_2}{V_1} = \dfrac{N_2}{N_1}$; $\dfrac{12}{3} = \dfrac{4}{1}$

The ratio of turns if therefore 4:1, so 40 turns on the primary and 10 turns on the
secondary.

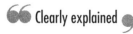**Clearly explained**

b)

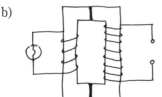

You understand the circuit and the principle of a transformer. Also correct ratio of turns.

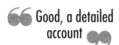**Good, a detailed account**

c) Current flows backwards and forwards through the primary coil, and sets up
an alternating magnetic field in the core, which induces a current of the same
frequency in the secondary coil.

**Yes, you have established the main points**

d) An alternating current is needed which changes direction to induce an EMF in
the secondary coil

REVIEW SHEET

✎ Complete the diagrams by putting the correct arrows on the lines to show magnetic field patterns.

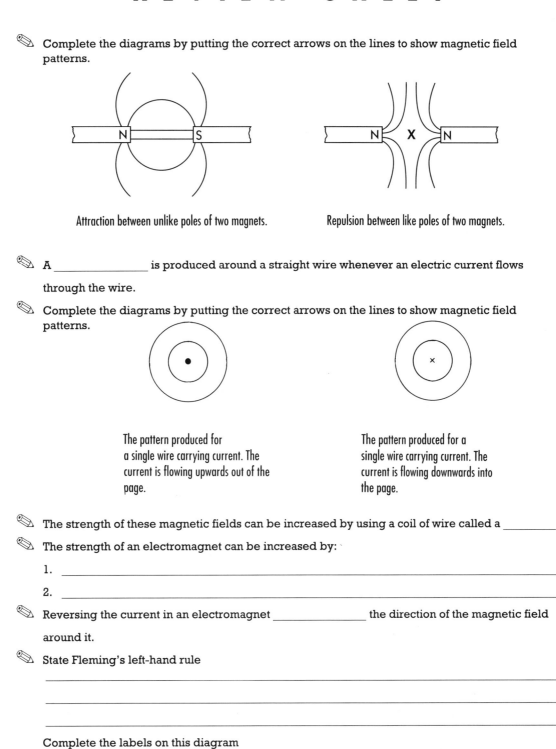

Attraction between unlike poles of two magnets.

Repulsion between like poles of two magnets.

✎ A _____ is produced around a straight wire whenever an electric current flows through the wire.

✎ Complete the diagrams by putting the correct arrows on the lines to show magnetic field patterns.

The pattern produced for a single wire carrying current. The current is flowing upwards out of the page.

The pattern produced for a single wire carrying current. The current is flowing downwards into the page.

✎ The strength of these magnetic fields can be increased by using a coil of wire called a _____

✎ The strength of an electromagnet can be increased by:

1. _____

2. _____

✎ Reversing the current in an electromagnet _____ the direction of the magnetic field around it.

✎ State Fleming's left-hand rule

_____

_____

_____

Complete the labels on this diagram

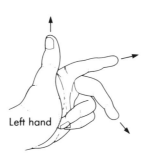

Left hand

✎ In an electric motor, the _____ is a split ring made of copper.

✎ _____ transfer kinetic energy to electrical energy.

✎ List four ways by which the current produced by alternators can be increased.

1. _____

2. _____

3. _____

4. _____

✎ A _____ is used to change voltage.

✎ Identify each type of transformer in the diagram.

a) _____ transformer   b) _____ transformer

✎ Complete this formula for calculating the voltage induced in the secondary coil.

$$\frac{\text{voltage across secondary coil}}{\text{voltage across primary coil}} \quad = \quad$$

✎ Suggest uses for each type of transformer

1. Step-up transformer _____

2. Step-down transformer _____

CHAPTER 17

GETTING STARTED

When you listen to the radio, watch TV, read a magazine, or sit by a fire, you are making use of the different effects of a group of waves known as electromagnetic waves. These waves, together with sound waves, seismic waves and water waves all transfer energy *without* the transfer of matter.

An earthquake is the result of a very large amount of energy travelling through the Earth. This energy can cause great destruction of buildings, roads and bridges, and great loss of life. Waves at sea also carry very large amounts of energy, and research is being carried out into ways in which this energy can be used to generate electricity.

WAVES

ESSENTIAL PRINCIPLES

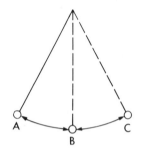

Fig. 17.1

1 ▶ OSCILLATIONS

If you hang an object on a piece of string and let it swing backwards and forwards, then you are allowing it to 'oscillate'. Eventually the oscillations slow down and the object comes to a stop. When you start it moving the size of the oscillations is large and then become gradually smaller. So one complete oscillation is from A to B to C and back to A, as shown in Figure 17.1.

A child on a swing is oscillating backwards and forwards. If the child makes 10 complete swings in 60 seconds then the frequency of the oscillation is 0.16 cycles per second or 0.16 Hertz.

OSCILLATIONS AND THE BODY

The oscillations produced by a ship which is rolling from side to side at sea can cause people to feel seasick. A drum beat which produces very low frequency oscillations can make people feel giddy and cause blurred vision. Sometimes people who work in factories are affected by the oscillations of the machinery which they operate. Musical instruments, such as a piano, produce sounds because of the oscillations of the piano strings.

2 ▶ WAVE MOTION

There are two types of waves, longitudinal and transverse. Electromagnetic waves and waves in water are examples of *transverse* waves. These are like the waves produced in a piece of rope when it moves up and down as shown in Figure 17.2.

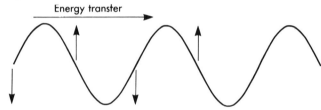

Energy transfer

Fig. 17.2 Energy is being transferred along this transverse wave, but the particles only move up and down.

Each part of the rope is oscillating up and down, as the energy is being transferred along the rope.

Sound waves are the only waves which are *longitudinal* waves. These waves are like the waves produced by a long spring, as shown in Figure 17.3. The energy is being transferred along the spring, but the particles are oscillating from left to right.

Energy transfer

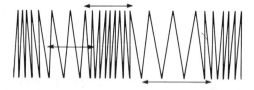

Fig. 17.3 Energy is being transferred along this longitudinal wave, but the particles are oscillating from left to right.

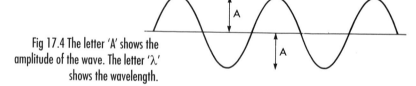

Fig 17.4 The letter 'A' shows the amplitude of the wave. The letter 'λ' shows the wavelength.

AMPLITUDE AND WAVELENGTH

The length of each complete oscillation of the wave is the *wavelength*. The *size of the wave* is the *amplitude* as shown in Fig. 17.4.

The distance marked λ (lambda) is the *wavelength,* and is the distance between two troughs or two crests. The distance marked A is the *amplitude,* and is the amount by which a particle is displaced up or down.

FREQUENCY

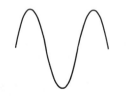

Fig. 17.5a) A low frequency wave.

Fig. 17.5b) A high frequency wave.

The *frequency* of the wave is the number of complete cycles per second, measured in Hertz (Hz). (Imagine standing on a beach and counting the waves as they come towards you. This would give you the frequency of the waves.) Figure 17.5a) shows a wave with a low frequency and large amplitude, and Figure 17.5b) shows a wave with a high frequency and small amplitude.

SPEED, FREQUENCY AND WAVELENGTH

$$\text{Speed (in metres per second)} = \text{frequency (in Hertz)} \times \text{wavelength (in metres)}$$

For example, if a wave is travelling with a frequency of 30 Hz and has a wavelength of 3 m, its speed or velocity is 90 m/s. The waves in the *electromagnetic spectrum* all travel at the same velocity of 300 000 000 metres per second, or 3×10^8 m/s. *Sound waves*, however, travel much more slowly, at approximately 330 metres per second. For example, if a sound wave has a wavelength of 0.6 m, and travels at 330 m/s, its frequency is 550 Hz.

$$\text{frequency} = \frac{330}{0.6} = 550 \text{ Hz}$$

3 > **ELECTRO-MAGNETIC AND MECHANICAL WAVES**

The chart below summarises the main points of difference between electromagnetic waves, such as radio waves, and mechanical waves, such as sound waves.

Electromagnetic

- transverse waves
- travel through a vacuum, do not need a material medium
- travel very fast (3×10^8 m/s)

Mechanical

- longitudinal waves
- need a material such as air to travel
- much slower speed (e.g. speed of sound in air is 300 m/s approx.)

ELECTROMAGNETIC WAVES

These are a group of *transverse* waves which have electric and magnetic properties. They are all produced by changing magnetic fields and changing electric fields, and travel at the very high speed of 300 000 000 metres per second. Figure 17.6 shows the position,

Fig. 17.6

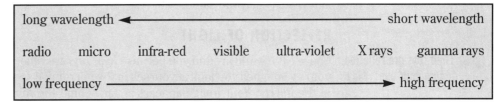

relative wavelength and frequency of the different electromagnetic waves.

The chart below summarises the different waves and their uses:

Type of wave		Uses	Source
radio wave:	long wave medium wave short wave }	radio communication	radio transmitters
	VHF UHF	stereo radio television	electronic circuits
	micro waves }	satellite communication, radar, microwave ovens	
infra-red		electric fires, ovens	any hot object
visible light		electric lights	very hot objects
ultra-violet		suntanning	extremely hot objects glowing gases
X-radiation		used in hospitals to photograph bones	X-ray tubes
gamma rays		used to irradiate food to kill germs; can penetrate very dense metal	radioactive materials

The different types of radiation have different effects on living cells.

- *microwaves* are absorbed by the water in living cells; the heat released may damage or kill the cells;
- *infra-red radiation* is felt as heat when it is absorbed by the skin;
- *ultra-violet (UV) radiation* passes through the upper layers of the skin to the deeper tissues; darker skin absorbs more ultra-violet so that less reaches the deeper tissues;
- *X-radiation* and *gamma radiation* pass through most living tissue although some may be absorbed by the cells; low doses of UV, X-radiation and gamma radiation can cause cells to become cancerous; higher doses may kill normal cells.

A MORE DETAILED LOOK AT X-RADIATION

X-rays are electromagnetic waves which have a very short wavelength between 10^{-9} and 10^{-12} of a metre. They are produced when a beam of high energy electrons strikes a metal target, such as tungsten. The penetrating power of X-radiation depends on the wavelength of the radiation and the type of material the rays fall on. X-rays are able to pass through many materials and are used to 'see' through dense objects. For example, at many airports suitcases are passed through an X-ray machine to search for any dangerous objects. In hospitals, X-rays are used by a radiographer to identify where bones may be broken.

X-rays are also used by scientists to help determine the internal structure of materials such as crystals, and used in industry to show hidden flaws in metal.

 **4 ▷ REFLECTION**

When a wave hits a barrier it is *reflected* away from the barrier. If a plane wave hits the barrier at *right angles*, it 'bounces back' along its original path, at the same wavelength, frequency and velocity. If the wave hits the barrier at an *angle*, it is reflected at the same angle away from the barrier, as shown in Figure 17.7.

The angle of incidence equals the angle of reflection, and the wavelength, frequency and velocity stay the same.

REFLECTION OF LIGHT

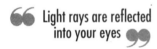 66 Light rays are reflected into your eyes 99

You see the world around you because *light rays* are reflected from different objects into your eyes. When you look at yourself in the mirror you see an image of yourself reflected in the mirror. Your image appears as far behind the mirror as you are in front of the mirror. The image is described as a *virtual* or *imaginary* image. It is the same way up as you are but the left and right sides are reversed. Figure 17.8 shows how an image is formed by a plane mirror.

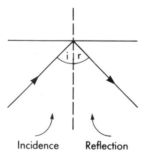

Incidence   Reflection

'I'

'O'

Fig 17.7 The angle of incidence equals the angle of reflection.

Fig. 17.8 The image 'I' of the object 'O' appears to be behind the mirror.

5 ▷ REFRACTION

Waves travel at a certain speed in air, but when they pass into a different medium, such as water, the speed slows down. The velocity of waves will also decrease as they pass from deeper to shallower water, ie their speed slows down.

REFRACTION OF LIGHT

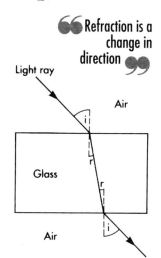

> 66 Refraction is a change in direction 99

Light ray

Air

Glass

Air

Fig.17.9 The light ray is bent or 'refracted' as it enters and leaves the glass.

When light rays cross the boundary from one substance to a different substance their speed changes and this may cause a change of direction known as *refraction*. For example, as light rays pass from air into glass, 'Perspex' or water their speed slows down, their wavelength becomes shorter and their direction may be changed, unless their direction of travel is along the normal.

If a ray of light enters a glass block at 90°, then it leaves the block in the same direction. It is when the light ray enters *at an angle* that its direction changes, both on entering and leaving the glass.

Light refracts or bends *towards* the normal (an imaginary line at 90° to the glass surface) as it enters the glass, which is more dense than the air. The light ray then refracts or bends *away from* the normal as it leaves the glass and passes into the air, a less dense medium.

SOME COMMON EFFECTS OF REFRACTION

If a thick glass block is placed over some print then the print and the bottom of the glass appear raised. If a stick is placed in water it appears to bend upwards. Both of these effects are due to the refraction of light rays away from the normal as they pass from a denser medium to another less dense medium. In the above examples: glass to air, water to air.

REFRACTIVE INDEX

Light is refracted as it enters and leaves the glass block because its speed changes according tot he refractive index of the material.

$$\text{Refractive index (n)} = \frac{\text{Speed of light in air}}{\text{Speed of light in material}} = \frac{C_{air}}{C_{medium}}$$

> 66 The greater the refractive index, the more the light is slowed down 99

For example light travels at 300 000 km/s in air, but at 200 000 km/s in glass. The refractive index of the glass is 3/2.

The greater the refractive index of the medium, the more the light is slowed down.

6 **TOTAL INTERNAL REFLECTION: CRITICAL ANGLE**

When light travels from a denser to a less dense medium, fir example, glass to air, there is a strong refracted ray and a weak ray reflected back into the glass (Figure 17.10(a)). When the angle of incidence reaches a certain *critical angle* of incidence the angle of refraction is 90° (Figure 17.10 (b)). As the angle of incidence is increased then *total internal reflection* occurs and all the light rays are reflected inside the glass block (Figure 17.10 (c)). The critical angle of incidence for glass is about 42° and for water about 48°.

Fig. 17.10

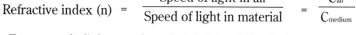

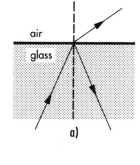

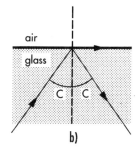

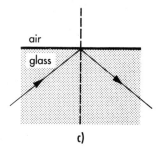

a)   b)   c)

Periscopes and optical fibres are two ways in which total internal reflection is made use of as shown in the diagram (Fig. 17.11).

An optical fibre consists of *two* types of glass (the *core glass fibre* and the *cladding glass fibre*). When light passes through the optical fibre it is continually being totally internally reflected, 'bouncing' along the fibre; it does not matter if the fibre is coiled or knotted, the light will still get through. The two types of glass must be very pure, ensuring that this is so is the most difficult part of the manufacturing process.

Optical fibres are now being used instead of copper cable to carry telephone messages. The messages are carried as pulses of light. Optical fibres are better than copper cables in that they can carry many more messages for the same thickness of cable.

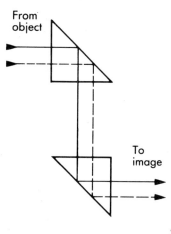

From object

To image

Fig. 17.11 Periscope

7 > THE SPECTRUM

White light is made up of seven different colours, each of which has a different wavelength. When a ray of white light enters a prism, each of the different wavelengths is refracted or bent by different amounts, because they travel through the prism at different speeds. This effect produces a spectrum of all the different colours which make up white light.

The rainbow effect

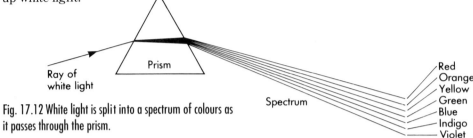

Fig. 17.12 White light is split into a spectrum of colours as it passes through the prism.

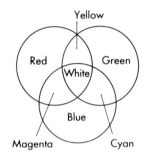

Fig. 17.13 The three primary colours make all the other colours.

COLOURED LIGHT

Red, green and blue are the three *primary colours* which *cannot* be made by mixing any other colours. All the other colours *can* be made from two or three of these primary colours, as shown in Figure 17.13.

When you *mix* two primary colours on a white screen, a new colour, called a *secondary colour* is produced. For example, mixing red and green light produces yellow light. If the third primary colour, blue, is now mixed with the yellow, white light is produced.

COLOUR MIXING OF PAINTS

Coloured dyes in paints and clothes *absorb* part of the spectrum of colours and *reflect* the other colours into our eyes so that we see a particular colour. For example, a red dress absorbs green and blue and reflects red, the colour we see. Green plants look green because the pigment in the leaves absorbs red and blue light and reflects the green.

When two coloured paints are *mixed together*, for example red and yellow, the paint appears to be orange, the colour that is *not absorbed* by either red or yellow. The red paint absorbs green and blue and reflects red and orange. The yellow paint absorbs red and blue and reflects orange, yellow and green. So *both* paints reflect orange.

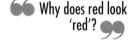

Why does red look 'red'?

HOW COLOURED PICTURES ARE PRODUCED ON A TV SCREEN

1 When a TV scene is filmed, light enters the camera, and is split into red, blue and green light.
2 These different signals then go to three different 'tubes', which then send out the corresponding signal on ultra-high frequency waves, to the three electron guns at the back of the TV screen.
3 The electrons hit millions of tiny red, green and blue dots covering the TV screen, which glow when the electrons hit them.
4 Depending on which coloured dots glow, the different colours are produced on the screen.

8 > LENSES

There are two main types of lenses: converging (convex) and diverging (concave). Both lenses refract (bend) light but diverging lenses cause parallel rays of light to spread out (diverge) whereas converging lenses cause parallel rays of light to come closer together (converge).

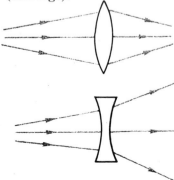

Fig. 17.14

FOCAL LENGTH

When a convex lens is set up a few centimetres away from a small lamp the image of the lamp can be focussed on a screen. The image is real (it exists in space) and inverted (upside down). If the object is moved closer to the lens, the screen must be moved further away to focus the image (Fig 17.15).

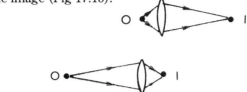

Fig. 17.15

When the object is moved far away, the rays reaching the surface of the lens are almost parallel and the image is formed close to the lens at a point called the *principal focus* (F). The distance from the centre of the lens to the principal focus is the *focal length* (Fig. 17.16).

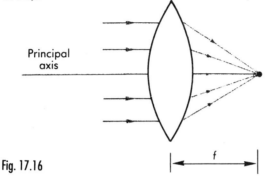

Principal axis

F

f

Fig. 17.16

You can measure the focal length of a lens by focussing rays from a distant object on to a screen and measuring the distance from the lens to the screen.

FINDING THE POSITION OF THE IMAGE

If the focal length and the distance of an object from the lens is known, then the position of the image can be found by *scale drawing*. Two rays can be drawn from any point on the object; one ray is drawn parallel to the axis, and then, after it is bent by the lens, it must pass through the principal focus of the lens; the second ray can be drawn so it passes through the centre of the lens without being bent. The image is formed where the two rays meet; as shown in the diagram (Figure 17.17).

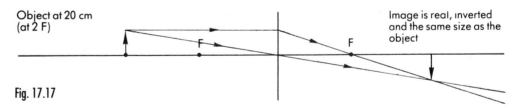

Object at 20 cm (at 2 F)

Image is real, inverted and the same size as the object

F

F

Fig. 17.17

CONVERGING LENSES AS MAGNIFYING GLASSES

Converging (convex) lenses can be used as a magnifying glass if the object is closer to the lens than the focal length, as shown in the diagram (Figure 17.18).

To the person looking at the object, the light rays appear to come from a point further away, so creating a large upright image because the light rays entering the eye are diverging. The image is described as *virtual* because no light rays originate from the image.

Converging lenses are also used in cameras, where they produce a small area inverted image; and in projectors, where a large real image is projected onto a screen.

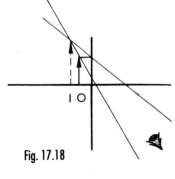

I O

Fig. 17.18

9 ❯ **THE EYE**

Light is refracted or bent as it enters the eye through the transparent *cornea*. It is then refracted even more by the convex lens of the eye, and focused on the *retina* at the back of the eye. The retina consists of light sensitive cells called rods and cones which are connected to the brain by nerve fibres. The *cones* are concerned with colour vision and vision in bright light. They are sensitive to red, green or blue light. The *rods* are concerned with non-colour vision and vision in dim light. When these cells are stimulated by light an impulse is sent to the brain via the optic nerve. The brain then forms images as a result of the impulses it receives. Fig. 17.19 shows the structure of the main parts of the eye.

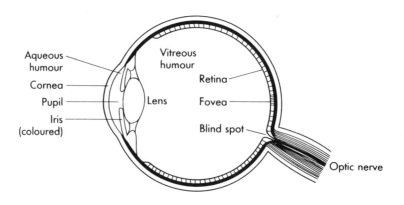

Fig. 17.19 The structure of the eye.

The chart shows a summary of the main parts of the eye:

The main parts of the eye and their function

■ **cornea**	refracts (bends) the light entering the eye
■ **aqueous humour**	supplies nutrient to the lens and cornea
■ **iris**	controls the amount of light entering the eye by adjusting the size of the pupil
■ **pupil**	the aperture which allows light into the eye
■ **lens**	refracts the light rays and changes shape to allow for fine focusing
■ **ciliary muscle**	controls the shape of the lens
■ **suspensory ligaments**	attach lens to ciliary muscle
■ **vitreous humour**	maintains the shape of the eye
■ **retina**	contains light sensitive cells which convert light energy into a nerve impulse
■ **fovea**	very sensitive region of retina where most light is focussed
■ **optic nerve**	carries impulses to the brain where they are interpreted

ACCOMMODATION

The ciliary muscles control the shape of the lens so that the eye can see objects which are near or far away. This is known as *accommodation*. To focus light from distant objects on the retina the lens needs to be thin and this is brought about by the contraction of the radial ciliary muscles. To focus light from near objects on the retina the lens becomes thicker due to contraction of the circular ciliary muscles. This action is a reflex action and some of the ability of the lens to change shape is lost with age.

Short and long sight

Sometimes the lens is unable to accommodate, so that objects which are close to or far away from the eye appear blurred. A short-sighted person is unable to see distant objects clearly and the light rays are focused in front of the retina usually due to the eyeball being too long. To correct this defect a concave lens is used which diverges (spreads out) the rays before they enter the eye, as shown in Fig.17.20).

A long-sighted person is unable to see objects close to their eye as their lens is too short. A convex lens helps to bend the light rays before they enter the eye.

Eye defect	Cause	Correction
Long sight (hypermetropia)	Short eyeball: near objects cannot be focused 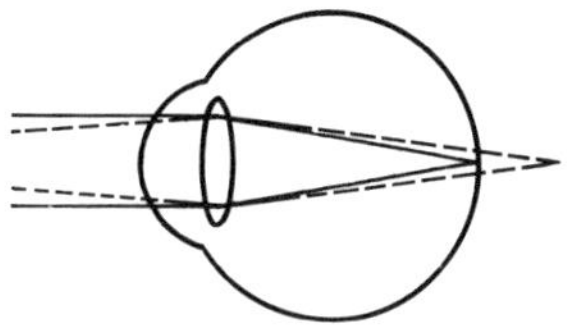	Converging lens 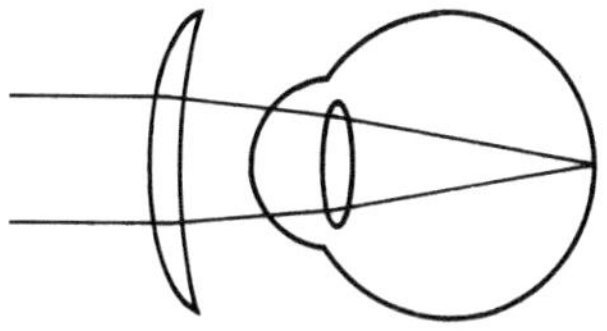
Short sight (myopia)	Long eyeball: distant objects cannot be focused 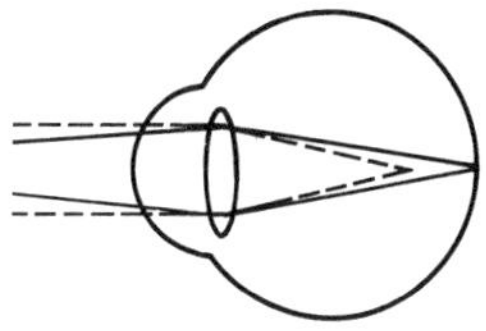	Diverging lens 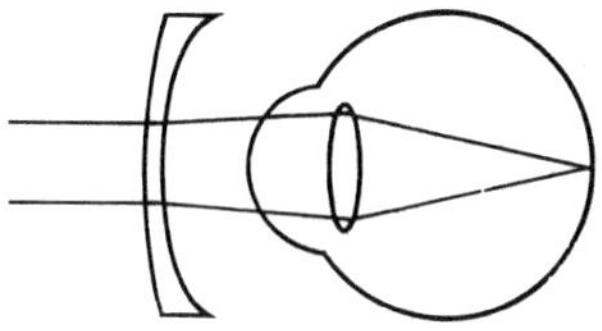

Fig. 17.20

10 > SOUND

Sound waves are longitudinal waves produced by vibrating sources such as a guitar, the human voice, a bell hitting a gong. Sound requires a substance or medium to travel through such as metal, air or water. The particles in the medium vibrate with the same frequency as the sound and along the same direction as the sound is travelling. The need for a medium can be demonstrated in the laboratory by hanging an electric bell in a glass jar and pumping all the air out of the jar. The bell can be seen to be hitting the gong but no sound can be heard. The sound waves cannot pass through a vacuum.

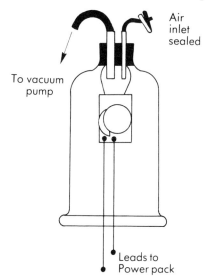

Air inlet sealed

To vacuum pump

Leads to Power pack

Fig. 17.21

SPEED OF SOUND

66 See page 329 for equation 99

You may remember a simple experiment you have done to determine the speed of sound. If you stand about 100 metres from a wall and clap your hands together you can hear the echoes of the clapping. If you increase the rate of clapping until the echo corresponds to the next clap, you know that the sound has travelled to the wall and back, a distance 2d, in the time taken between claps. If you time the interval between 20 claps you can find the time for one interval (t). Knowing the distance (d) from the source of the sound to the wall enables you to find the speed of sound in air   = 2d/ t.

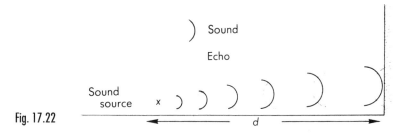

Sound

Echo

Sound source

Fig. 17.22

The speed of sound depends on the material through which it is travelling; for example in air the speed is 330 m/s, whereas in sea water it is 1 200 m/s and in steel it is 2 500 m/s.

LOUDNESS AND AMPLITUDE, PITCH AND FREQUENCY

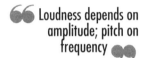

Loudness depends on amplitude; pitch on frequency

The loudness of a sound is determined by the size or amplitude of the vibrations. A musical note sounds louder if more energy is put into producing a note, for example, hitting a drum with more force increases the amplitude of the note and it sounds louder. (Fig. 17.23).

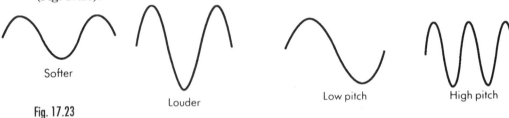

Softer   Louder   Low pitch   High pitch

Fig. 17.23

The pitch of a sound is determined by its frequency, i.e. the number of vibrations per second. A high pitch note has a high frequency and a short wavelength as shown in Fig. 17.23.

11 > THE EAR

The ear drum detects the compressions and rarefactions of the air which are caused when sound waves are produced from a vibrating source. The vibrations of the ear drum are passed through the three small bones or *ossicles* in the middle ear which amplify the vibration. The fluid in the cochlea or inner ear then vibrates and impulses are passed via the auditory nerve to the brain.

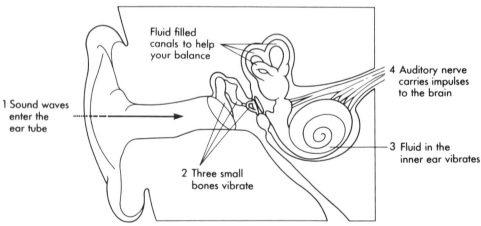

Fluid filled canals to help your balance

4 Auditory nerve carries impulses to the brain

1 Sound waves enter the ear tube

3 Fluid in the inner ear vibrates

2 Three small bones vibrate

Fig. 17.24 The structure of the ear.

Humans can detect sounds within the frequency of about 20 Hz to 20 000 Hz. The upper limit decreases with age. Sound is measured in decibels using a sound meter or decibel meter. One decibel is about the smallest amount of sound you can detect. Very loud noise over 100 decibels can be extremely unpleasant and may be harmful to your ears. People who are subjected to noise over 97 decibels for more than 2 hours a day can suffer from temporary or even permanent deafness. For example, listening to a personal stereo for several hours at a time can affect your eardrums and may make you unable to hear higher frequency sounds.

Sound devices

Microphones convert sound vibrations into electrical vibrations of the same frequencies. The pattern of vibration can then be amplified and sent over long distances by radio waves, along wires or by optical fibres. Loudspeakers convert electrical vibrations into sound waves of the same frequencies.

Resonance

Objects which are able to vibrate or oscillate have their own natural frequency of vibration. If the object receives impulses from another vibrating system oscillating at the same frequency then the object can respond by vibrating sometimes at very large amplitudes. This can cause problems say, in a car, if the engine is vibrating at the natural frequency of the metal body work of the car and can cause large vibrations to be set up which weaken the metal.

Ultrasonic waves

Sound waves with frequencies higher than 20 000 Hz can be produced by electronic systems. One of the uses of these ultrasonic waves is in hospitals for pre-natal scanning of a foetus. An image of the foetus is produced on a screen so that the radiographer can check that the foetus has no abnormalities.

12 > INTERFERENCE DIFFRACTION AND POLARISATION

INTERFERENCE

When waves from two or more sources meet, a process known as *interference* takes place. Where two sets of light waves for example have the same frequency, wavelength and amplitude and are in time with each other (in phase) they combine with each other to give a single wave of maximum amplitude. This is known as *constructive interference*, and the amplitudes of the individual waves are *added* (Fig. 17.25).

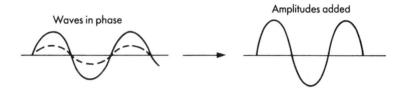

Fig. 17.25

Sometimes the waves are pushing the medium in opposite directions, so that the waves cancel each other. If two opposing 'peaks' (i.e. a peak and a 'trough') arrive at the same place at the same time, the waves are 'out of phase' and the amplitudes of the individual waves are *subtracted*. Indeed equal amplitudes would exactly cancel. This is called *destructive interference* (Fig. 17.26)

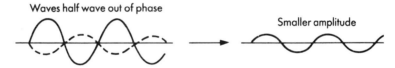

Fig. 17.26

A similar effect can happen with sound waves from two loudspeakers in a large room. If the loudspeakers are connected to the same signal generator one can hear areas of 'sound' and areas of 'silence' as one moves across the room. The areas of sound represent constructive interference so the resultant amplitude is high. The areas of silence represent destructive interference so the resultant amplitude is zero.

DIFFRACTION

When waves pass through a small opening or around the edge of an obstacle they can change the shape of their wavefront so that they spread out from the edges. This effect is known as *diffraction*. The velocity, frequency and wavelength do not change. You may have seen this effect in a ripple tank. As plane waves approach a barrier or pass through a gap they spread out beyond the edges as seen in Fig. 17.27.

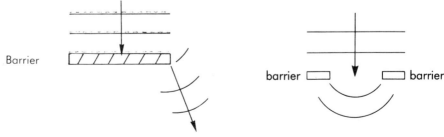

Fig. 17.27

POLARISATION

Light is made up of transverse waves with vibrations in all directions at right angles to the direction of travel and is described as *unpolarised*. If a ray of unpolarised light is passed through a polariser then the vibrations are restricted to one direction only and the light is said to be *polarised* in that direction. A common polariser is a material called 'Polaroid' which is a thin transparent film made of sheets of plastic containing minute crystals. 'Polaroid' is commonly used in camera filters and sunglasses to reduce glare. Polarised light has many uses, for example in chemical analysis and in the measurement of stress in materials.

EXAMINATION QUESTIONS

MULTIPLE CHOICE

QUESTION 1

Which one of the following is an example of a longitudinal wave?
A infra-red radiation   D sound waves
B micro waves   E X-rays
C radio waves

QUESTION 2

The diagram shows the position of the waves in the electromagnetic spectrum.

	micro-waves		visible light		X-rays	P

What type of radiation is at position P?
A gamma; B infra-red; C radio; D soundwaves; E ultra-violet

QUESTION 3

The diagram shows a simple wave form.
Which letter – A, B, C, D, or E – shows the wavelength?

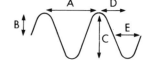

QUESTION 4

Which one of the following waves has the longest wavelength and lowest frequency?
A gamma; B infra-red; C radio; D ultra-violet; E visible light

QUESTION 5

A swinging pendulum makes 80 complete swings in 20 seconds. What is the frequency of the oscillation?
A 2 Hertz; B 4 Hertz; C 8 Hertz; D 20 Hertz; E 80 Hertz

QUESTION 6

A sound wave travels at 300 metres per second and has a frequency of 60 Hertz. What is its wavelength?
A 0.2 m; B 5 m; C 60 m; D 360 m; E 18 000 m

QUESTION 7

Which one of the following types of radiation is used to irradiate food and kill germs?
A micro-waves   D X-rays
B infra-red   E gamma rays
C ultra-violet

QUESTION 8

Which one of the following diagrams correctly shows the path of a ray of light as it passes through a glass block?

A   B   C   D   E

QUESTION 9

A narrow beam of white light is passed through a glass prism and forms a spectrum on a screen. The lines drawn show the limits of the visible spectrum.
What colour of light appears at X?
A blue; B green; C red; D violet; E white

White light → [prism diagram] → X

STRUCTURED QUESTIONS

QUESTION 10

Waves were produced in a ripple tank as shown in the diagram below. A ruler was placed along the edge of the tank.

The wave motion was frozen by a stroboscope set at 7 flashes per second.

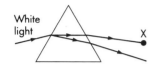

0   10   20   30 cm

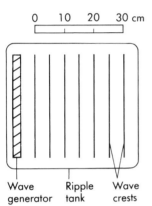

Wave   Ripple   Wave
generator   tank   crests

a) i) What is the wavelength of the water waves in cm?

_____
                                                        (1)

ii) Suggest **two** possible frequencies of the wave motion.

1 _____
                                                        (1)

2 _____
                                                        (1)

iii) What would be the effect on the wavelength if the wave generator produced more waves per second?

_____
                                                        (1)

b) Light is also a wave motion and forms part of the electromagnetic spectrum. The following experiment was set up using white light and a prism.

i) Complete the diagram, showing the dispersion and refraction of white light by the prism to form a spectrum.   *(3)*

ii) Show clearly where you would expect to find red light on the screen.   *(1)*

Screen

White light →

Triangular prism

Spectrum

c) i) Name the types of radiation that would occur at A and B in the electromagnetic spectrum shown below.

radiowaves

microwaves

A _____
                                                        (1)

visible light

ultra-violet light

B _____
                                                        (1)

γ-radiation

ii) Which radiation shown in the spectrum has the shortest wavelength?

_____
                                                        (1)

d) Give a practical use for:

    i) microwaves: (2 lines available)   *(1)*

    ii) γ – radiation: (2 lines available)   *(1)*

                                                       (MEG)

QUESTION 11

Ultrasonic waves and X-rays can both be used to examine the interior of the human body.

a) Describe how each of them is produced

    i) X-rays (8 lines for your answer)   *(5)*

    ii) Ultrasonic waves (2 lines for your answer)   *(1)*

b) Explain fully why it is often preferable to use ultrasonic waves rather than X-rays to examine patients. (9 lines for your answer)   *(6)*

                      [Co-ordinated Science NEAB, WJEC, ULEAC]

Now try Question 13 on page 357.

O U T L I N E   A N S W E R S

MULTIPLE CHOICE

ANSWER 1

Key D. Sound waves are the only longitudinal wave on the list, all the others are electromagnetic waves and are transverse.

ANSWER 2

Key A. Gamma radiation has a shorter wavelength than X-rays. The position of visible light and microwaves gives you a clue.

ANSWER 3

Key A. The wavelength is the distance from one crest to another. Option B marks the amplitude.

ANSWER 4

Key C, radio waves. Option A gamma rays have the shortest wavelength and the highest frequency.

ANSWER 5

Key B, 4 complete cycles per second. Divide the number of complete swings by the time. $80 \div 20 = 4$.

ANSWER 6

Key B, 5. Remember speed = frequency x wavelength, so divide speed by the frequency to find the wavelength. $300 \div 60 = 5$.

ANSWER 7

Key E, gamma rays, are involved in irradiation of food. Option A micro-waves just heat up food so it can be eaten hot!

ANSWER 8

Key A. The light ray bends away from the normal as it leaves the denser glass block. Option D is the closest, but light doesn't follow the 'normal' path straight through the block.

ANSWER 9

Key C. Red light is refracted the least by the glass block.

ANSWER 10

a) i) 5 cm (measure the distance using the ruler above the diagram)

ii) 7 Hz, 14 Hz

iii) The wavelength would decrease.

b) i) , ii) see diagram

c) i) A infra-red
       B X-rays

ii) gamma rays

d) i) cooking food

ii) sterilising equipment.

ANSWER 11

This question is targeted at level 9 and is an example of extended writing. The number of lines available and the number of marks in brackets indicates the length of answer required. You should attempt to make specific points in your answer. Each point should gain one mark.

a) i) electrons gain energy (1)
        leave heated wire (1)
        accelerated by electric field (1)
        hit metal target (1)
        emit some of their energy as X-rays (1)

ii) ultrasound is produced electronically (1)

b) X-rays can damage living cells (1)
    may cause cancers (1)
    radiographers at risk (1)
    X-rays suitable for viewing hard tissue e.g. bone (1)
    ultrasound used for soft tissue, e.g. organs (1)
    does not damage living cells e.g. foetus (1)

A STUDENT'S ANSWER WITH
EXAMINER'S COMMENTS

a) The diagram below shows an observer in an underground shelter.

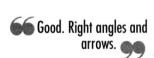
Good. Right angles and arrows.

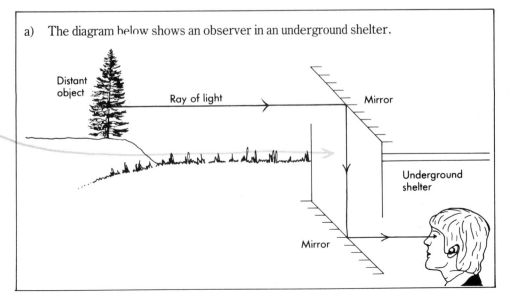

i) Complete the ray of light from the object to the observer's eye.
ii) Suggest another use for such an arrangement of mirrors.

in a submarine.

(2)

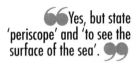
66 Yes, but state 'periscope' and 'to see the surface of the sea'. **99**

b) i) Complete the path of the ray in the diagram below.

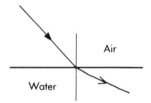

Air

Water

66 No, the light ray bends towards the 'normal'. **99**

ii) Explain what is happening.

the light ray bends away from the normal.

66 No, incorrect. As the light is entering a denser medium, it bends *towards* the normal. **99**

iii) What is the name given to this effect?

Bending of light.

66 *Refraction* is the word required. **99**

(3)

c) i) Complete the diagram below to show dispersion of white light as it passes through a prism.

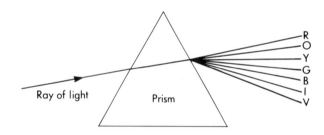

Ray of light   Prism

R O Y G B I V

66 Oh dear! See Figure 17.12. The ray is split as it *enters* the prism. **99**

ii) Visible light is part of the electromagnetic spectrum. Place the following in order of *increasing* wavelength:

radiowaves, infra-red, visible light, X-rays

Shortest wavelength:

X-rays ✓
visible ✓
radio waves X
infra-red X

66 Wrong order here. **99**

iii) Explain how selective absorption of light produces the following effects.

1 White paper: it reflects all the light.

66 Yes, but state it does not 'absorb' light, as the question asks. **99**

2 Black ink: does not reflect any light.

66 Yes, but it *absorbs* all the light. **99**

3 A red apple: absorbs green and blue, and reflects red.

66 Good, well done. **99**

(9)
(ULEAC)

R E V I E W   S H E E T

 Electromagnetic waves and waves in water are examples of _____ waves.

 Sound waves are an example of _____ waves.

 The length of each complete oscillation of a wave is its _____, and is the distance between two troughs or two crests (peaks).

 In the diagram what does each letter stand for?

x _____

y _____

 The strength of an electromagnet can be increased by_____

 The number of complete cycles of the wave per second is called the _____ of the

wave, and is measured in _____

 Complete this equation

Speed   =

(in metres per second)

 List three ways in which an electromagnetic wave *differs* from a mechanical wave

1. _____

2. _____

3. _____

 Fill in the *types of electromagnetic wave* which could be placed in the various positions along the spectrum shown in the diagram.

long wavelength ◄───────────────────── short wavelength

low frequency ─────────────────────► high frequency

 Complete this equation

The angle of incidence   =

 When light rays cross the boundary from one substance to a different substance their speed

changes and this may cause a change of direction known as _____

 Complete this equation

Refractive index (n)   =

 The _____ the refractive index of the medium, the _____ the light is slowed down.

 When the angle of incidence of light travelling from glass to air is around 42°, the angle of

refraction is _____

 _____ occurs when all the light rays are reflected inside the glass block.

✎ List the colours in the spectrum

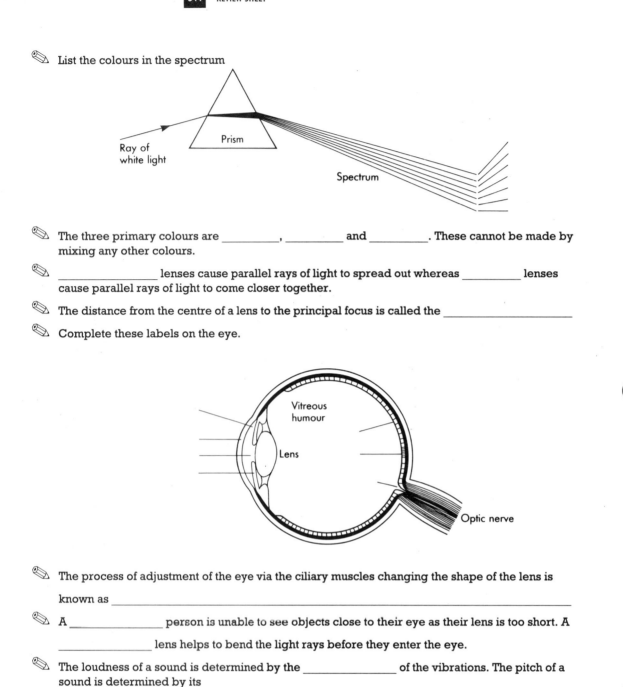

✎ The three primary colours are _____ , _____ and _____ . These cannot be made by mixing any other colours.

✎ _____ lenses cause parallel rays of light to spread out whereas _____ lenses cause parallel rays of light to come closer together.

✎ The distance from the centre of a lens to the principal focus is called the _____

✎ Complete these labels on the eye.

✎ The process of adjustment of the eye via the ciliary muscles changing the shape of the lens is

known as _____

✎ A _____ person is unable to see objects close to their eye as their lens is too short. A

_____ lens helps to bend the light rays before they enter the eye.

✎ The loudness of a sound is determined by the _____ of the vibrations. The pitch of a sound is determined by its

_____

✎ Sound is measured in _____

FORCE AND MOTION

GETTING STARTED

Walking, running, swimming, cycling and flying are all ways in which you may have moved at different *speeds*. The speed at which you travel depends on two factors: *how far* you have moved and *how long* it has taken. Light waves and sound waves also travel at *different* speeds, with both waves moving a large distance in a short time.

You have probably experienced *acceleration* when sitting in a car or bus which has started moving and then got faster and faster. You may also have experienced *deceleration* as friction from the brakes caused the car or bus to slow down. Forces are needed to change the *motion* of moving bodies. For instance you will have worn a seat belt when travelling in a car, or when taking off and landing in an aeroplane.

E S S E N T I A L   P R I N C I P L E S

1 > SPEED

Speed is the distance travelled in a unit of time, such as metres per second, or kilometres per hour.

The formula is:

$$\text{speed (m/s)} = \frac{\text{distance travelled (m)}}{\text{time taken (s)}}$$

In the laboratory you may have made measurements to speed using a *ticker-timer*. This instrument is a type of clock which produces 50 ticks every second, equal to 5 ticks every 0.1 second. These ticks appear as dots on a strip of ticker tape paper, which shows how far the tape has moved between each dot. The time interval between each dot is 0.02 seconds. When the dots are close together the tape has been moved slowly. When the dots are far apart the tape has been moved quickly.

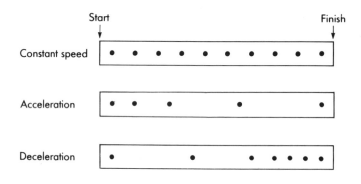

Fig. 18.1 Each piece of ticker tape shows a different type of movement.

The ticker tape is usually attached to a moving trolley to study how the trolley moved. The tape shown in Figure 18.2 was produced by a trolley moving down a runway.

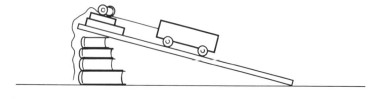

Fig. 18.2 The ticket tape shows how the trolley accelerated.

The trolley started slowly and then accelerated.

2 > ACCELERATION

The *acceleration* of an object is the rate at which its speed in a particular direction changes. The formula is:

$$\text{acceleration (m/s}^2\text{)} = \frac{\text{change in speed (m/s)}}{\text{time taken for change (s)}}$$

When a long piece of tape is pulled through the ticker-timer, the tape can be cut up into 5-dot lengths, each representing a time interval of 0.1 s and fixed on to paper as shown in Figure 18.3.

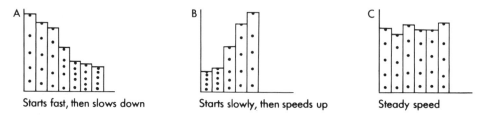

Fig. 18.3 The tape is cut into 5 dot lengths and made into a graph.

The velocity for each piece of tape can be found by measuring the distance travelled in 0.1 seconds.

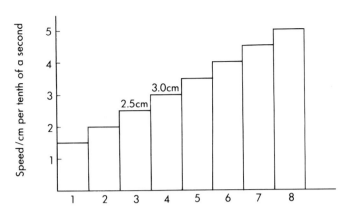

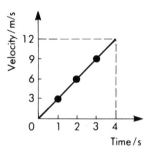

Fig. 18.4 Each length of tape is the distance travelled in 0.1 seconds.

Fig. 18.5 A graph showing constant acceleration.

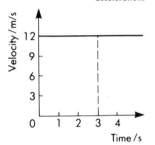

Fig. 18.6 A graph showing constant velocity.

The length of strip 3 is 2.5 cm, which means the trolley moved 2.5 cm in 0.1 s (25 cm/s). In strip 4 the distance moved was 3.0 cm in 0.1 second (30 cm/s), so the change in velocity is 5 cm/s in 0.1 second and the acceleration is 50 cm/s^2. The information from ticker tapes can be shown on a *velocity-time* graph.

Figure 18.5 shows a *constant acceleration* of 3 m/s^2

$$\text{acceleration} = \frac{\text{change in velocity}}{\text{time taken}}$$

$$a = \frac{(12 - 0)}{4} = 3 \text{ m/s}^2$$

The *distance travelled* is the *area under the graph*, which equals the area of the triangle ie: area = $\frac{1}{2}$ x base x height.
In this example it is $\frac{1}{2}$ x 4 x 12 = 24 m.

Figure 18.6 shows a trolley moving with constant velocity.

The trolley is moving with constant velocity of 12 m/s, so in 3 seconds the car will have travelled 36 metres. This is equal to the area under the graph.

3 ▶ FORCE AND ACCELERATION

When an object is at rest, a force such as a push or a pull must be exerted on the object to make it move. A force is required to make it go faster or accelerate. The *amount of force* required depends on the *mass of the object* and is given by the formula below:

$$\textbf{force (N)} = \textbf{mass} \text{ (kg) x } \textbf{acceleration} \text{ (m/s}^2)$$
$$F = ma$$
$$\text{or} \qquad a = F/m.$$

The amount of acceleration produced depends on two factors – the size of the force, measured in Newtons, and the mass of the object, measured in kilograms. If the force doubles, or the mass is halved, then the acceleration is doubled. For example, if a force of 15 N acts on a mass of 3 kg, then its acceleration is 5 m/s^2. If the force doubles to 30 N, then the acceleration is 10 m/s^2.

FRICTION

When you push an object to start it moving, the object will eventually slow down and stop, owing to the force of *friction* which resists motion. The direction of the force of friction is always *opposite* to the direction in which the object is moving. When travelling in a car, friction between the tyres and the roads is essential if the car is going to travel safely and not skid about. Friction between the brake pads and the wheels of a bicycle and between the tyres and the road are essential if you need to stop the bicycle moving.

However, friction means that energy has to be used to *overcome* it, and so there are many ways of reducing friction as described below:

 **Friction can be useful**

1 Oil is used in car engines to reduce the friction of the parts rubbing against each other.
2 Air is used in hovercraft to reduce the friction between the boat and the water.
3 Ball bearings are used to reduce the friction between the wheel and the axle of a skateboard.

PAIRS OF FORCES

When an object is acted on by a force, then the object exerts an equal force in the opposite direction. For example, if you kick a ball, then your foot exerts a force on the ball, and the ball exerts an equal and opposite force on your foot; a rocket moves forward when the rocket engine pushes out a large mass of waste gases behind the rocket.

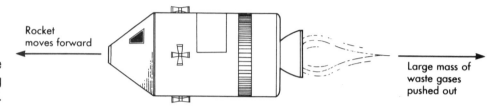

Rocket moves forward

Large mass of waste gases pushed out

Fig. 18.7 The rocket accelerates due to the force of the gases being pushed out.

FREE-FALL

An object which is allowed to fall freely near the Earth's surface has a *constant acceleration* of 10 m/s². For example, if two objects one of 5 kg and one of 20 kg were dropped from a weather balloon, they would both have the same acceleration. The larger object would need *more force* to accelerate its greater mass.

The force which is acting on free-falling objects is the force of *gravity* caused by the Earth's gravitational field. This is described as the *weight* of the object.

weight = mass x gravitational field strength

The weight of an object depends on how far it is from the Earth's centre. The gravitational pull of the Earth is decreased the further away an object is, so the weight is reduced. At the Earth's surface, the force acting on 1 kilogram is 10 Newtons. Therefore:

the weight of the 5 kg mass is 5 x 10 = 50 N
the weight of the 20 kg mass is 20 x 10 = 200 N

$$\text{acceleration} = \frac{\text{force}}{\text{mass}}$$

for the smaller object $\quad a = \dfrac{50}{5} = 10 \text{ m/s}^2$

for the larger object $\quad a = \dfrac{200}{20} = 10 \text{ m/s}^2$

5 kg   20 kg

Fig. 18.8 Both the 5 kg object and 20 kg object would have the same acceleration.

(assuming negligible air resistance).
■ the greater the mass of an object the greater its weight
■ the stronger the gravitational field acting on an object the greater its weight

ACCELERATION DUE TO GRAVITY (*g*)

One way of measuring *g* by free fall is to time how long it takes for a ball to drop through a known height. The acceleration of the ball can be calculated. The apparatus used is shown in Figure 18.9.

When the power supply to the electromagnet is switched off, the ball starts to drop and an electronic timer is automatically switched on. When the ball hits the gate and opens it, the timer is switched off. It is usual to repeat this timing several times and obtain an average time: t seconds, over s metres.

$$g = 2s/t^2$$

> ❝ *g* is acceleration due to gravity ❞

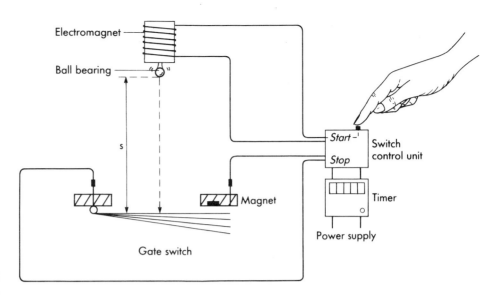

Fig. 18.9 Apparatus for measuring the acceleration due to gravity.

WEIGHT ON THE MOON

The mass of the Moon is smaller than that of Earth, so the gravitational pull of the Moon is about one sixth that of Earth. An object of mass of 10 kg would weigh 16 N on the Moon, whereas on Earth it would weigh 100 N.

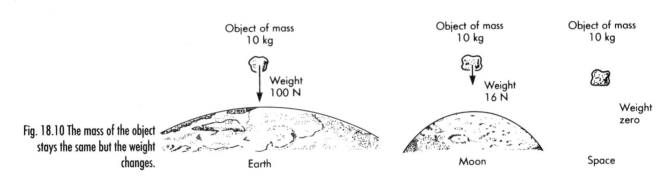

Fig. 18.10 The mass of the object stays the same but the weight changes.

SATELLITES IN ORBIT

The gravitational pull of the Earth provides the pull required to make a satellite follow a circular path around the Earth. For a satellite to orbit just above the atmosphere it needs to orbit at about 8000 m/s. The Moon, a natural satellite of Earth, orbits much further away from Earth at a speed of about 1000 m/s.

When an object is at a point above the ground it has *gravitational potential energy*. If you hold a book above your desk, the book has gravitational potential energy, equal to the amount of work which you did to lift it to that height, which is given by force x distance moved. On Earth the gravitational field strength is about 10 N/kg.

The **gravitational potential energy** of an object is *mgh*

where *mg* is the upward force needed to lift the object, and *h* is the vertical height above the ground.

For example, if the book has a mass of 2 kg, and is held 3 m high, then:

$$\text{gravitational potential energy} = 2 \text{ kg} \times 10 \text{ m/s}^2 \times 3 \text{ m}$$
$$= 60\text{J}$$

The *kinetic energy* (E) of a moving object depends on the mass (m) of the object and its velocity (v), as stated in the formula

$$E = \tfrac{1}{2} \, m \, v^2$$

An object has more kinetic energy
- the greater its mass
- the greater its speed

If a person of mass 60 kg is travelling with a velocity of 2 m/s, the kinetic energy =
$\frac{1}{2}$ x 60 x $(2 \text{ m/s})^2$ = 120 J
If the same person is travelling twice as fast, at 4 m/s, the kinetic energy =
$\frac{1}{2}$ x 60 x $(4 \text{ m/s})^2$ = 480 J
The kinetic energy has increased four times, as the speed has doubled.
If the *mass* of the person doubled to 120 kg, and the speed stayed at 2 m/s, the kinetic energy would be doubled:

$$E = \tfrac{1}{2} \times 120 \times (2 \text{ m/s})^2 = 240J$$

MOMENTUM

The *momentum* of an object is a product of its mass and its velocity. The greater the mass of an object, and the greater its speed in a particular direction (its velocity), the more momentum an object has.
The formula is:

momentum (kg m/s) = mass (kg) x velocity (m/s)

In a collision the total momentum after a collision in a particular direction is the same as the total momentum in that direction before the collision. This is known as *conservation of momentum*.

CARS ON THE MOVE

These ideas about kinetic energy are very important when applied to real life situations such as the braking distances of cars. When a car brakes to a stop, the kinetic energy is transferred to the brakes and to the road. The amount of energy transferred is equal to the braking force times the distance taken to stop.

If a car has twice the mass of another car, but is travelling at the same speed, it will have twice the amount of energy and need twice the braking distance for the same braking force. If two cars have the same mass but one is travelling twice the speed of the other car, it will have four times the amount of energy and need four times the braking distance. Wet road surfaces and smooth tyres will also increase the braking distance, as will the time it takes for the driver to react to a situation and to think about applying the brakes of the car.

 Travelling *twice* as fast needs *four* times the stopping distance

---

7 WORK AND ENERGY

Work is done and energy is transferred whenever a force moves an object through a distance.

The formula is

work done (J) = force applied (N) x distance moved (m)

For example, if a person pushes a box with a force of 200 N over a distance of 10 m they have done 200 x 10 = 2000 J of work (Fig. 18.11)

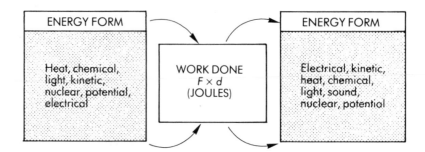

Fig. 18.11

---

8 POWER

Power is the rate of doing work or the rate of transfer of energy.

The formula is

$$\text{power (W)} = \frac{\text{work done (J)}}{\text{time taken (s)}}$$

For example if a person lifts 10 boxes onto a shelf 2m high using a force of 50 N per box in 40 seconds, you can calculate their rate of doing work:

work done = energy transferred

= 10 x 50 x 2 = 1 000 J

power developed = $\dfrac{1000}{40}$ = 25 W

In some calculations you may be given the mass of an object so you need to multiply the mass figure by 10, as the force acting on 1 kg is 10 N/kg. For example, if a person has a mass of 65 kg and climbs a flight of stairs 4 m high in 5 seconds, then you can calculate the power developed as follows:

65 kg weight (65 x 10) newtons
work done = 65 x 10 x 4 = 2 600 J

power developed = $\dfrac{2\,600}{5}$ = 520 W

When energy is supplied to a substance the temperature of the substance rises and the particles gain kinetic energy. The amount of heat energy required to raise the temperature of a substance depends on three factors:

- the mass of the substance being heated

- the temperature rise produced

- the type of substance

The energy required to raise the temperature of 1 kg of a substance by 1°C is known as its *specific heat capacity*. For example the specific heat capacity of water is 4200 joules per kilogram per degree Celsius (J/kg ° C). This means that to raise the temperature of 1 kg of water by 1°C, 4200 joules of energy are required. The specific heat capacity of copper is 380 J/kg °C so only 380 joules are required to raise the temperature of copper by 1°C.

The amount of energy transferred to a substance when its temperature changes can be calculated using the formula

energy transferred = specific heat capacity × mass × change in temperature
(J)   (J/kg°C)   kg   (°C)

If you have to calculate the amount of energy transferred you will be given the relevant formula and all the measurements you need. One common error is being told that the mass of say water heated is 500 g and inserting 500 g into the formula. You need to convert the 500 g to 0.5 kg before using it in the formula.

For example, 500 g of water at 20°C was heated to 60°C. Calculate how much energy had been transferred to the water. (The specific heat capacity of water is 4200 J/kg °C).

energy transferred = 0.5 kg x 4200 x 40°C = 84000 joules = 84 kJ

10 ⟩ **MOMENTS**

The *moment* of a force is its turning effect.

The formula for moments is

moments (Nm) = force (N) x perpendicular distance between the line of action and the pivot (m)

To reach equilibrium, when an object is not turning, the total moments of forces tending to turn it in one direction must be exactly balanced by the total moments of forces tending to turn it in the opposite direction. This can be expressed as

sum of clockwise moments = sum of anticlockwise moments

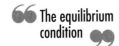 The equilibrium
condition

Fig. 18.12 shows the moment of the 4 N force is (4 x 6) = 24 N clockwise. To reach equilibrium both moments must be equal.

$$24 \text{ Nm} = 8x$$
$$3 \text{ m} = x$$

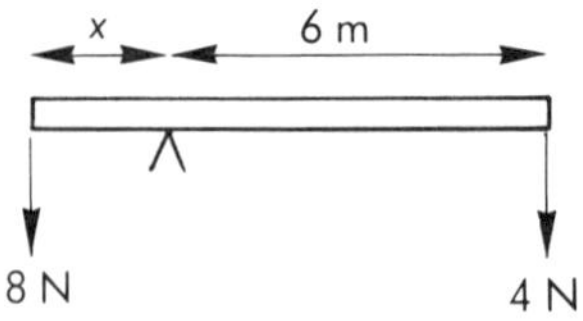

Fig. 18.12

8 N   4 N

The force of 8 N on the other side of the pivot must be 3 m distance from the pivot (8 x 3) = 24 Nm.

11 > PRESSURE

Pressure is the effect of force on an area.

The formula is

$$\text{pressure (Pa)} = \frac{\text{force (N)}}{\text{area (m}^2)}$$

The units of pressure are newtons per square metre (N/m^2) also called a *pascal* (Pa).

The same force acting over a large and small area will give a smaller pressure over the large area. The greater the force which acts on an area the greater the pressure. Large heavy animals such as camels and elephants have feet with a large surface area to reduce the pressure the animal exerts on the ground. You may be requested to calculate the pressure exerted by a person standing on the ground. For example, a person who weighs 500 N stands on an area of shoes of about 250 cm².

Therefore the pressure exerted on the floor is

$$\frac{500}{250} = 2 \text{ N/cm}^2$$

There are 100 x 100 centimetre squares in 1 m², so the pressure is

$$2 \times 100 \times 100 \text{ N/m}^2 = 20 \text{ kN/m}^2$$

FLUID PRESSURE

Remember   (i)   pressure increases with depth
           (ii)   pressure increases with the density of the fluid

Practical applications include hydraulic machines such as hydraulic brakes. These machines use liquid pressure to transfer a force from one place to another. They work on three basic properties of liquids:

1   They are incompressible, i.e. liquids cannot be compressed.
2   At the same depth, liquid pressure is the same in all directions.
3   Any change in liquid pressure is transmitted instantly to all parts of the liquid.

The diagram (Figure 18.13) shows the basic principle on which hydraulic brakes and jacks work.

Since A_2 is greater than A_1, a small force applied at the smaller cylinder is multiplied to become a large force applied at the larger cylinder. Although the force is made greater, energy is still conserved and at best work done by F_1 = work done by F_2. In Fig. 18.13

$$F_1 \times d_1 = F_2 \times d_2$$

So if the force is increased 10 times, the distance moved is decreased in the same proportion.

     This is the basic principle behind hydraulic jacks and hydraulic brakes.

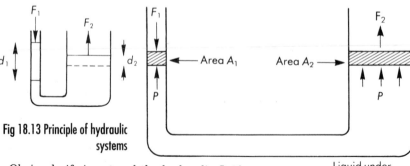

Fig 18.13 Principle of hydraulic systems

Obviously if air entered the hydraulic fluid, the system would not work well since gases can be compressed and pressure would not be transmitted instantly from one side of the system to the other.

Liquid under pressure

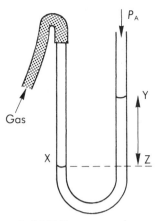

Fig 18.14 Manometer used to measure gas pressure

If a force is applied to the smaller piston 1 the pressure is transmitted through the liquid and is now applied at the larger piston 2. As the area of cylinder 2 is larger than that of cylinder 1 a small force applied at cylinder 1 is multiplied to become a large force applied at the cylinder 2.

Manometers

In the laboratory, gas pressure is measured using a *manometer* which is connected to the gas tap. The manometer contains a liquid on which the pressure is the same on both sides. When the gas pressure is turned on, the gas exerts a pressure on surface X causing level Y to rise as shown in the diagram (Figure 18.14).

The pressure of the liquid column YZ equals the amount by which gas pressure exceeds atmospheric pressure.

UPTHRUST IN FLUIDS: FLOTATION

When an object is immersed in a fluid, a force is exerted on it which tries to push the object upwards. This force is described as *upthrust* and is brought about because the pressure under the object is greater than that above the object.

The upthrust force = weight of liquid displaced by the object.

Any object will float if the upthrust force is greater than , or equal to, its own weight. A floating ship displaces a large weight of liquid equal to the total weight of the ship.

A balloon filled with hydrogen weighs less than the weight of air it displaces. The upthrust is greater than its weight, so the balloon rises.

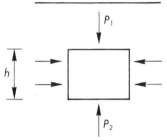

Fig 18.15 Pressure is greater below the block than above it

EXAMINATION QUESTIONS

MULTIPLE CHOICE

QUESTION 1

During an investigation into how objects move, the ticker tape sample shown below was produced by a moving model vehicle.

← Direction

Which one of the following correctly describes how the vehicle moved?
A   got faster and then slowed down
B   steady, constant speed all the time
C   steady, constant speed and then slowed down
D   steady, constant speed and then got faster
E   started slowly and then got faster.

QUESTION 2

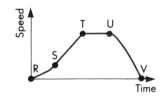

The graph opposite represents the journey of a car

During what part of the journey is the car braking?
A R–S; B S-T; C T-U; D U-V

QUESTION 3

What is the average speed of a vehicle which travels 30 kilometres in 15 minutes?
A 2 km/h; B 45 km/h; C 120 km/h; D 250 km/h; E 450 km/h

QUESTION 4

The graph opposite shows how the speed of an object varies with time.

The object is
A falling freely
B moving with constant speed
C moving with constant acceleration
D moving with constant deceleration.

QUESTION 5

The force on a 10 kg mass is 25 N. The acceleration is
A 0.4 m s^{-2} C 25 m s^{-2}
B 2.5 m s^{-2} D 250 m s^{-2}

QUESTION 6

Using the pattern

Energy = $\frac{1}{2}$ x mass x speed^2

what is the energy of a car of mass 6000 kg moving at a speed of 10 m/s?
A 6000 J   D 300 000 J
B 30 000 J   E 600 000 J
C 60 000 J

QUESTION 7

The Moon's gravitational field strength is one sixth that of Earth. An object on Earth has a mass of 60 kg and a weight of 600 N. What is the mass and weight of the object on the Moon?

	Mass	Weight
A	10	100
B	10	600
C	60	100
D	60	600

QUESTION 8

Using the formula

gravitational potential energy = m g h,

what is the gravitational potential energy of an object which has a mass of 5 kg and is 6m above the ground?
A 30 J; B 50 J; C 60 J; D 300 J; E 600 J

STRUCTURED QUESTIONS

QUESTION 9

The graph below represents the movement of a car during a short journey.

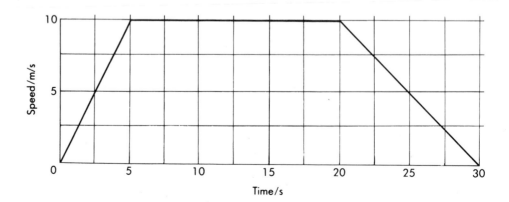

a) What is happening to the car

    i) in the first 5 seconds?

_____

(1)

    ii) between 5 seconds and 20 seconds?

_____

(1)

b) How far does the car travel between 5 seconds and 20 seconds?

_____

(1)

c) Between 20 seconds and 30 seconds the car comes to rest without the use of brakes. Explain how this could happen. (2 lines available)

(1)

(MEG)

QUESTION 10

The astronaut shown in the diagram below has a weight of 690 N on Earth.

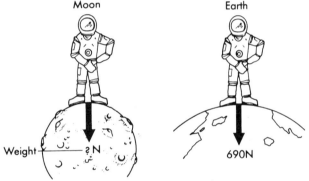

a) If the force of gravity on the Moon is $\frac{1}{6}$ (one sixth) that on Earth, what would be his weight on the Moon? Show how you arrive at your answer. *(2)*

Weight on Moon = _____ N

b) By reference to part a) explain briefly why an astronaut who walks on the Moon wears heavy boots. (3 lines available)

(2)

(NICCEA)

QUESTION 11

On 17th May, 1974, the first geostationary weather satellite was launched from Cape Canaveral. The satellite was capable of detecting visible light and infra-red radiation on a continuous 24-hour basis. It was placed in a position 36 000 km above the Equator at 45° W. The satellite recorded the development of a frontal wave over the Atlantic Ocean between 2100 hours on 12th June and 0900 GMT on 13th June, and transmitted this information to Earth.

a) What was the main advantage in this case of having the infra-red detectors on the satellite? *(2)*

Geostationary satellites appear to be stationary in the sky.

b) What does this tell you about the orbiting speed of the satellite compared to the rotation of Earth? *(1)*

c) What force keeps the satellite in orbit around the Earth? *(1)*

d) Explain how and why the weight of the satellite would change when it is in orbit compared to its weight on Earth. *(2)*

e) Suggest how a satellite could be constructed to meet its own energy needs over a long period of time. *(2)*

(MEG)

QUESTION 12

A car of mass 1000 kg starts off from rest at traffic lights, and accelerates away uniformly, as shown in the graph below.

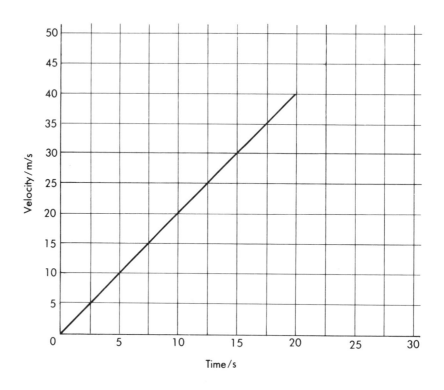

a) i) What is meant by 'accelerates'? (2 lines available) *(1)*

    ii) Calculate the acceleration of the car and state the units. (4 lines available) *(3)*

b) The kinetic energy of a moving body can be found from the pattern

    Energy $= \frac{1}{2}$ mass x (velocity)^2

    Find the kinetic energy of the car at 10 seconds after the start, stating the units. (4 lines available) *(3)*

c) The input energy is produced by petrol burning in the engine. Car engines waste some of this input energy, because not all of it can be converted to kinetic energy.

    i) What is the other main form of energy produced?

        (1)

    ii) What use can be made of this energy? (3 lines available) *(1)*

    The car has an input energy of 400 kJ 10 seconds after the start.
The efficiency of the engine is found from the pattern:

    Efficiency $= \dfrac{\text{kinetic energy}}{\text{input energy}}$ x 100

    Calculate the efficiency of the engine after 10 seconds. (3 lines available) *(3)*

d) 20 seconds after the start, the driver of the car puts on the brakes and comes to a stop in 5 seconds.

    Force = mass x acceleration

    Calculate the braking force, stating the units. (3 lines available) *(3)*

    (15)

    (ULEAC)

QUESTION 13

(aimed at levels 6–8, for Science Attainment Target 4)

a) i) The diagram below (Fig. 18.16) shows part of a telephone.

Choose the words from the list in the box below which completes the sentence which follows. *(2)*

| chemical | electrical | gravitational | heat | light | nuclear | sound |

The microphone in the mouthpiece changes _____

energy into _____ energy.

ii) The earpiece contains a loudspeaker. The diagram below shows a sectional view of a loudspeaker.

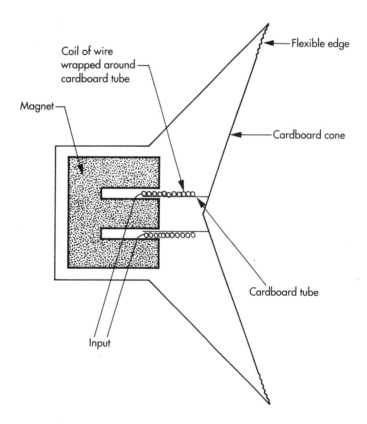

A) When an electric current flows through the wire of the coil the cardboard cone vibrates. Explain why. (4 lines available) *(3)*

B) Explain how the sound produced by the loudspeaker reaches the ear of a listener. (5 lines available) *(3)*

b) Sound wave patterns can be shown as traces on the screen of an oscilloscope. The diagrams which follow show traces for two sound waves, **A** and **B**.

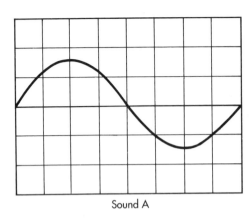
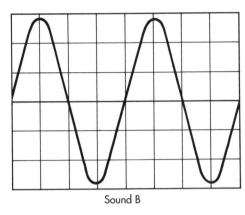

Sound A   Sound B

i) Which sound wave has the highest pitch? Give a reason for your answer. *(2)*

Sound wave _____ because _____
(2 lines available)

ii) Which sound wave is the loudest? Give a reason for your answer. *(3)*

Sound wave _____ because _____
(2 lines available)

c) i) What equation should be used to find the **speed** of a wave from its **frequency** and **wavelength**? *(1)*

_____

ii) A sound wave has a wavelength of 0.25 metres (m). Use your equation to calculate its frequency. The speed of sound is 330 metres per second (m/s).
(4 lines available) *(4)*

d) Sounds above 20 000 Hz are known as ultrasound. Some singers who can sing notes of very high frequencies are supposed to be able to break wine glasses when they make these high notes. People suffer great pain if 'kidney stones' grow in their kidneys. These stones are formed from calcium compounds. Doctors in some hospitals are trying to break up kidney stones using beams of ultrasound focussed at the stones. Explain why the ultrasound beam could cause the break up of the kidney stones (4 lines available). *(3)*

e) Smoke alarms are designed to produce a sound signal when smoke is detected. The graph below shows the different hearing abilities of a person aged 13 and a person aged 65.

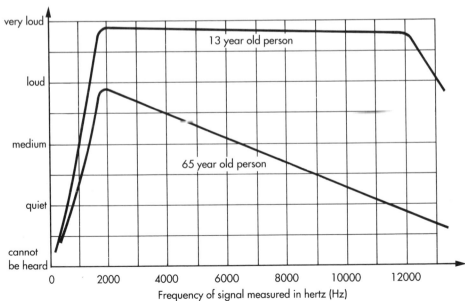

i) Use the information in the graph to suggest the best frequency for the signal produced by the smoke alarm. Give the reason for your choice.   *(2)*

Frequency _____

Reason _____

_____

ii) Most smoke alarms set off a sound signal rather than a visual one, such as a flashing light.

A) Give **four** different advantages of sound signals rather than visual ones. (6 lines available)   *(4)*

B) Explain why an alarm with both sound and visual signals is sometimes necessary. (6 lines available)   *(2)*

[SEG Science Double Award, Paper 7, Intermediate Tier, levels 6–8]

Question 14

(aimed at Levels 6–8, 8–10)

In this question parts (a) and (c) are common to both tier I (level 6–8) and tier H (level 8–10). Parts (b) and (d) are only for level H.

The table below gives some details about a jet aircraft, and some information and two equations you will need to use to answer the questions.

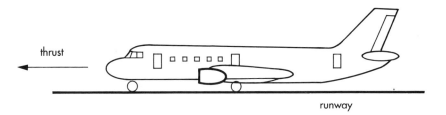

Maximum take-off mass	= 250 t
Maximum take-off thrust force of all the engines	= 670 k N
Total thrust force when cruising	= 290 kN
Speed at take-off (rotation)	= 90 m/s
Cruising speed	= 320 m/s
Cruising altitude	= 11 000 m
1 t = 1000 kg 1 kN = 1000 N Kinetic energy= $\frac{1}{2}$ mass × (velocity)^2 Force = mass × acceleration	

a) Calculate the acceleration at the start of the take-off when the aircraft is fully loaded (3 lines available)   *(3)*

b) Calculate the kinetic energy of a passenger of mass 70 kg when the aircraft is just about to lift-off. (3 lines available)   *(3)*

c) i) What is the size of the force which acts against the motion of the aircraft when it is cruising at 11 000 m? Give a reason for your answer. (2 lines available)   *(1)*

ii) Give **two** reasons why the same aircraft flying at a lower altitude, in the same weather conditions, needs more thrust to maintain the same speed. (4 lines available)   *(2)*

d) The diagram below shows a turbojet used in high speed passenger aircraft.

Turbojet

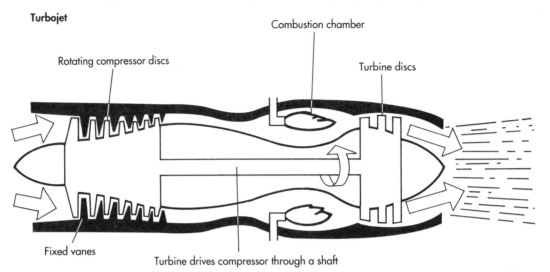

With acknowledgements to 'Flight in Focus' (1986), publ. Hobsons (Cambridge)

In the turbojet engine, air enters the front of the jet and is compressed, mixed with fuel and ignited. It then travels out of the exhaust as shown. Explain in terms of momentum OR a law of forces how the action of the jet engine is able to give the aircraft a forward thrust when the pilot starts the take-off run. (5 lines available)

(3)

[SEG/ULEAC Science Double Award, Modular]

ANSWERS TO EXAMINATION QUESTIONS

ANSWER 1

Key C, constant speed then slowed down. As the dots are not evenly spaced, option B is wrong. The direction the tape is moved indicates that it is slowing down instead of getting faster, so options A, D and E are incorrect.

ANSWER 2

Key D, U-V. Options A and B show the speed increasing, and option C, region T-U, shows constant speed.

ANSWER 3

Key C, 120 km/h. The catch here is km/h. The distance travelled is for 15 minutes, so multiply by 4 to find the speed in one hour. Option A is for people who divide the 30 by 15.

ANSWER 4

Key B. The straight horizontal line shown on the graph represents moving with constant speed.

ANSWER 5

Key B. Acceleration is force divided by mass, $25 \div 10 = 2.5$.

ANSWER 6

Key D, 300 000 J. Multiply 6000 by $\frac{1}{2}$, then multiply the answer by 10 x 10.

ANSWER 7

Key C. Remember the mass on the Moon stays the same, so it is 60 kg. The weight is one sixth, so 600 divided by 6.

ANSWER 8

Key D, 300J. Multiply 5 x 10 x 6.

STRUCTURED QUESTIONS

ANSWER 9

a) i) It is accelerating constantly.   ii) It is moving at constant speed.
b) 150 metres (at 10 m/s for 15 seconds, 10 x 15 = 150)
c) The car could be moving uphill, or the person could take their foot off the accelerator pedal.

ANSWER 10

a) The weight is 690 ÷ 6 = 115 N.
b) Heavy boots are needed to keep the astronaut on the surface, as there is very little gravity on the Moon.

ANSWER 11

a) The frontal system developed during the night from 9 pm to 9 am. The satellite was able to detect infra-red radiation instead of visible light.
b) The speed is the same.
c) The gravitational pull of the Earth.
d) The weight would become less, as the effect of the Earth's gravitational pull is less.
e) Solar panels could be used to convert solar energy into electricity.

ANSWER 12

a) i) The velocity of the car increases.

ii) acceleration $= \dfrac{\text{change in velocity}}{\text{time taken}}$

$= \dfrac{20-0}{10}$

$= 2 \text{ m/s}^2$

$= 2$ metres per second per second

b) (The mass of the car is stated above the graph, the velocity can be read from the graph.)
kinetic energy $= \frac{1}{2} \times 1000 \text{ kg} \times 20^2$
$= 500 \times 400$
$= 200\,000 \text{Joules}$
$= 200 \text{ kJ}$

c) i) heat energy   d) force $= 1000 \text{ kg} \times 8 \text{ m/s}^2$
    ii) to heat the inside of the car $= 8,000$ Newton
    iii) efficiency $= \dfrac{200 \text{ kJ}}{400 \text{ kJ}} \times 100$
    The efficiency is 50%.

ANSWER 13

a) i) In the mouthpiece sound energy (1) is changed into electrical energy (1).

Note: in the earpiece electrical energy would be changed into sound energy.

ii) A the cardboard cone vibrates because the coil of wire becomes an electromagnet

(1)

the coil is in a magnetic field (1); interaction between the 2 magnetic fields causes movement / attraction / repulsion (1)
B the molecules of air vibrate (1); energy is passed on (1)
mention of compressions where molecules are closer together or rarefactions where molecules are further apart (1)

b) i) Sound wave B (1) has the highest pitch because it has a higher frequency (1)

   ii) Sound wave B (1) is the loudest because it has the highest amplitude (1)

c) i) speed = frequency x wavelength (1)

   ii) 330 = frequency x 0.25 (1)
       frequency = speed/wavelength
                  = 330/0.25 (1)
                  = 1320 Hz (2) {if units missing then (1)}

   Note: if you do not show your working here you would only gain 2 marks instead of 4.

d) this uses the principle of resonance (1); the frequency of the ultrasound waves should match the natural frequency of the stones (1); so the stones break up or disintegrate (1)

e) i) the best frequency is 2000 Hz (1)
       the sound seems loudest for both age groups (1)

   ii) A Note the question asks for 4 points;
          possible answers here might include
          1 you would be woken up by a sound if you were asleep
          2 you can hear a sound even if the door is closed
          3 sound travels through dense smoke
          4 people outside the house can hear the sound

       B people who are deaf or who work where it is noisy (1) can see the visual signal (1)

ANSWER 14

a) Use the information in the table to convert the figures for mass from tons to kilograms, and the thrust force from kilonewtons to newtons by multiplying by 1000

   the acceleration = force / mass
                     = 670 000/250 000
                     = 2.7 m/s^2 (2 marks with correct unit)

b) (level 8–10 only)
   use the formula given for kinetic energy
   KE = $\frac{1}{2}$ mass x (velocity)^2
       = 0.5 x 70 x (90)^2
       = 283500 J (2 marks with correct unit)

c) i) the force which acts against the motion of the aircraft
       is the total thrust force from the table = 290 kN (1)

   ii) at lower altitude there is more air resistance/drag (1)
        net force is smaller for same speed (1)

d) (level 8–10 only)
   you are given a choice here; you can either answer in terms of momentum or in terms of action and reaction (Newton's Third Law)

   momentum before = momentum after (1)
   the change of momentum of exhaust gases must equal
   change of momentum forward (1)
   change of momentum per second gives forward thrust (1)

OR

   action and reaction are equal and opposite (1)
   the exhaust gases provide the action force (1)
   the reaction force on the jet gives the jet a forward thrust (1)

INDEX